self-instructional
workbook
for

emergency
care
fifth edition

J. David Bergeron
with Alan Braslow, Ph.D.

D1501380

A BRADY BOOK
PRENTICE HALL BUILDING
Englewood Cliffs, New Jersey 07632

Editorial/production supervision: Colleen Brosnan
    and Lynda Santamaria
Cover design: Ray Lundgren
Cover photo: George Dodson
Manufacturing buyer: Dave Dickey

Printed in the United States of America

10 9 8 7 6 5 4 3 2 1

ISBN 0-89303-235-2

Prentice-Hall International (UK) Limited, *London*
Prentice-Hall of Australia Pty. Limited, *Sydney*
Prentice-Hall Canada Inc., *Toronto*
Prentice-Hall Hispanoamericana, S.A., *Mexico*
Prentice-Hall of India Private Limited, *New Delhi*
Prentice-Hall of Japan, Inc., *Tokyo*
Simon & Schuster Asia Pte. Ltd., *Singapore*
Editora Prentice-Hall do Brasil, Ltda., *Rio de Janeiro*

contents

acknowledgments

The amount of work necessary to develop and write a self-instructional workbook can be greatly reduced by the help of many dedicated professionals. This was true for the first four editions of this workbook and remains the case for the fifth edition.

The acquisitions editor for the fifth edition of this project was **Claire Merrick** at the Brady Company. Claire's understanding of education and her dedication to the EMS field allow her to alert authors to the classroom needs of students and instructors. Her insight and understanding are greatly appreciated.

The supplements editor for this edition was **Mariann Hutlak** and the production editor was **Lynda Santamaria**. We wish to acknowledge their skills and dedication that were essential in the making of this book.

introduction

This is a self-instructional workbook. It has been designed to allow you to work at your own pace, helping you to evaluate your learning progress as you move through each chapter. Any textbook or workbook that is self-instructional demands more from the user than a standard text. To benefit from this workbook, you will have to follow the procedures in this introduction. Thousands of students before you have used this workbook as a part of their emergency medical training. The System works, having helped them to learn and to pass the critical examinations required for certification. It is hoped that you will put your work into each chapter as directed. Not only will you benefit, but so will all those to whom you deliver emergency care.

This workbook is designed to accompany the fifth edition of the textbook *Emergency Care*. No attempt has been made to cover all the materials found in the text. You will find that the workbook has been designed to review the most significant areas of emergency care and to highlight those areas that may be overlooked during your first reading of the textbook. The workbook is not meant to replace the textbook, nor is it meant to substitute for a well-designed course in emergency care.

Each section of this workbook requires you to complete 6 steps. Leaving out one of these steps, or hurrying through any one of them, will significantly reduce your learning. The six steps you must follow are:

Step 1.	There are two parts to Step 1. You will be given a Reading Assignment that includes a list of Objectives. Before beginning the assigned reading, go through the entire list of objectives. These objectives will tell you the things you should know and be able to do before you finish each unit of study. Once you know the objectives, complete the reading assignment. Do not attempt to do any of the workbook activities until you have read the entire assignment given here, or assigned by your instructor.

Step 2.	After you have completed Step 1, reread the Objectives.

Step 3.	The third step is the programmed text. Every learning section of this workbook has a portion of programmed text, providing you with a step-by-step guide to learning a unit of information. The program will present the information and then ask you to demonstrate how well you have learned and understood this information. More will be said about the programmed text later.

Step 4.	The fourth step is to begin the activities found at the end of each programmed section. Start with the Terminology. Define each term and check your definitions with the ones given in the Glossary of the textbook. As you check the Glossary, practice pronunciation of each term. Since the life of a patient may depend on your ability to communicate with the other members of the medical care team, correct pronunciation is essential. Do not go on to the other activities until you have completed the Terminology section. You will need many of these terms to complete the remaining activities.

Step 5.	The fifth step is the completion of the remaining activities. These will take the form of Labeling, Matching, Multiple Choice, Forming Medical Terms, and short essay Exercises. The answers to all but the Exercises are given at the end of the activities section. Page references to your textbook are given for each exercise so that you can check your answers.

Step 6.	There are three parts to Step 6. First, check your answers. Next, use the references to textbook pages to study again the material concerning any of the questions you missed. Finally, after you have checked the information in your text, re-read the Objectives at the beginning of the textbook section. Your studying is not finished until you can meet all of these objectives.

Most students find the 6 steps easy to follow except for the programmed sections. The problem with programmed text is not the text, but how the student approaches it. If you move too quickly through a program, you will learn very little. If you look up answers before responding, you will believe that you know the information while actually knowing very little. A programmed text gives you information and then requires you to recall and use this information as you continue to read.

Approach the programs in this book properly and you will not only learn a great deal about emergency care, you will also know what you do not understand about the material presented. This is a rare opportunity for a learner, knowing immediately what has not been understood or retained.

Each paragraph of programmed text is called a frame. A piece of information is given in one frame and then must be given back within the next few frames. You will notice blanks in the programmed text requiring you to give back materials you should have learned in preceding frames. The answer to each blank can be found in the margin. The whole purpose of the program will be defeated if you look at the answers before responding to the blank to be filled in.

It is very difficult to read a programmed text without having your eyes jump ahead to the answers. A simple solution to this problem is to use something to mask the section containing the answers. You can use a large index card, or a lightweight piece of cardboard. The following sample fits the programmed text exactly and can be used as a guide. The small notch at the top of this mask will allow you to read a line while keeping the answer covered.

Whenever you reach a blank to be filled in, write down your response. This is the only sure way for you to tell whether you know the correct answer. This also will keep you from moving too quickly through the program. If you do not respond with the correct answer, go back to the frame where the information was presented and re-read the entire frame before you continue with the program. Throughout this entire process, practice saying medical terms out loud to improve your pronunciation. The guides in the Glossary will help you.

After you have completed all the chapters in this workbook, you can complete the 10 Emergency Care Situations found toward the end of this book. These are not unusual or special situations. Many are very simple if you know the information presented in a basic emergency care course. Test your ability to put together the information you have learned.

Once you have completed your responses to the situations, you are ready to take the Post-Test found at the back of this workbook. Follow the directions completely, including the time requirements. This Post-Test will help you to get ready for any final examinations you may have to take in your course, and it also should be good practice before taking any certification examination.

It is hoped that your study of emergency care will be both enjoyable and fascinating, leaving you with the desire to know even more. The Author welcomes not only your comments and suggestions concerning this self-instructional workbook, but also any comments you may have in general about the learning of emergency care.

1 *the emergency medical technician*

Reading Assignment: Emergency Care, 5th ed., pp. 3–29

THE EMERGENCY MEDICAL SERVICES SYSTEM

THE CHAIN OF HUMAN AND PHYSICAL RESOURCES

The links in the chain of the Emergency Medical Services (EMS) system include the public, the dispatcher, first responders, emergency medical technicians, the rescue squad, the emergency department staff, the surgical staff, the medical staff, and the rehabilitation specialists. Emergency medical care and services have improved greatly in the last 20 years. One of the primary reasons is the new specialized training of ambulance attendants, rescue squad workers, firefighters, and others to develop their skills to the level of the Emergency Medical Technician (EMT).

Improved assessment skills and the knowledge of emergency care methods have upgraded ambulance attendants and rescue squad workers to the professional level called the _____ .

EMT (emergency medical technician)

Once at the hospital, a patient can be treated swiftly in the emergency department and transferred to the care of the surgical, medical, and rehabilitative staffs. The EMT should consider the ambulance as an extension of the hospital _____ _____. At the emergency scene and during transport, the _____ must supervise and administer necessary care. Consider this extension of the hospital emergency department as having three components: the EMTs, the ambulance, and the supplies and equipment carried on the ambulance.

emergency department
EMT

THE EMERGENCY MEDICAL TECHNICIAN

Before the EMT can supervise and administer necessary _____, a prompt and efficient response to the scene is required. This is not accomplished by excessive driving speed, but by driving the ambulance carefully to the address given by the dispatcher, taking the most expeditious route, and observing all state and local traffic ordinances and regulations, followed by safe and proper parking at the scene.

care

The driver-EMT drives the ambulance _____ to the address received from the _____. Considering traffic conditions, weather, and a number of other factors, the EMT uses the most _____ route. While en route, the driver-EMT observes all state and local traffic _____ and _____ that apply to the driving of an emergency vehicle. Upon arrival at the emer-

carefully (safely)
dispatcher

expeditious
ordinances, regulations

1

2

gency scene, the driver-EMT is responsible for the _____ and proper _____ of the ambulance.

After a _____ and _____ response to the emergency scene, the EMTs may have to supervise or help other authorities control the scene (traffic, onlookers, etc.). The primary responsibility of the EMT is the care of the patient; however, the EMT must ensure his or her personal safety by avoiding injury and infectious diseases. Unless a physician is present, the responsibility for patient care is the EMT's. Following _____ of the emergency scene, the EMTs should administer prompt and effective care. This may include gaining access to the patient, utilizing various sources of information, detecting and treating life-threatening problems, assisting with extrication from the wreckage, and providing emotional comfort to the patient and his loved ones. At every emergency, care should be taken to ensure personal safety. This includes protecting the EMT from _____ and _____ _____.

To properly do the job of an EMT, you will be called upon to do more than treat life-threatening problems. Before you can assess and treat a patient, you must be able to gain _____ to the patient. You will have to know all the possible sources of _____ and how to use them. In addition to taking care of the patient's physical needs, you will also have to provide _____ comfort to both the patient and his loved ones.

Before the patient can be transferred to the ambulance, EMTs often have to help with _____ from the wreckage. Prompt and effective _____ administered at the scene should be continued during the safe transport of the patient to a medical facility. The EMTs should deliver the patient and, whenever possible, his personal effects to the medical facility. In addition, they should deliver any patient status and treatment information, either by communications en route or directly to the emergency department staff. The EMT is a professional supplying other professionals on the medical team with information needed to ensure the best care for the patient.

The EMTs should deliver the patient, his personal effects, and _____ to the staff of the emergency department. _____ should be accomplished without excessive speed, sudden stops or swerves, or unnecessary use of the siren and horn. Through all steps, communications are essential. To be sure that information is not lost and that the planned routine of care is efficient, reporting and record keeping are a must.

Additional tasks for the EMT may include proper actions to comply with all regulations that govern the disposition of the deceased, correct conduct at the scene of a crime, and assisting of the emergency department staff. Regardless of the activities performed, a critique of the run should be made. Remember, an efficient run will include both _____ and _____ keeping

For the cycle to begin again with a prompt and efficient _____ to the scene, care for the vehicle and its special equipment is also the responsibility of the EMTs. Each cycle begins and ends with preparation. Keep in mind that even the best cared for equipment is only as good as the personnel who use it. Proper training, emotional control, appropriate conversation,

---

safe
parking
prompt, efficient

control

injury, infectious
diseases

access
information

emotional

extrication
care

information (status)
Transport

reporting
record
response

and proper manners and dress are all important in providing the community with the best emergency care possible.

IMPORTANT: You may think that your responsibilities as an EMT will include only assessment and care. In complex emergency situations, you will be called upon to do any or all the EMT tasks mentioned. Learn all you can about each of these tasks. The more you know and the more you can do, the better you will be at providing patients with the best of care.

THE EMT AND THE LAW (MEDICAL-LEGAL PROBLEMS)

The threat of lawsuits does exist in the practice of emergency care. Mistreatment of a patient caused by gross negligence or wanton misconduct could lead to the EMT being sued. However, if the EMT acts in good faith to the best of his abilities, utilizing the training he has had, there is little chance of a successful suit being brought against him.

The majority of emergency care lawsuits are filed claiming negligence. In such cases, an EMT with a duty to act is accused of failing to provide the standard care required for a situation. This improper action must have harmed or injured the patient if the suit is to be successful.

The EMT must understand when a _____ to act exists and be able to deliver care to the _____ of care. Failure to do so may harm or injure a patient. This could lead to the EMT being sued for_____.

Added protection is given the EMT in many states in the form of the Good Samaritan laws. These laws protect emergency care personnel from lawsuits, provided they act in good faith and to the best of their _____, utilizing the _____ they have had. There are no laws to protect the EMT from a charge of patient abandonment.

The EMT is protected from lawsuits in many states by the _____ _____ laws. These laws do not protect the EMT from charges of mistreatment of a patient caused by gross _____ or wanton _____ There are no laws that will protect the EMT guilty of patient _____.

The EMT needs to understand the difference between actual and implied consent. If an adult patient has the mental and physical capabilities to make a judgment concerning his own care, you must seek his consent before you begin to administer emergency care.

Implied consent allows the EMT to give emergency care to the unconscious, extremely ill, or seriously injured patient. If an adult patient has the mental and physical capabilities to decide for himself, _____ consent is needed.

As in the case of an unconscious patient, if a child's parent or legal guardian is not present, the EMT can consider this to be a case of _____ consent and initiate proper emergency care.

Even with many states having _____ _____ laws and laws governing _____ consent, the EMT should be aware of special laws and situations that will present legal problems. The emergency care team should follow special routines for the handling of mentally disturbed patients, intoxicated patients, suspected felons, and attempted suicide victims.

Police assistance is needed when treating and transporting a mentally

duty
standard

negligence

abilities, training

Good
Samaritan
negligence
misconduct
abandonment

actual

implied
Good Samaritan
implied

4

disturbed patient. The EMT does not have the legal right to capture and restrain (check your own state laws). Humane restraints can be applied by the police, or by the EMTs under police orders or under the orders of a physician.

When transporting a female patient suffering from a mental disorder, always have another female accompany the patient. Call in to your dispatcher and give your time of departure and the odometer reading. If the patient must be restrained, do so only under the order of a _____ or if a police officer is present.

physician

NOTE: Some states have emergency care provisions that allow for the capture and humane restraint of anyone who is acting in a manner that could lead to personal injury or to the injury of others. Be certain to check the laws in your state.

A person should not be assumed to be intoxicated until you have considered any possible medical reasons for the observed behavior. Also, remember that an intoxicated person may have sustained injuries, possibly unknown to him, caused by falls, etc. If necessary, _____ restraints can be applied by the police or under a _____ supervision.

humane
physician's

Police assistance is desirable when dealing with attempted suicide victims. This is also true for cases of _____ disturbed patients, intoxicated patients, possible child abuse victims, and suspected felons. Your first duty is to provide needed _____ _____. However, you may be called upon to apply humane _____, protect evidence, or even to collect information of past abuse so as to alert the emergency department staff to the possibility of unhealed injuries.

mentally

emergency care
restraints

THE AMBULANCE

An ambulance is defined as a vehicle for emergency care that provides a driver compartment and a patient compartment.

For an emergency vehicle to meet the definition of an ambulance, it must have a driver compartment and a _____ compartment that can accommodate two EMTs and two litter patients. The positioning of the patients has been defined, stating that at least one patient must be able to be positioned for intensive life support during transport.

patient

An ambulance should have a patient compartment and a _____ compartment. The patient compartment should accommodate _____ EMTs and at least _____ _____ patients. It should be possible to position the patients so that at least one can be given intensive _____ _____ during _____. This means that the ambulance must carry the equipment and supplies needed for emergency care at the scene and during transport.

driver
two, two litter

life support, transport

The ambulance should have two-way radio communications and any form of telecommunications needed for any specialization of care assigned to the ambulance. This will help the EMTs to provide optimum emergency care at the _____ and during _____. Protection of patient and staff is to be considered in the equipment design and the ambulance design to allow for safe operating procedures at hazardous scenes and during transport.

scene, transport

According to federal specifications, there are three types of ambulances. A type I ambulance is a modular ambulance body mounted onto a conventional cab and chassis. The body can be lifted off and the cab and chassis replaced. There is no passageway between crew compartment and patient compartment.

A type II ambulance is a van type, where body and cab are an integral unit. This is an advantage over the type I ambulance, which lacks a _____ _____ between the _____ and _____ compartments. The type III ambulance is very much like the type II in that it is a _____ type, having a cab and integral body. The body of the type III is larger than the type II body.

A van-type ambulance with a typical body size is a type _____ ambulance. If the ambulance has a larger integral body cab, it is classified as a type _____. A type I ambulance has a _____ ambulance body mounted onto a conventional cab and chassis.

Even though there are _____ distinct types of ambulances, all such emergency vehicles need to be colored and marked so that they are easily recognized as ambulances. White background, orange striping, and blue lettering are commonly used. The star-of-life emblem may be used to help identify the vehicle. The word AMBULANCE should be a mirror-imaged word painted on the front of the ambulance, positioned so as to be easily read in rearview mirrors.

An ambulance should have warning lights and flashing lights in the upper corners of the vehicle body.

passageway, driver (crew)
patient
van

II

III, modular

three

AMBULANCE EQUIPMENT AND SUPPLIES

The ambulance should be equipped with basic supplies and equipment for transfer of patients, ventilation and resuscitation, oxygen inhalation, suction, and cardiac compression. Basic supplies are those items that protect the patient, provide for his personal needs, and provide for patient monitoring activities.

Items such as blankets, emesis bags, and a stethoscope are examples of _____ supplies to be carried on the ambulance. Wheeled stretchers are provided for the _____ of patients. Special transfer and transport equipment must be on hand for newborn infants.

Various airways and devices must be carried to provide for _____ and resuscitation. Along with such equipment _____ inhalation equipment should be carried.

An ambulance should have a fixed suction system and a portable suction device. Various spine boards and CPR boards should be part of the equipment available for use in _____ compression efforts.

The well-equipped ambulance has equipment and supplies to provide for the protection of the patient and for his personal needs. Such items are called _____ supplies. Equipment should be on hand to allow for proper patient _____and transport, including the special needs of _____ _____.

Equipment is needed for ventilation and _____, oxygen _____ procedures, fixed and _____ _____units and equipment for cardiac _____.

An ambulance should be equipped with supplies used for immobilization of fractures, dressing and bandaging wounds, treatment of shock, and treatment of acute poisoning.

Various padded board splints, inflatable splints, and traction splints should be carried to allow for the _____ of frac-

basic
transfer

ventilation
oxygen

cardiac

basic
transfer
newborn infants
resuscitation
inhalation, portable
suction, compression

immobilization

6

tures. The ambulance should be equipped with supplies for _____ and _____ wounds and for the care of _____ and acute _____.

All ambulances should have supplies for childbirth, including a sterile childbirth kit (obstetric or OB kit) and all the equipment and supplies needed for the _____ and _____ of the newborn infant.

In addition to the supplies and equipment mentioned, the ambulance should have special equipment for physicians and qualified paramedics, access and disentanglement equipment; personnel safety equipment, fire extinguishing equipment, and communications equipment.

dressing
bandaging, shock
poisoning

transfer, transport

TERMINOLOGY

Define the following terms. Check your definitions with those in the Glossary of your textbook.

Abandonment—

Actual Consent—

Ambulance—

Emergency Medical Technician—

Good Samaritan Laws—

Implied Consent—

Negligence—

MULTIPLE CHOICE

Circle the letter of the best answer for each question. The answers are given at the end of test. Note that page references to the textbook are listed.

1. Many states help protect the EMT from lawsuits with (p. 19):
   A. Professional associations
   B. Full immunity laws
   C. Good Samaritan laws
   D. Abandonment laws

2. The EMT can treat and transport an unconscious patient because of the legal consideration known as (p. 19):
   A. Implied consent
   B. Applied consent
   C. Immunity consent
   D. Triage consent

3. In an emergency situation, when parents or legal guardians are not present, the child's consent is *(p. 19)*:
   A. Still needed
   B. Actual
   C. Implied
   D. Meaningless, parental consent is still essential

4. In most cases, when EMTs have to transport an emotionally disturbed patient, they should *(p. 20)*:
   A. Wait until the patient is calm
   B. Capture and transport
   C. Capture and restrain
   D. Wait for police assistance

5. If an EMT with a duty to act fails to provide the standard of care, and if this failure causes harm or injury to the patient, the EMT may be accused of *(p. 17)*:
   A. Breach of promise
   B. Negligence
   C. Abandonment
   D. Assault

6. An ambulance with the body and cab formed as an integral unit is a _____ ambulance *(p. 22)*:
   A. Type I
   B. Type II
   C. Type III
   D. Type IV

7. An ambulance with a conventional cab and a chassis on which a modular ambulance body is mounted is a _____ ambulance *(p. 22)*:
   A. Type I
   B. Type II
   C. Type III
   D. Type IV

8. The basis for most EMT training programs is the national standard curriculum developed by the *(p. 11)*:
   A. American Red Cross (ARC)
   B. American Heart Association (AHA)
   C. United States Department of Transportation (DOT)
   D. National Institutes of Health (NIH)

EXERCISES

1. In terms of general groupings, list the basic items of supply to be carried on an ambulance *(pp. 22–23)*.

2. Define what is meant by "basic supplies" *(p. 22)*.

3. List the 9 main duties of an EMT *(p. 12)*.

4. List at least 10 desirable traits of an EMT *(p. 15)*.

8

5. List at least 8 possible reasons why an EMT may be sued and held liable (*pp. 16–17*).

ANSWERS: Multiple Choice

1. C
2. A
3. C
4. D

5. B
6. B
7. A
8. C

2 the human body

Reading Assignment: Emergency Care, 5th ed., pp. 31-59

THE LANGUAGE OF EMERGENCY MEDICAL CARE

MEDICAL TERMS

Medical terms are made up of stems that usually refer to a body organ or structure. You can add prefixes to the front of this stem or suffixes to the end. For example, *gastro-* refers to stomach. With the suffix *-itis*, the word becomes *gastritis*, an inflammation of the stomach. Whenever you see the suffix *-itis*, it will mean an inflammation of the structure referred to by the stem part of the term.

The prefix *peri-* means around. This prefix can be added to a stem word to mean a structure around a given organ, gland, blood vessel, etc. The sac that lies around the heart is the _____-cardial sac. *Peri-* is an example of a _____. An inflammation of the heart sac is _____.

peri
prefix, pericarditis

Exercises on medical terminology are included in Chapters 3 through 20 of this workbook. They will help you to understand the formation of medical and anatomical terms.

NOTE: See Appendix 6 of your textbook for more practice with medical terminology.

ANATOMICAL TERMS

Today's EMTs must have a working knowledge of human anatomical terms and medical terms. The majority of these terms make reference to the human body as it appears when it is in the erect position with arms down at the sides and the palms facing forward. This is called the *anatomical position*. The positioning of the palms facing forward is very important for the naming of blood vessels, nerves, and bones.

The EMT needs to have a working knowledge of both medical and _____ terms. Most terms relating to the human body assume it to be in the _____ _____ , standing erect with the arms down at the sides and the palms facing _____. In this position, surfaces to the front are called *anterior* or *ventral*, while surfaces to the back are called *posterior* or *dorsal*.

anatomical
anatomical position
forward

The front of an organ is its _____ surface, and the back of an organ is its _____ surface. If you are considering the midline of the body or of an organ, the term *medial* (or *mesial*) is used. Toward this midline is *medial*. Away from this midline, that is, to the sides, is *lateral*.

anterior (ventral)
posterior (dorsal)

Consider the vertical midline of the body. Now, compare the positioning of an eye and an ear to this midline. The ear is _____ to the eye, while the eye is _____ to the ear.

lateral
medial

The head end of the body is the cephalic region and the tail end is the *caudal* region. Thus, an injury to the head has taken place in the _____ region of the body.

cephalic

10

The directional term that means toward the head or _____ region is *superior*. Superior also can be applied to the top of an organ. The directional term *inferior* means away from the head, or the bottom of an organ. The top of the heart is its_____ surface and the bottom of the heart is its _____ surface.

cephalic

superior
inferior

When comparing the position of the eyes in relation to the nose, the eyes are said to be _____ to the nose, while the nose is _____ to the eyes. Even though the nose is said to be inferior to the eyes, the nose can be said to be _____ to the mouth. This means that something can be either superior or inferior in position, depending on what it is being compared to in the reference.

superior
inferior
superior

The term *palmar* refers to the inner surface (the palms) of the hands. In the anatomical position, the palmar surfaces are facing _____. *Plantar* refers to the sole of the foot.

forward

A blood vessel that arches through the palm of the hand can be called a _____ arch. A wart on the sole of the foot can be called a _____ wart.

palmar
plantar

Along the trunk of the body, toward the head is _____ and toward the feet is _____. When considering the arms and legs, the terms *proximal* and *distal* are used. These two terms are always used to relate 2 things back to an origin. For example, when compared to the shoulder, the elbow is proximal and the wrist is distal.

superior
inferior

When compared to the hip, the knee is _____ and the ankle is _____. If you compare the wrist or the fingers to the shoulders, the wrist is_____ and the fingers are _____.

proximal
distal
proximal, distal

The human body and its structures can be divided by planes. A *transverse plane* will divide the body or one of its organs into a top and bottom. A *sagittal plane* will divide the body or one of its organs into a right and left side. A *coronal* or *frontal plane* will divide the body or one of its organs into a front and back portion.

The heart can be divided into a top and bottom by a _____ plane. The top surface is said to be _____ and the bottom surface is _____. The heart also can be divided into a right side and a left side by a _____ plane. The heart also can be divided into a front and a back by a _____ plane. The front surface is called _____, while the back surface is called _____.

transverse, superior
inferior
sagittal
coronal (frontal)
anterior
posterior

Certain anatomical terms describe the direction of movement. Movement toward the body's midline is *adduction* and movement away from the midline is *abduction*. To rotate away from the midline of the body is a _____ rotation, while any rotation toward the midline is a _____ rotation.

lateral
medial

When the arm is pulled in toward the midline, this action is called _____. If the arm is pulled away from the midline, _____ has taken place.

adduction
abduction

NOTE: Think of "toward the midline" as adding to the body, thus, AD-Duction. Remember that person carried away is abducted, If the arm is moved away from the midline, it is abducted.

If you bend your arm at the elbow, this is called a *flexion*. When you straighten your arm, this is an *extension*. Thus, flexion and extension are terms that describe _____ of movement.

direction

When the head is bent forward, a _____ has taken place. **flexion**
When the head is returned to the upright position and the neck is straight,
an _____ has taken place. **extension**

Terms relating to body posture are very important. The anatomical position calls for the body to be standing in the _____ position. **erect**
When a person is lying on his back, the person is in a supine position. When lying face down, a person is in the prone position.

A person is found lying face up. He is in the _____ position. **supine**
If found lying on his right side, the patient is said to be in the *right lateral recumbent* position.

A person is found lying face down. He is in the _____ position. **prone**
tion. Your directions call for moving him onto his left side, or the left
_____ _____ position. **lateral, recumbent**

TOPOGRAPHIC ANATOMY

Consider the body to be composed of the head and neck, the trunk, and the extremities. Knowing the body regions and the body landmarks is essential to learning emergency medical care.

THE HEAD AND NECK

The body is considered to be composed of the trunk, the extremities, and the _____ and _____. The head is composed of the *cranium*, which **head, neck**
is toward the top or _____ position, and the face. The face makes **superior**
up the front or _____ portion of the head. It is located in an **anterior**
_____ position to the cranium. **inferior**

The *mandible*, or lower jaw, is part of the _____. Any structure of the **face**
head that is not part of the face is part of the _____. **cranium**

THE TRUNK

The trunk is the body minus the head and neck and the
_____. The chest region is called the *thorax* or tho- **extremities**
racic portion. Below, or _____ to the thorax is the *abdomen*. **inferior**

The chest is called the _____ region. Inferior to the thorax is **thoracic**
the _____ region, divided into *quadrants*. These quadrants **abdominal**
are the right upper quadrant, the left upper quadrant, the right lower quadrant, and the left lower quadrant. Therefore, if a patient has pain on his right side, above the umbilicus (navel), the pain is reported to be in the
_____ _____ quadrant. **right, upper**

In addition to the abdomen being divided into _____ areas or quad- **4**
rants, there are also 9 regions to the ventral abdominal wall. Of these, the
EMT should know the *epigastric* region, just above the navel or
_____ , and the *suprapubic* (hypogastric) region, just above **umbilicus**
the genitals.

THE EXTREMITIES

The human body is made up of the extremities, the head and neck, and
the _____. Each upper extremity extends from the shoulders to **trunk**
the finger tips. Each lower extremity extends from the hip to the tips of the toes. Many common terms may be used in reference to the extremities, such as elbows, wrists, knees, and ankles.

12

BODY CAVITIES

The front or _____ of the body contains 2 cavities separated by a dome-shaped muscle called the diaphragm. The top or _____ cavity is the thoracic cavity, enclosed by the rib cage.

There are _____ anterior body cavities. They are separated by the _____. The superior cavity is the_____ cavity, containing the lungs, heart, great blood vessels, and parts of the trachea (windpipe) and esophagus.

The thoracic cavity is enclosed by the _____ _____. It is separated from the lower or _____ anterior cavity by the diaphragm. The inferior cavity is the abdominopelvic cavity.

Below the diaphragm is the inferior _____ body cavity known as the _____ cavity. It is sometimes thought of as having two portions, the abdominal and the pelvic cavities, even though there is really only one cavity. The pelvic cavity is protected by the bones of the pelvic girdle. There is no bony protection for the abdominal cavity except the inferior portion of the rib cage.

The pelvic cavity is protected by the bones of the _____ _____ . The thoracic cavity and the superior portion of the _____ cavity are protected by the _____ _____.

The back or _____ of the body also has _____ cavities, the cranial and the spinal cavity. Both of these cavities are protected by bone. The only body cavity having a large region unprotected by bone is the _____ cavity.

The 2 posterior cavities are the _____ and the _____ cavities. The cranial cavity is the braincase of the skull, housing the brain. The other posterior cavity, the _____ cavity, runs through the center of the backbone (vertebrae). It protects the spinal cord.

The heart and lungs are found in the_____ cavity. This cavity is protected by the _____ of the rib cage. The brain is protected by the bones surrounding the _____ cavity.

anterior
superior
2
diaphragm, thoracic
rib cage
inferior
anterior
abdominopelvic
pelvic
girdle
abdominal, rib cage
posterior, 2
abdominal
cranial, spinal
spinal
thoracic
bones
cranial

NOTE: The anatomical plates that follow page 43 in your textbook can be useful in your study of body cavities. The *Membranes* plate shows the thoracic and abdominopelvic cavities. The cranial and spinal cavities are shown on the *Nervous System* plate. The *Respiration, Digestion, Excretion, and Reproduction* plates will aid you in defining the major body cavities and learning the positions of the major body organs.

TERMINOLOGY

Define the following terms. Check your definitions with those in the Glossary at the end of your textbook.

Anatomical Position—

Diaphragm—

Duodenum—

Thorax—

LABELING: Abdominal Quadrants

Label the following illustration of abdominal quadrants. See the end of this chapter for the answers.

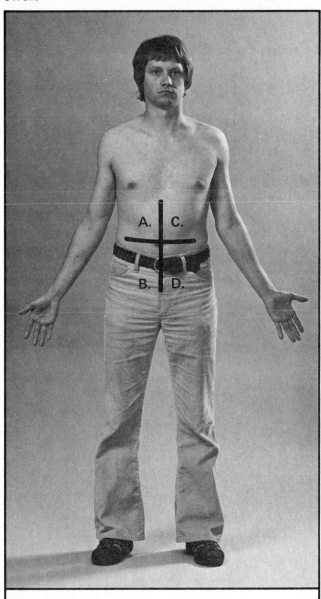

A. _____

B. _____

C. _____

D. _____

Figure 2.1 (*p. 38*)

LABELING: Anatomical Postures

Identify the following anatomical postures. The answers can be found at the end of this chapter.

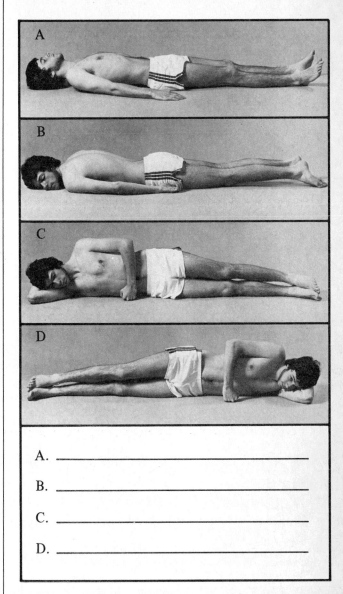

A. _____

B. _____

C. _____

D. _____

Figure 2.2 (*p. 35*)

LABELING: Direction of Movement

Identify the directions of movement shown below. The answers can be found at the end of this chapter.

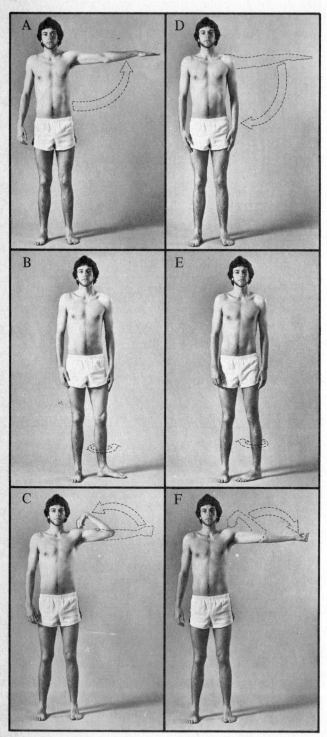

Figure 2.3 (*p. 35*)

A. _____

B. _____

C. _____

D. _____

E. _____

F. _____

LABELING: Body Organs

Draw the positions of the following organs on the photograph provided below: heart, lungs, diaphragm, stomach, spleen, and kidneys. Check your drawing with the illustrations on page 40 of your textbook.

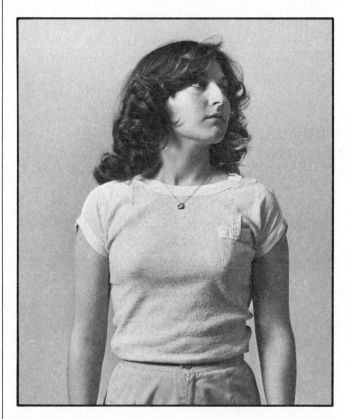

Figure 2.4

15

MULTIPLE CHOICE

Circle the letter of the correct answer for each question. The answers are given at the end of this chapter. Note page references to *Emergency Care, 5th ed.*

1. Which of the following terms describes the direction of movement when the arm is pulled toward the body's midline? *(p. 34)*
   A. Abduction
   B. Lateral rotation
   C. Flexion
   D. Adduction

2. A patient found lying on his back is in the position *(p. 33)*.
   A. Anatomical
   B. Supine
   C. Prone
   D. Lateral recumbent

3. When compared to the hip, the knees are said to be _____ and the toes are _____ *(p. 33)*.
   A. Inferior, superior
   B. Proximal, distal
   C. Superior, inferior
   D. Distal, proximal

4. The anterior trunk of the body is composed of the abdomen, pelvis, and *(p. 36)*:
   A. Thorax
   B. Neck
   C. Extremities
   D. Head and neck

5. Most of the liver is located in the _____ quadrant *(p. 38)*.
   A. Right lower
   B. Left lower
   C. Right upper
   D. Left upper

6. The two anterior body cavities are separated by the *(p. 37)*:
   A. Meninges
   B. Diaphragm
   C. Spinal column
   D. Duodenum

7. The heart is located in the _____ cavity *(p. 37)*.
   A. Thoracic
   B. Cranial
   C. Cardiac
   D. Sagittal

8. The heart is _____ to the stomach *(p. 33)*.
   A. Proximal
   B. Distal
   C. Medial
   D. Superior

9. Which of the following structures is located posterior to the abdominopelvic cavity? *(p. 38)*
   A. Gallbladder
   B. Kidneys
   C. Spleen
   D. Small intestine

10. Which of the following is found in all 4 abdominal quadrants? *(p. 38)*
    A. Lungs
    B. Urinary bladder
    C. Kidneys
    D. Large intestine

EXERCISE

Complete the following exercise and check your answer with the information presented on page 38 of your textbook.

List 11 of the body systems and give one function for each.

ANSWERS

Labeling—Abdominal Quadrants— *Figure 2-1*

A. Right upper quadrant
B. Right lower quadrant
C. Left upper quadrant
D. Left lower quadrant

Labeling—Anatomical Postures—*Figure 2-2*

A. Supine
B. Prone
C. Right lateral recumbent
D. Left lateral recumbent

Labeling—Direction of Movement—*Figure 2-3*

A. Abduction
B. Lateral rotation
C. Flexion
D. Adduction
E. Medial rotation
F. Extension

Multiple Choice

1. D
2. B
3. B
4. A
5. C
6. B
7. A
8. D
9. B
10. D

3 patient assessment

Reading Assignment: Emergency Care, 5th ed., pp. 61-109

THE PATIENT ASSESSMENT PROCEDURE

The patient evaluation procedure consists of three major activities: the emergency scene evaluation, the primary survey, and the secondary survey. During assessment and care, you must ensure your own personal safety. Always avoid contact with the patient's blood and body fluids. Use the appropriate protective equipment required by your EMS system. Your first concern will be to identify and attempt to correct any life-threatening problems. Next, you will have to identify and provide care that will help to stabilize the patient and reduce the severity of his or her problem.

The most important concern in patient assessment is to detect and provide immediate care for_____ -_____ problems. After this is done, you must attempt to _____ the patient and reduce the _____ of his or her major problems. Your third concern will be to keep the patient stable and continue reassessing to detect changes in the patient's condition.

Assessment and care should be done without risk to the rescuer. Keep in mind that direct contact with the patient's _____ and body _____ may expose you to infectious disease. Use appropriate _____ equipment to minimize this risk.

life-threatening
stabilize
severity

blood
fluids
protective

THE RESCUE SCENE EVALUATION

Not all injuries and illnesses are obvious. The EMT should obtain information from first aiders, first responders, relatives, and witnesses. Additional information can be obtained by studying the situation and by talking to the patient.

Upon arrival at the emergency scene, the EMT can obtain information from first aiders, first responders, _____ , and _____. Additional information can be collected by observing both the patient and the _____.

In case of injury, the EMT should relate the major categories of accidents to the classification of injuries, by observing both the _____ and the situation. There may be soft tissue injuries, fractures to bone and cartilage, dislocations, and internal injuries.

Injuries are not always obvious. You should relate possible injuries to the major categories of _____. For example, fire can cause burns, which are _____ tissue injuries. However, the patient may have fallen during the fire, causing _____ to bone and cartilage. Gases from the fire may have poisoned the patient, causing _____ injuries.

Knowing the mechanism of injury is also essential. A bent steering wheel could imply chest injuries. A lap safety belt could mean pelvic or ab-

relatives
witnesses
scene

patient

accidents
soft
fractures
internal

18

dominal injuries. Not all injuries are obvious. You must know the _____ of injury.

> mechanism

Look for blood around the patient and estimate the patient's blood loss. Look for obvious injuries and their resulting deformities. Spinal cord damage is suggested if the patient's arms are over his head or if priapism (involuntary erection of the penis) has occurred. Fractures and dislocations can be obvious because of the resulting _____. Before moving the patient, check for protruding or impaled objects at the scene of accident.

> deformities

Is there profuse bleeding? Look for blood _____ the patient and _____ the blood loss. See if there are any other clues (signs) such as vomitus with undigested pills, or any strange odors that suggest toxins have been ingested.

> around
> estimate

Look for a medical alerting device such as the Medic Alert Emblem worn on a necklace or bracelet. Some of these medical _____ devices are carried in wallets or purses. Remember, the patient may have spinal injuries. Do NOT move a patient to get to his wallet before you have properly cared for any possible spinal injuries.

> alerting

Sources of information are available to the EMT at the emergency scene. First aiders and first _____ are trained to pass on information. The EMT should listen to witnesses and _____. The EMT needs to be a trained observer, looking for the _____ of injury. The EMT should look for_____ around the patient and any _____ injuries, _____ and other clues. Finally, the EMT can obtain valuable information from any _____ _____ device.

> responders
> relatives
> mechanism
> blood
> obvious, deformities
> medical
> alerting

THE PRIMARY SURVEY

The patient evaluation procedure consists of the emergency _____ _____ , the primary survey, and the _____ _____ . Of these, the primary survey is concerned with those life-threatening emergencies that must receive immediate attention. Respiratory arrest, cardiac arrest, and profuse bleeding are examined for and cared for during the primary survey.

> scene evaluation
> secondary survey

The most important examination sign is respiration. The EMT should ensure that the airway is open, (use the head-tilt, chin-lift or jaw-thrust) and that breathing is adequate (look, listen, and feel). Artificial ventilation may have to be given to a patient. If artificial ventilation does not produce spontaneous breathing, the patient may be in cardiac arrest.

The most important examination sign is _____. The patient's airway must be _____ and breathing must be _____. Should artificial ventilation fail to produce _____ breathing, the patient may be in _____ arrest. The easiest method to check for heart action is to take a carotid pulse rate. If there is a pulse, the EMT should assume only respiratory arrest and go back to artificial _____. If there is no pulse, cardiopulmonary resuscitation (CPR) is immediately called for.

> respiration
> open, adequate
> spontaneous
> cardiac

> ventilations

The primary survey deals with _____ -_____ emergencies. In cases of respiratory arrest, _____ _____ should be started by the EMTs. Should the patient be in cardiac arrest, _____ resuscitation should be initiated. During the primary survey, the EMT should also look for and control _____ bleeding.

> life-threatening
> artificial
> ventilations
> cardiopulmonary

> profuse

THE SECONDARY SURVEY

After completing the _____ survey, the EMT should turn his attention to the discovery of those problems that do not pose an immediate threat to the patient's survival, but may become critical if allowed to go uncorrected. The secondary survey consists of the subjective interview and the objective examination. If the patient has a life-threatening illness or injury, it may not be possible to complete the secondary survey before starting to transport the patient.

primary

The objective examination consists of determining the patient's vital signs and doing a head-to-toe survey. This usually follows the subjective _____, a conversational information-gathering effort between patient and EMT.

interview

Make sure, if at all possible, that the patient can see you. Identify yourself and reassure the patient. The _____ interview can now begin as an _____ gathering effort between you and the patient. Learn and record the patient's name, age, and primary complaint.

subjective
information

After learning the patient's name and _____, the EMT must find out the patient's _____ _____. Once the complaint is known, the circumstances of the complaint should be determined. In other words, you know *what*, now you are finding out *how*.

age
primary complaint

After learning the patient's _____, age, primary complaint, and the _____ of the complaint, learn of any previous relevant experiences by asking the patient if this has ever happened before. Ask if the patient is under a physician's care and what medication, if any, the patient is taking.

name
circumstances

Learn of _____ relevant experiences and if the patient is under a physician's care. If the patient is taking any _____, find out what they are. Finally, determine whether the patient has any allergies. If the patient is not conscious, then elicit information from a friend or _____.

previous
medications

The subjective interview is followed by the _____ _____. The patient's _____ signs are determined and the head-to-toe survey is made. Remember to observe your patient. Is he alert? How does he respond? How stable does he appear to be?

witness
objective
examination, vital

VITAL SIGNS

Vital signs are pulse rate and character, respiratory rate and character, blood pressure, and body or skin temperature. Be sure to explain to the patient what you are doing.

Obtaining vital signs should be a smooth process. With the stethoscope positioned correctly around your neck and the blood pressure cuff in place on the patient's arm, begin with pulse rate and _____. The easiest way to measure heart action is _____ rate. In adults, the "at rest" pulse rate is 60 to 80 beats per minute. For children, the rate is usually between 80 and 150 beats per minute. An infant can have a pulse rate up to 180 beats per minute.

character
pulse

In the primary survey you determined heart action by checking for a _____ pulse. In the secondary survey, a radial or wrist pulse is taken. The first three fingers are used to palpate a radial pulse. Count the pulse beats for 30 seconds and multiply this rate by 2 to get the pulse beats per minute.

carotid

A _____ pulse rate is taken during the secondary survey. Count the beats for _____ seconds and multiply by _____. The "at rest" pulse rate for an adult should be between _____ and _____ beats per minute. However, at the scene of an accident or other stressful situation, do not be surprised to find pulse rates ranging from 100 to 150 beats per minute. Always recheck a suspicious rate after a few minutes have elapsed. Any adult "at rest" rate that stays at a rate below 50 or above 120 should be treated as a true emergency and transport should take place as soon as possible.

While taking the pulse rate, also notice the _____ of the pulse. Note if the pulse rhythm is regular or irregular. Is the pulse normal and strong or weak and thin? A strong pulse is described as being full, a weak pulse is described as thready. A normal adult at rest would have a pulse rate between _____ and _____ beats per _____, and the character of the pulse would be _____ and _____.

Before taking the patient's blood pressure, determine the rate and character of the patient's _____. Count the number of breaths the patient takes in 30 seconds and multiply by two to determine the rate per minute. For the adult at rest, the normal range is 12 to 20 breaths per minute. The respiratory _____ for children is faster, with infants breathing as fast as 35 to 60 breaths per minute.

In addition to the respiratory rate, you will want to know the rhythm and depth of the respirations. Is breathing regular or irregular? Are respirations deep or shallow? For a normal adult at rest the respiratory rate is from _____ to _____ breaths per minute. A respiratory rate that stays above 30 per minute for an adult at rest should be treated as a true emergency and transport should take place as soon as possible.

Along with respiratory _____, rhythm, and_____, note any unusual sounds such as snoring, crowing, or gurgling. These may indicate an airway obstruction. Note also any red frothing that may indicate internal injuries.

After determining the _____ rate and character and the _____ rate and character, turn your attention to _____ _____, and then take the temperature. There are two readings for blood pressure. One, the systolic pressure, represents the pressure exerted on the arterial walls when the heart is contracting. The other, diastolic pressure, represents the pressure exerted on the arterial walls when the heart is at rest.

A typical blood pressure reading is 120/80, read as 120 over 80. Both of these figures are expressed in millimeters of mercury (mmHg). The 120 mmHg represents the pressure during heart contraction and is called the _____ pressure. The 80 _____ is the pressure when the heart is relaxing and is called the _____ pressure.

A quick rule of thumb for the normal blood pressure expected for a male patient at rest is as follows. When his heart is contracting, the pressure is 100 plus the patient's age. This is the _____ pressure. This is not an absolute law, so expect variations. There are limits to the rule of thumb. This is a fairly good tool when working with young adult males. However, a systolic pressure of 160 _____ for a 60-year-old person may not be a life-threatening emergency, but it is not considered normal or good.

During heart relaxation, the _____ blood pressure is usually between 60 and 90 _____. For females, both pressures tend to be 8 to 10 mmHg less than those for a male of the same age.

---

radial
30, 2
60, 80

character

60, 80, minute
regular, full

respirations

rate

12, 20

rate, depth

pulse
respiratory
blood pressure

systolic, mmHg
diastolic

systolic

mmHg

diastolic
mmHg

For a 26-year-old male, the normal systolic blood pressure would be _____ mmHg and the normal diastolic pressure should be between _____ and _____ mmHg. For an adult, a reading of 90/50 mmHg or less is a low blood pressure called hypotension. A reading of 145/90 or higher is hypertension. A drop of pressure to below 90/60 is reliable sign of shock.

126
60, 90

Too low a blood pressure is called _____, occurring when the reading is below _____/_____ mmHg. High blood pressure is called _____ and occurs when readings are above _____/_____ mmHg.

hypotension
90, 50
hypertension
145, 90

Blood pressure can be determined by one of two methods: auscultation or palpation. Both methods require the use of a sphygmomanometer or blood pressure cuff. Characteristic sounds are listened for with a stethoscope during auscultation of blood pressure. For palpation, the radial pulse is palpated with the fingertips. Needless to say, the methods for blood pressure determination cannot be learned by reading a textbook. Practice both auscultation and palpation.

After taking and recording blood pressure, determine skin or body _____. The body temperature must be taken with a thermometer. Temperature in healthy individuals will range from 97°F to 99°F. Other than the body temperature, the EMT can determine the patient's _____ temperature. This is not a vital sign but it is a useful indicator. Hot, dry skin could indicate heatstroke. Cool, clammy skin could indicate shock.

temperature

skin

THE HEAD-TO-TOE SURVEY

NOTE: Consider all unconscious patients to have possible spinal injuries.

A head-to-toe examination is part of the _____ survey; however, it should be designed to consider the patient's chief (primary) complaint, the mechanism of injury, or the nature of the illness.

secondary

Palpate the cervical (neck) spine for tenderness and deformity. If tenderness is found, stop and immobilize the head and neck. Be sure you have checked the anterior neck to see if the patient is a neck breather. Always make sure you can see the _____ (ventral) surface of the neck so that you can check for a _____ or tracheostomy tube. Always examine the anterior and sides of the neck before applying a rigid collar.

anterior
stoma

After _____ the cervical spine for _____ and _____ the EMT should check the scalp for lacerations (cuts) and contusions (bruises). He should check for lumps that may indicate bleeding under the scalp, and he should check the skull for depressions that might indicate the bone has been fractured or crushed.

palpating
tenderness, deformity

When examining the head, the EMT should check for lacerations and contusions of the _____, lumps that may indicate _____ under the scalp, and depressions of the _____ that could indicate that the bone has been _____ or crushed.

scalp, bleeding
skull
fractured

After examining the skull, be certain to check the face for deformities and other signs of injury, especially injury to the facial bones.

Unless injuries to the _____ bones are obvious, gently palpate the cheekbones, forehead, and lower jaw.

facial

Next, the EMT should inspect the pupils of the eyes to see if they react to light and if they are both equal in size and reaction. The pupils may be di-

22

lated in shock and unconsciousness, constricted in drug overdose, or unequal in size in head injuries and stroke.

The state of consciousness can be an examination sign. Apparent unconsciousness can be confirmed if the pupils are _____ . After inspection of the pupils, look for contact lenses and remove them from the eyes of an unconscious patient. You should know how to remove both hard and soft (flexible) contact lenses.

dilated

While examining the pupils to see if they _____ to light and if they are _____ in size, also check the inner surfaces of the eyelids. They should be pink. If they are pale, internal blood loss is a possibility. If they are yellow, jaundice is suspected.

react
equal

Next, the EMT should examine the ears, nose, and mouth of the patient. This is done after the inner surfaces of the _____ have been inspected. The ears and nose should be checked for clear fluid and for blood. The mouth should also be inspected for blood and any possible or potential causes of airway obstruction. Be sure to sniff for odd breath odors that may be caused either by poisoning or by a diabetic condition.

eyelids

After noting whether the inner eyelids have their normal _____ color, look for _____ and _____ in the ears and nose. Check the mouth for possible airway obstruction and _____. Sniff for breath _____.

pink
fluids, blood
blood
odors

The other areas of the body are to be examined after you complete your examination of the _____. Clothing may hinder the examination. Where noted, and whenever you think there is an injury site, clothing should be opened or removed for proper site examination (follow local protocols). To expose an injury site, cut away clothing to avoid additional injury.

head

Remove or open articles of clothing on the patient when necessary to expose examination areas. _____ away clothing over any injury site. Next, check the chest for penetrations, fractures, and equal expansion. Using your stethoscope, listen for sounds of equal air entry.

Cut

Once the chest has been inspected for fractures, _____ expansion, and _____, the stethoscope should be used to listen for sounds of equal _____ _____. Next, the abdomen should be checked for penetrations, tenderness, rigidity, and spasms.

equal
penetration
air entry

Once the EMT has checked the head, neck, _____, and abdomen for injuries, he should check the lower back for point tenderness and deformity and then palpate the pelvis for possible fractures.

chest

The lower back should be examined for_____ tenderness and deformity, and the pelvis should be checked for _____. The genital region should be inspected for any obvious injuries, including nonmenstrual bleeding and priapism (involuntary erection).

point
fractures

One possible sign of spinal injury in the male is the involuntary erection of the penis. This is called _____. After inspecting the genital region, check both lower extremities for injury and paralysis and then both upper extremities for injury and paralysis.

priapism

The extremities are inspected after examining the _____ region. The extremities are checked for both injury and for _____. This is easier if the patient is conscious, since he can be asked if he has feeling in his limbs and if he can move his feet, move his legs, wiggle his toes, move his fingers and arms, etc.

genital

paralysis

A neurologic assessment is done for the conscious trauma patient to help detect injury and _____ of the extremities. A neurolog-

paralysis

ical assessment can be done for the unconscious patient by applying a painful stimulus to the tops of the feet and the backs of the hands.

WARNING: Field tests for neurologic function when the patient is unconscious are very unreliable. Always assume that the unconscious trauma patient has spinal injuries.

The assessment of the extremities of a conscious trauma patient should include testing for _____ function. Extremity assessment also should include an evaluation of circulation by checking for a distal pulse in each limb. The pulse used for the lower extremity can be the dorsalis pedis pulse or the posterior tibial pulse. The pulse used for the upper extremity is the same pulse that was used for the taking of vital signs, the _____ pulse. If a distal pulse is absent, check skin temperature and color, and test the time required for capillary refill.

Circulation in the extremities is assessed by checking for a _____ pulse. In most cases, the radial pulse and the _____ tibial pulse sites are used.

After checking for paralysis and _____ to the _____, the EMT should check for wounds to the back surfaces, including the buttocks.

All of the survey does not have to be performed on every patient. The survey should be geared to the patient's chief _____ and the nature of the illness or accident.

neurologic

radial

distal
posterior
injury
extremities

complaint

TERMINOLOGY

Define the following terms. Check your definitions with those in the Glossary of your textbook.

ABC's of emergency care—

Auscultation—

Mechanism of Injury—

Palpation—

Priapism—

Primary Survey—

Secondary Survey—

Sign—

Symptom—

Vital Signs—

MATCHING

Match the letter of the correct answers to the statements listed below. See the end of this chapter for the answers.

_____ 1. Primary survey
_____ 2. Secondary survey
_____ 3. Diastolic
_____ 4. Respiration rate (at rest)
_____ 5. Systolic

A. Paralysis

B. Heart contraction

C. Pulse

D. Heart relaxation

E. 12 to 20 per minute

F. 60 to 80 minute

MULTIPLE CHOICE

Circle the letter of the best answer to each question. The answers are given at the end of this chapter. Note that page references to the textbook are listed.

1. The EMT should gather information at the scene by (p. 65):
   A. Talking to patients
   B. Talking to bystanders
   C. Observing the patient
   D. All of the above

2. Which of the following is the most accessible distal pulse site for assessing circulation in the lower extremities? (p. 101)
   A. Femoral pulse
   B. Dorsalis pedis pulse
   C. Posterior tibial pulse
   D. Distal radial pulse

3. The look, listen, and feel method is used to assess (p. 72):
   A. Breathing
   B. Neurologic function
   C. Distal circulation
   D. The development of shock

4. To gather information, the EMT should know (p. 69):
   A. Types of accidents
   B. Types of injuries
   C. Mechanisms of injuries
   D. All of the above

5. Using a simple rule of thumb, the normal systolic blood pressure of a young male can be estimated by taking his age and adding (p. 88):
   A. 120
   B. 100
   C. 90
   D. 80

6. In shock, the blood pressure usually shows a (p. 88):
   A. Marked drop
   B. Rise
   C. Rapid rise
   D. Normal reading

7. Blood pressure is taken with a stethoscope and a (p. 75):
   A. Hydometer
   B. Photometer
   C. Pressoreceptor
   D. Sphygmomanometer

8. The most important diagnostic sign is (p. 70):
   A. Body temperature
   B. Pulse
   C. Heart action
   D. Respiration

9. The easiest method to check heart action is (p. 72):
   A. Pulse
   B. Stethoscope
   C. ECG
   D. EEG

10. The typical pulse rate for an adult male at rest is _____ beats per minute. *(p. 85)*:
    A. 60 to 72
    B. 70 to 75
    C. 60 to 80
    D. 70 to 100

11. Cool and clammy skin could indicate *(p. 90)*:
    A. Heatstroke
    B. Exposure to cold
    C. Mild fever
    D. Shock

12. Hot and dry skin could indicate *(p. 90)*:
    A. Heatstroke
    B. Exposure to cold
    C. Mild fever
    D. Shock

13. Dilated unresponsive pupils may indicate *(p. 94)*:
    A. Head injury
    B. Brain damage
    C. Unconsciousness
    D. Spinal injury

14. The order of the primary survey is *(pp. 71–73)*:
    A. Pulse, respiration, bleeding
    B. Respiration, pulse, bleeding
    C. Bleeding, pulse, respiration
    D. Respiration, bleeding, pulse

15. If, during the secondary survey, the head is found fixed in an abnormal position, the EMT should *(p. 91)*:
    A. Avoid neck examinations
    B. Raise the head
    C. Stabilize the head and neck
    D. Roll the head to a recumbent position

16. Constricted pupils could mean *(p. 94)*:
    A. Central nervous system damage
    B. Stroke
    C. Head injury
    D. Unconsciousness

17. Foot wave in a conscious patient probably indicates *(p. 102)*:
    A. Spinal cord damage
    B. Intact nerve pathways
    C. Muscle damage
    D. Damaged nerve pathways

18. Which of the following methods will give you both systolic and diastolic blood pressure *(pp. 88–89)*:
    A. Palpation
    B. Auscultation
    C. Oscillation
    D. All of the above

EXERCISES

1. List the vital signs *(p. 82)*.

2. List and describe the five steps of the primary survey *(pp. 71-73)*:

3. Describe how an EMT can check for lower limb paralysis in a conscious patient and in an unconscious patient *(p. 102)*.

4. List five of the problems that can interfere with patient assessment (p. 64).

5. List the eleven rules that must be followed during the secondary survey (pp. 105, 107).

6. What is the "AVPU" method for assessing a patient's level of consciousness (p. 83)?

7. What two factors are added together to find the total trauma score for a patient (p. 78)?

8. List the following activities of the secondary survey in the correct sequence from 1 to 20. See the end of this chapter for the answers (pp. 91-105).
   A. Inspect chest for penetration _____
   B. Palpate pelvis for fractures _____
   C. Inspect scalp for wounds _____
   D. Check each upper limb for injury and paralysis _____
   E. Inspect the back surfaces _____
   F. Inspect pupils for equality and reactivity _____
   G. Inspect mouth for blood _____
   H. Inspect genital region for obvious injury _____
   I. Inspect chest for fractures _____
   J. Palpate lower back for point tenderness _____
   K. Inspect ears and nose for blood or clear fluids _____
   L. Check each lower limb for injury and paralysis _____
   M. Inspect chest for equal expansion _____
   N. Inspect abdomen for penetration _____
   O. Inspect mouth for airway obstructions _____
   P. Inspect inner surfaces of eyelids _____
   Q. Palpate abdomen for tenderness _____
   R. Palpate the cervical spine for point tenderness and deformity _____
   S. Sniff for an odd breath odor _____
   T. Inspect neck for stoma or tracheostomy _____

ANSWERS

Matching

1. C   2. A   3. D   4. E   5. B

Multiple Choice

1. D	7. D	13. C
2. C	8. D	14. B
3. A	9. A	15. C
4. D	10. C	16. A
5. B	11. D	17. B
6. A	12. A	18. B

Exercise 8

A. 10	H. 17	O. 7
B. 16	I. 11	P. 5
C. 3	J. 15	Q. 14
D. 19	K. 6	R. 1
E. 20	L. 18	S. 9
F. 4	M. 12	T. 2
G. 8	N. 13	

4 basic life support i: the airway and pulmonary resuscitation

Reading Assignment: Emergency Care, 5th ed., pp. 111–135

THE RESPIRATORY SYSTEM

All cells in the body need oxygen (O_2) for survival. Lethal changes will begin to take place in the brain within 4 to 6 minutes without a constant and adequate supply of _____.

    oxygen

Atmospheric air is inhaled through the nose or the mouth. This air is 21% O_2 and 79% nitrogen and other gases. Without the _____ in the air we breathe, lethal changes will begin to take place in the brain in _____ to _____ minutes. Brain cells will die in 10 minutes if they do not receive a constant supply of oxygen.

    oxygen

    4, 6

Interruption of air flow is very dangerous. Since air is inhaled through the _____ or the _____, an obstruction in these areas could _____ the flow of air and cause lethal changes to begin in the _____ in 4 to 6 minutes. Brain cells will die in _____ minutes.

    nose, mouth

    interrupt

    brain, 10

Air passes from the nose and mouth into the pharynx (throat). In order to reach the trachea (windpipe), the air must pass through the larynx. Air cannot pass from the nose (or mouth) to the larynx if there is an obstruction in the _____.

    pharynx

At the beginning of the larynx is the epiglottis. This structure prevents liquids and solids from entering the larynx. If an obstruction does pass the epiglottis and enters the _____, air will not be able to flow from the pharynx to the _____.

    larynx

    trachea

The trachea gives rise to the bronchi, which branch into the bronchioles. The bronchioles end in tiny air sacs called alveoli. This is where the _____ in the air is transferred to the blood. If there is any form of an obstruction, the O_2 in the air will never reach the _____ to be transferred to the _____. Without O_2, all the cells of the body will _____.

    oxygen

    alveoli

    blood

    die

The inside of the lungs consists of the bronchi, the bronchioles ending in tiny air sacs called _____, and the blood vessels that pick up _____ from the air. The outside of the lungs is surrounded by a double-wall sac called the pleura. One layer of the pleura attaches to the chest wall, while the other layer attaches to the lungs.

    alveoli

    oxygen

When air flows into the lungs, the process is called inspiration. For an inspiration to occur, the diaphragm and the muscles between the ribs (intercostal muscles) must contract. Expiration, or the flow of air from the

27

28

lungs back into the atmosphere, requires the intercostal muscles and the _____ to relax. The average adult male takes 12 to 20 breaths per minute. During the single inspiration, 500 cc of air will move _____ the lungs. This is known as the tidal volume.

diaphragm

into

PULMONARY RESUSCITATION

NOTE: Make certain that you follow your EMS system's guidelines for personal safety so that you can avoid contact with the patient's blood and body fluids.

The superior method of pulmonary resuscitation is mouth-to-mouth resuscitation. Mechanical ventilation devices are very useful in emergency care, but their use takes up valuable time. As an EMT, you will learn how to provide pulmonary _____ with and without special equipment. Equipment like a pocket face mask with one-way valve or a bag-valve-mask is recommended because its use protects you from infectious disease. However, current American Heart Association guidelines require that you must also master the techniques of mouth-to-mouth and mouth-to-nose resuscitation.

resuscitation

Mechanical ventilation devices offer you protection from _____ disease, but their use can take up valuable _____. Also, such devices can fail to perform. When a patient requires basic life support, pulmonary _____ should be started without delay. If you are off duty and the proper equipment is not available, you should know how to give the patient _____-to-_____ resuscitation. You should realize, however, that this technique may expose you to infectious disease.

infectious, time

resuscitation

mouth, mouth

There are many advantages to using the mouth-to-mouth technique of pulmonary _____. It requires no special _____ and can be done by one person. The effectiveness of this method is easy to evaluate simply by looking for breathing _____, _____ for airflow, and _____ for air exchange. Be sure to take at last 5 seconds to assess the patient's breathing.

resuscitation

equipment

movements, listening

feeling

To be effective, maximum extension of the airway must be accomplished by tilting the patient's _____ backward (no spinal injuries). The nose must be sealed off, the mouth opened widely and sealed by the EMT's mouth during the inflow of air. This should be done at the rate of 12 breaths per minute. The correct volume of air will not reach the patient's lungs if there is improper _____ of the patient's head, the nose is not _____, the mouth is not opened _____ enough, and if the EMT's mouth does not properly _____ the patient's mouth during the inflow of air.

head

tilting

sealed, widely

seal

Before initiating mouth-to-mouth resuscitation, first ensure an _____ airway. For the maximum airway opening, use the _____-tilt, chin-lift maneuver. The patient is placed on his back in the _____ position. Kneeling beside the patient, place one hand on his forehead to ensure a head-tilt and use your other hand to lift his chin, keeping the mouth opened.

open

head

supine

The head-tilt, _____-_____ maneuver can be used to open a patient's airway. Another maneuver, the jaw-thrust, can be used to open a patient's airway in cases that may involve spinal injury. This maneuver allows for the forward displacement of the jaw without a major lifting of the neck or tilting of the _____.

chin-lift

head

Before the first mouth-to-mouth ventilation can take place, the patient's _____ must be sealed off and his mouth opened widely and _____ by the EMT's _____ . The EMT exhales into the mouth of the patient until he sees the patient's chest rise and feels resistance offered by the patient's expanding lungs. Two breaths are delivered, allowing the patient to passively exhale between each breath. The breaths must be adequate, taking 1 to 1.5 seconds per ventilation.

nose, sealed mouth

After the EMT provides the patient with _____ _____ breaths, he should stop and monitor the patient's breathing and pulse rate. If there is a pulse, but the patient has not begun _____ respiration, the EMT can begin the pattern of _____ breaths per minute delivered at the rate of 1 breath every 5 seconds. If there is no pulse, the EMT will have to initiate CPR.

2 adequate

spontaneous

12

There are variations of the mouth-to-mouth technique. Since air can enter the airway by 1 of 2 ways, mouth-to-mouth can be replaced with mouth-to-_____ when there is lower jaw or mouth damage.

nose

For infants and small children, the EMT should cover both the mouth and nose. Infants should receive 1 _____ breath every 3 seconds, while children should receive 1 adequate breath every 4 seconds. These rates differ from the rate for adults which is 1 adequate breath every _____ _____. If a pocket face mask is used, it should be the correct size for the patient.

adequate

5

seconds

During artificial ventilation, gastric distention may occur. This is the condition of air being forced into the stomach. A slight distention is of no real significance in an emergency situation. A marked distention may cause problems and indicates that there may be an airway obstruction.

The patient with marked _____ distention may vomit. The pressure of his air-filled _____ may push up against the primary muscle of respiration, the _____ . Current guidelines discourage attempts to relieve gastric distention unless suction devices are on hand. Usually, gastric distention can be avoided by positioning the patient's head properly, delivering ventilations so that each breath takes _____ to _____ seconds to deliver, and watching the patient's _____ _____.

gastric

stomach

diaphragm

1, 1.5

chest rise

The EMT should attempt to relieve gastric distention if there is _____ equipment on hand. Place the patient on his side and use the flat of your hand to apply moderate pressure on the patient's abdomen, between the navel and the edge of his _____ _____ . *Be prepared for patient vomiting*. You must suction or sweep the mouth clear immediately.

suction

rib cage

Another special case is the treatment of a patient who has had a laryngectomy. His larynx has been surgically removed and the trachea has been attached to a permanent opening in the neck called a stoma. Since no air can be conducted from the mouth and nose to the lungs, mouth-to-mouth techniques must be replaced by mouth-to-_____ resuscitation. Some EMS systems approve the use of a pediatric-sized pocket face mask over the top of the stoma. The neck-breather, that is, someone who has a _____ , should be given resuscitation at the same rate as applied to an adult. The rate should be _____ breaths per _____ .

stoma

laryngectomy

12, minute

Before initiating mouth-to-stoma ventilation, check to see if the _____ patient's stoma has a breathing tube. If it does, the tube may be clogged. Also, before beginning any resuscitative measures, check to see if the laryngectomy patient's trachea is clear. If necessary, quickly clean the opening using a gauze pad. The trachea can be cleared using a sterile suction catheter (see Chapter 6).

laryngectomy

AIRWAY OBSTRUCTION

Many deaths in cases of heart attacks and accidents could be prevented by a well-trained EMT applying modern resuscitative techniques (artificial ventilation) immediately at the scene. Since brain damage can occur in a matter of minutes, the EMT should remove any obstructions blocking the airway and begin artificial ventilation _____.

immediately

The airway can be blocked by a complete or partial obstruction. The EMT should remove any _____ and begin _____ _____ immediately. If this is not done, irreparable damage to the brain cells will begin in _____ to _____ minutes. As the vital cells of the body die and the functions of the heart, brain, and lungs cease, asphyxia occurs.

obstruction

artificial ventilation

4, 6

Foreign matter such as mucus, blood, or food can obstruct the airway. Vital cells will die, giving rise to the condition known as _____. In addition to the airway being blocked by _____ _____, the state of unconsciousness can cause the neck to be flexed at such an angle that the tongue will be forced against the pharynx. This will obstruct the flow of air form the mouth and nose to the _____ and the rest of the airway. The EMT should begin by properly placing the head of the patient. If breathing is not restored, he should check for and remove any _____ and start _____ _____ immediately.

asphyxia

foreign matter

pharynx

obstructions, artificial ventilation

The EMT must be able to quickly recognize an airway obstruction. The patient's head should be properly positioned. Next, the EMT should look for breathing movements, listen for airflow at the mouth and nose, and feel for air exchange. As the EMT _____ for breathing movements, he should position his ear close to the patient's mouth and nose to _____ for airflow and to _____ for air exchange. A partial _____ can cause noisy breathing. The EMT should _____ to detect snoring, crowing, or gurgling sounds.

looks

listen, feel

obstruction

listen

The conscious patient with a partial airway obstruction may still be able to speak and cough. A complete airway obstruction in a conscious patient is easily recognized since the patient will not be able to _____ or _____. This patient will not be breathing. He may even show indications of cyanosis, the turning of skin and lip color to blue. Most of these individuals will give you a distress signal by clutching their neck between the thumb and index finger.

talk

cough

The unconscious patient with a partial airway obstruction will have _____ breathing. The conscious patient with a partial obstruction of the airway may still be able to _____ and _____. Any patient with a complete airway obstruction will not be _____ . The conscious patient will not be able to speak and cough. He may show indications of _____. Many of these patients will give you a _____ _____ by clutching their neck with the thumb and fingers.

noisy

talk, cough

breathing

cyanosis

distress signal

CORRECTING AIRWAY OBSTRUCTIONS

If the patient is conscious and has a partial airway obstruction, he should still be able to speak and _____. Watch this patient carefully, but *do not* interfere with his efforts to expel the obstruction.

cough

The conscious patient with a complete airway obstruction will need your assistance to expel the foreign object that is causing the obstruction. You im-

mediately will have to use manual thrusts (usually _____ | **abdominal**
thrusts). Remember, before you take any action, ask the patient if he or she
can talk or _____. | **cough**

You should begin to correct an airway obstruction by asking the patient
if he or she can _____ or cough. If the patient cannot do one of these, | **speak**
the obstruction is _____. Deliver 6 to 10 abdominal thrusts | **complete/(total)**
in _____ succession. Continue with the manual thrusts until the | **rapid**
object is expelled or the patient loses consciousness. If there is a loss of con-
sciousness, open the airway and attempt to _____, deliver 6 | **ventilate**
to 10 abdominal thrusts, attempt finger sweeps, and reattempt to ventilate.
Continue until you are successful.

The most common form of manual thrust is the abdominal thrust. This
thrust can be delivered if the patient is standing or sitting. A patient lying
on his stomach is in the _____ position. To utilize abdominal | **prone**
thrusts, roll the patient onto his back, placing him in the _____ | **supine**
position.

The most common form of manual thrust is the _____ thrust. | **abdominal**
This maneuver can be used for patients who are sitting, standing, or lying in
the _____ position. For patients sitting or standing, begin by plac- | **supine**
ing yourself behind the patient and wrapping your arms around his waist.
Place the thumb side of one fist along the midline of the patient's abdomen,
above the navel and below the rib cage. The emphasis of the hand position
is done with the heel of the fist. Do not jam your knuckles into the patient's
abdomen. Grasp this positioned hand and press it into the patient's | **6 to 10**
abdomen with a quick upward thrust. This is to be done _____ times in | **rapid succession**
_____ _____. | **supine**
 | **abdominal**

If the patient is lying down, he must be moved to the _____ | **supine**
position before the _____ thrust will be effective. Kneel | **abdominal**
close to his side, facing his chest. (**NOTE:** In some cases, straddling the
patient will be more effective.) Place the heel of one hand on the patient's
abdomen along the _____, slightly above the _____ and | **midline, navel**
below the _____ _____. Place your other hand over the positioned hand, | **rib cage**
your shoulders are directly over the patient's abdomen. Press toward the
patient's diaphragm in a quick upward thrust. This is to be done _____ | **6 to 10**
times, in _____ _____. | **rapid succession**

The chestthrust method also is very effective for expelling an airway
obstruction. Begin by standing behind the standing or sitting patient. Your
hands will be positioned the same as for the abdominal thrust, except they
will be placed over a point on the chest that is 2 finger-widths above the
xiphoid process (see CPR). For the chest thrust, the force is applied directly
backward, instead of _____ as in the abdominal thrust. | **upward**

The chest thrust can be used for patients lying down as long as they are
in the _____ position. Again, follow the procedure for the | **supine**
_____ thrust, but position your hands over the sternum, | **abdomial**
_____ finger-widths above the _____ process. The force should | **2, xiphoid**
be aimed directly downward.

To correct a complete airway obstruction in a conscious patient, begin
by asking the patient if he can _____ _____ _____. If the pa- | **talk or cough**
tient cannot talk or gives you a distress signal, begin with _____ | **6 to 10**
abdominal thrusts delivered in rapid succession.

The unconscious patient with a complete airway obstruction will not be
breathing. Gently tap the patient's shoulders and talk to him to see if he is
responsive. Begin by attempting to establish an open _____. | **airway**

Check again for breathing and, if necessary, ventilate by providing _____ breaths. If this is unsuccessful, reposition the patient's head and attempt once more to _____. The second ventilation attempt should be followed by 6 to 10 _____ _____ delivered in rapid succession. Turning the patient's head to the side will reduce the chances of his breathing in (aspirating) vomitus if the manual thrusts induce vomiting.

    After applying manual thrusts, you should perform finger _____ using a gloved hand. The purpose of the finger sweep is to remove any foreign objects from the patient's mouth.

    Should your patient be an infant, cradle the infant in the face-down position and deliver four back blows. Turn the infant over and deliver four chest thrusts using the tips of two or three fingers. *Never* place an infant or small child with a partial airway obstruction in the head-down position as long as they are breathing adequately in the upright position.

2

ventilate
abdominal thrusts

sweeps

TERMINOLOGY

Define the following terms. Check your definitions with those in the Glossary of your textbook.

Alveoli—

Asphyxia—

Cyanosis—

Diaphragm—

Epiglottis—

Inspiration—

Laryngectomy—

Pleura—

Resuscitation—

FORMING MEDICAL TERMS

The following are some of the elements of medical terms used in this chapter. The answers are given at the end of the chapter.

Roots and Combining Forms

cyano (sigh-ah-no-): blue
laryngo (LAR-in-ge-o-): referring to the larynx
pulmo (PUL-mo-), *pulmono*-(PUL-mon-o-), pulmonary: referring to the respiratory system or specifically to the lungs
tracheo (TRAY-key-o): referring to the trachea

Prefixes

epi (EP-i): on or upon. The glottis is the opening of the airway in the larynx. A structure that is on the superior part of the larynx (above the glottis) would be called the _____.

Suffixes

-*al*: pertaining to (e.g., pleural membrane). If a structure is part of the trachea, it is a _____eal structure.

-ectomy (-EK-to-me): to surgically remove (excision, excised), as in the removal of the larynx. This surgery would be called a _____ectomy.
-osis (-o-sis): a conditon or disease. If a patient has a condition in which there is a blue discoloration of the skin, the patient is said to have _____ _____osis.
-stomy (-stow-me), *-ostomy* (-OS-to-me): to surgically create an artificial opening. such an opening in the trachea would be called a _____.

LABELING

Label the drawing in the lettered spaces provided (*p. 52*). The answers are given at the end of this chapter.

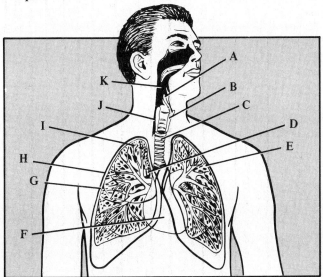

Figure 4–1

A. _____

B. _____

C. _____

D. _____

E. _____

F. _____

G. _____

H. _____

I. _____

J. _____

K. _____

MATCHING

Match the letter of the correct answer to each phrase. The answers are given at the end of this chapter.

_____ 1. Stoma
_____ 2. 500 cc
_____ 3. Inspiration
_____ 4. Snoring
_____ 5. Crowing
_____ 6. Gurgling

A. Diaphragm contraction

B. Obstruction by tongue

C. Concussion

D. Laryngectomy

E. Tracheal obstruction

F. Inspiration

G. Laryngeal spasms

H. 1000 cc

MULTIPLE CHOICE

Circle the letter of the best answer to each question. Answers are given at the end of this chapter. Note page references to *Emergency Care, 5th ed.*

1. Atmospheric air contains (*p. 120*).
   A. 10 percent oxygen
   B. 16 percent oxygen
   C. 21 percent oxygen
   D. 25 percent oxygen

2. Under normal conditions, once respiratory arrest begins, lethal changes in the brain will begin in (*p. 114*).
   A. 10 to 20 minutes
   B. 4 to 6 minutes
   C. 30 minutes to 1 hour
   D. 3 to 5 seconds

3. At the beginning of the larynx is a structure that can prevent liquids and objects from entering the respiratory tract. It is known as the (*p. 114*).
   A. Epiglottis
   B. Stoma
   C. Trachea
   D. Esophagus

4. At the begining of an inspiration, both the intercostal muscles and the _____ contract (p. 115).
   A. Alveoli
   B. Pleura
   C. Epiglottis
   D. Diaphragm

5. A double-walled sac surrounds each lung. It is called the (p. 115):
   A. Peritoneum
   B. Meninges
   C. Pericardium
   D. Pleura

6. Which of the following is the process in which the volume of the chest cavity increases and the lungs expand? (p. 115)
   A. Expiration
   B. Inspiration
   C. Compression
   D. Concussion

7. The tiny air sacs at the ends of the bronchioles are the (p. 114):
   A. Bronchi
   B. Papillae
   C. Microviilli
   D. Alveoli

8. When at rest, the average alult male will breathe (p. 116):
   A. 60 times a minute
   B. 75 to 100 times a minute
   C. 12 to 20 times a minute
   D. 30 times a minute

9. The average breath of an adult male at rest is (p. 116):
   A. 1000 cc
   B. 4500 cc
   C. 500 cc
   D. 150 cc

10. If the volume of the thoracic cavity increases, the pressure within the cavity (p. 115):
    A. Decreases
    B. Increases
    C. Stays the same
    D. At first increases, but then rapidly decreases.

11. In Caucasians, cyanosis will cause the skin to turn (p. 116):
    A. White
    B. Blue
    C. Light red
    D. Deep red

12. Respiratory failure is (p. 116):
    A. The cessation of normal breathing
    B. The reduction of breathing to where it is not sufficient to support life

C. Both A and B
D. None of the above

13. When an unconscious person's head is flexed forward the airway will be obstructed by the (p. 117):
    A. Tongue
    B. Epiglottis
    C. Carotid artery
    D. Pharynx

14. The very first step to aid a patient who is not breathing is to (p. 117):
    A. Clear the mouth
    B. Administer oxygen
    C. Apply positive ventilation
    D. Open the airway

15. To detect an obstruction of the airway, the EMT should look for breathing movements, and listen and feel for air exchange at the (p. 120):
    A. Mouth and nose
    B. Chest
    C. The nose only
    D. The mouth only

16. Which of the following sounds indicates spasms of the larynx? (p. 126)
    A. Snoring
    B. Crowing
    C. Gurgling
    D. Crackling

17. An EMT is trying to correct a complete airway obstruction in a conscious adult patient. The first maneuver is to deliver (p. 127):
    A. Abdominal thrusts
    B. Back blows
    C. Finger sweeps
    D. Ventilations

18. Which of the following is the correct sequence of steps for an EMT who has opened an unconscious patient's airway, attempted ventilations, and has detected an upper airway obstruction that is not visible? (p. 132)
    A. Back blows, finger sweeps, abdomial thrusts
    B. Abdominal thrusts, finger sweeps, ventilations
    C. Reattempt ventilations, abdominal thrusts, finger sweeps, ventilations
    D. Finger sweeps, reattempt ventilations, abdominal thrusts, ventilations

19. Usually, the most expedient form of artificial ventilation is (p. 120):
    A. Mouth-to-stoma
    B. Back-pressure, arm-lift
    C. Chest-pressure, arm-lift
    D. Mouth-to-mouth

20. In the mouth-to-mouth resuscitation of adult patients, the ventilation should be repeated once every *(p. 121):*
    A. Seconds
    B. 5 seconds
    C. 10 seconds
    D. 12 seconds

21. In the mouth-to-mouth resuscitation of an infant, the ventilation should be repeated once every *(p. 122):*
    A. Seconds
    B. 2 seconds
    C. 3 seconds
    D. 4 seconds

22. In the mouth-to-stoma resuscitation method (adult patient), the ventilation should be repeated once every *(p. 124):*
    A. Seconds
    B. 2 seconds
    C. 5 seconds
    D. 10 seconds

23. Which of the following is an advantage of the mouth-to-mouth method? *(p. 120)*
    A. Requires one person
    B. Done without delay
    C. Needs no equipment
    D. All of the above

24. After a laryngectomy, there is a permanent opening in the neck called a *(p. 123):*
    A. Catheter tube
    B. Meatus
    C. Stoma
    D. Papilla

25. When providing mouth-to-mouth and nose ventilations to an infant, use the *(p. 122):*
    A. Jaw-thrust method
    B. Head-tilt, chin-lift maneuver
    C. Simple head-tilt
    D. Head-tilt, neck-lift maneuver

26. When providing ventilation, each breath should take _____ to deliver *(p. 121).*
    A. 1 to 1.5 seconds
    B. 2 to 2.5 seconds
    C. 3 to 3.5 seconds
    D. 4 to 4.5 seconds

27. When applying back blows to an infant to correct a complete airway obstruction, the patient should be cradled *(p. 130):*
    A. In the supine position
    B. In the sitting position
    C. In an upright position
    D. In the face-down position

28. The recommended procedure for opening the airway of a patient with possible spinal injury is the *(p. 119):*
    A. Head-tilt
    B. Head-tilt, chin-lift
    C. Head-tilt, neck-lift
    D. Jaw-thrust

29. Before beginning any resuscitative procedures with the laryngectomy patient, the EMT should first check for obstructions in the *(p. 123):*
    A. Trachea
    B. Pharynx
    C. Larynx
    D. Nose and mouth

30. For the chest-thrust maneuver, the hands are placed *(p. 128):*
    A. Two finger-widths above the xiphoid process
    B. At the lower border of the rib cage
    C. Directly over the xiphoid
    D. Directly over the clavicle

EXERCISES

To check your answers to the Exercises, refer to *Emergency Care, 5th ed.*

1. Describe the breathing process in terms of volume changes in the chest cavity and pressure changes in the lungs *(p. 115).*

2. List the steps in the treatment of a complete airway obstruction in an unconscious adult patient *(p. 132).*

3. Describe the jaw-thrust maneuver *(p. 119).*

36

4. List the advantages of the mouth-to-mouth resuscitative technique (p. 120).

5 Describe step by step, mouth-to-mouth resuscitation (pp. 120–121).

ANSWERS

Forming Medical Terms

epiglottis, tracheal, laryngectomy (LAR-in-JEK-to-me), cyanosis, tracheostomy (TRAY-ke-OS-to-me)

Labeling—*Figure 4–1*

A. Epiglottis
B. Larynx
C. Trachea
D. Bronchi
E. Alveoli
F. Heart
G. Pleural space
H. Pleura
I. Lung
J. Esophagus
K. Pharynx

Matching

1. D   2. F   3. A   4. B   5. G   6. E

Multiple Choice

1. C	9. C	17. A	24. C
2. B	10. A	18. C	25. B
3. A	11. B	19. D	26. A
4. D	12. C	20. B	27. D
5. D	13. A	21. C	28. D
6. B	14. D	22. C	29. A
7. D	15. A	23. D	30. A
8. C	16. B		

the patient's feet, he locates the lower margin of the rib cage. Next, he moves his fingers along the rib cage until he finds where the ribs meet with the breastbone or _____. Keeping his middle finger resting over this point and his index finger resting over the lower end of the sternum, the EMT places the heel of his free hand on the midline of the chest so that the thumb side of his hand touches the index finger of the hand placed at the lower end of the sternum. The EMT's hand is now over the CPR _____ site.

sternum

compression

The EMT should position himself over the patient and place the _____ of one hand over the compression site on the _____. The heel of the other hand should be placed over the back of the first with the fingers pointing away from his body. The entire weight of the upper portion of the EMT's body is used to _____ the chest of the patient 1 1/2 to 2 inches. If two EMTs are working together, a rate of 80 to 100 compressions per minute is recommended. If one EMT is doing the CPR, he must not only be involved with artificial circulation, but also with artificial _____. It is recommended that he perform compressions at the rate of 80 to 100 per minute.

heel, sternum

compress

ventilation

CPR: ONE RESCUER

To determine if the patient is in cardiac arrest, the EMT should have observed no _____ and no _____. The ABC technique should be employed. The _____ must be cleared and _____ breaths given. If spontaneous respiration does not begin, then the chest must be compressed at a rate of_____ per minute. Proper technique calls for compressions and _____. After 15 compressions, the patient's head should be flexed back and his lungs inflated 2 times. The cycle of 15 compressions and _____ ventilations must be continued until the patient recovers or competent medical personnel relieve the EMT. Periodically (every few minutes) monitor the carotid pulse.

respiration, pulse
airway
2
80 to 100
ventilations

2

CPR: TWO RESCUERS

The same basic cycle is followed except one EMT performs chest compressions at the rate of _____ per minute, while the other EMT performs _____. The cycle for the 2-rescuer team is 5 compressions and 1 full breath. This differs from the 1-rescuer cycle of _____ compressions followed by _____ ventilations.

80 to 100
ventilations

15, 2

One advantage of 2-rescuer CPR is that the rescuers can switch positions, with the compressor EMT switching to ventilations and the ventilator EMT switching to compressions. When the EMT giving compressions moves to the ventilating position, he should monitor for a _____ _____ and spontaneous respirations. It is recommended that the ventilator use a protective device such as a pocket face mask with one-way valve or a bag-valve-mask.

carotid
pulse

CPR: INFANTS AND CHILDREN

Much less pressure is needed for compressions when working with infants and children. Only the tips of the index and middle fingers should be used for infants, compressing the chest (sternum) only 1/2 to 1 inch. For children, the heel of one hand will be enough to compress the _____ from 1 to 1 1/2 inches.

sternum

The EMT should compress the sternum of a child from _____ to

1

_____ inches, using the _____ of one hand. For infants, use the _____ of the _____ and _____ fingers to compress the sternum _____ to _____ inch.

1 1/2 , heel, tips
index, midle,
1/2 , 1

The CPR compression site for both the infant and the child can be found along the vertical midline of the _____. The infant's site is one finger-width below the intermammary line. The child's site is found the same as an adult's.

sternum

One hand is placed over the child's CPR compression site for the delivery of external chest compressions. Two or three finger tips are placed over the infant's CPR compression site. This site is _____ sternum, one finger-width below the _____ line.

mid-
intermammary

The compression rate over the child's _____ compression site should be delivered at the same rate as one-rescuer CPR, _____ compressions per minute. A compression rate of at least 100 per minute is used for infants. Only 1 ventilation after every 5 compressions is required.

CPR
80 to 100

Remember that the neck of an infant cannot be extended like that of an adult. Deliver 1 ventilation every _____ compressions. For the infant, the compression rate is at least _____ per minute.

5
100

EFFECTIVENESS OF CPR

The pupils of the patient's eyes may constrict, the patient's color may improve, but a _____ at the carotid artery *must* be felt with each cardiac compression. Because of the heart-lung-brain relationship, the EMT should consider spontaneous respiration as an indication that the patient is no longer in the state of _____ _____.

pulse

cardiac arrest

TERMINATING CPR

CPR is not to be terminated unless spontaneous circulation and respiration begin, or the patient is turned over to a qualified professional or medical facility, or the rescuer is too exhausted to carry on. The rescuer should realize that CPR has its physical limitations for the performer. You should not feel guilty if you cannot continue.

TERMINOLOGY

Define the following terms. Check your definitions with those in the Glossary of your textbook.

Brachial pulse—

Cardiac arrest—

Cardiopulmonary resuscitation—

Conduction system—

CPR compression site—

FORMING MEDICAL TERMS

The following are some of the elements of medical terms that were used in this chapter. The answers are given at the end of the chapter.

Roots and Combining Forms

cardio- (KAR-de-o-), *cardiac* (KAR-de-ak): referring to the heart.

Prefixes

hyper- (HI-per-): above, over, or in excess
intra- (in-trah-): inside of
inter- (in-ter-): between
peri- (per-i-): around

The septum between the two ventricles is called the _____ ventricular septum. The sac that surrounds the heart is the _____ial sac.

LABELING

Label the drawing in the lettered spaces. Mark the position of the CPR compression site *(p. 144)*. The answers are given at the end of this chapter.

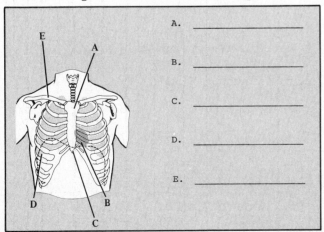

A. _____

B. _____

C. _____

D. _____

E. _____

Figure 5-1

COMPLETION

The following paragraph traces the path of blood through the heart. Enter the name of the correct structure in the lettered blanks. Use the drawing of the heart as a guide. See answers at the end of this chapter.

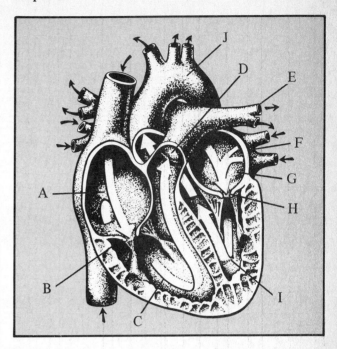

Figure 5-2

Blood from the body enters the right side of the heart into the (A) _____ _____. When this chamber contracts, it sends blood through a one-way (B) _____ into the (C) _____ _____. This chamber contracts, sending blood through another one-way (D) _____ into vessels going to the (E) _____. Oxygenated blood returns to the (F) _____ side of the heart into the (G) _____ _____. This chamber contracts, sending the blood through a one-way (H) _____ into the (I) _____ _____. When this lower chamber contracts, it forces blood through another one-way valve into the great artery called the (J) _____ into systemic circulation.

MATCHING

Match the letter of the correct answer to each phrase. The answers are given at the end of this chapter.

_____ 1. Carotid pulse
_____ 2. 10 minutes
_____ 3. Xiphoid
_____ 4. Brachial pulse
_____ 5. Thoracic

A. Sternum

B. Neck

C. Chest

D. Clinical death

E. Arm

F. Biological death

G. Wrist

MULTIPLE CHOICE

Circle the letter of the best answer to each question. Answers are given at the end of this chapter. Note page references to _Emergency Care, 5th ed._

1. Blood is sent from the heart to the _____ to pick up oxygen. _(p. 140)_.
   A. Brain
   B. Lungs
   C. Trachea
   D. Larynx

2. Signals from the _____ help to regulate the related activities of the heart and the lungs _(p. 139)_.
   A. Liver
   B. Spleen
   C. Celiac
   D. Brain

3. When the heart stops beating, the cells of the _____ usually will begin to die in 10 minutes _(p. 141)_.
   A. Heart
   B. Brain
   C. Liver
   D. Kidney

4. When the heart falters and stops because it is not receiving oxygen, the condition is known as _(p. 143)_:
   A. Coronary
   B. Pulmonary arrest
   C. Cardiac arrest
   D. CVA

5. After establishing unresponsiveness, the first primary survey sign of the condition in question 4 is _(p. 143)_:
   A. Pulmonary arrest
   B. Cardiac arrest
   C. Cyanosis
   D. Pupil dilation

6. During cardiac arrest, the pupils usually will _(p. 146)_:
   A. Constrict
   B. Not be visible because of eye roll back
   C. Dilate
   D. Appear normal

7. To examine for cardiac arrest, the EMT should check for a pulse at the _(p. 143)_:
   A. Radial artery
   B. Great saphenous vein
   C. Aorta
   D. Carotid artery

8. The heart is protected to the front by the ribs and the _____ in the middle of the chest. _(p. 144)_
   A. Clavicle
   B. Xiphoid
   C. Scapula
   D. Sternum

9. Which of the following structures is at the lower end of the sternum? _(p. 147)_
   A. Xiphoid
   B. Clavicle
   C. Scapula
   D. Mastoid

10. The CPR compression point is located halfway between a midpoint on the sternum superior to the _(p. 144)_:
    A. Ribs
    B. Substernal notch
    C. Hyoid
    D. Clavicle

11. In the ABC method of cardiopulmonary resuscitation, the A stands for _(p. 141)_:
    A. Air flow
    B. Arterial pulse
    C. Airway
    D. Aorta

12. In the ABC method of cardiopulmonary resuscitation, the C stands for *(pp. 142-143)*:
    A. Cardiac
    B. Compression
    C. Circulation
    D. Carotid

13. After clearing the airway, the EMT should inflate the patient's lung with *(p. 143)*:
    A. One quick, full breath
    B. Two adequate breaths
    C. One half breath
    D. Four quick, adequate breaths

14. Effective CPR consists of *(pp. 144-146)*:
    A. Compression
    B. Release
    C. Ventilation
    D. All of the above

15. To determine cardiac arrest in an infant, the EMT should use the *(p. 155)*:
    A. Brachial pulse
    B. Carotid pulse
    C. Femoral pulse
    D. Apical pulse

16. When the heel of the hand is placed over the CPR compression site, the fingers should be *(p. 145)*:
    A. Curved on top of the ribs
    B. Curled into a fist
    C. Pointing away from the rescuer's body
    D. Held together

17. During the CPR of an adult, the sternum should be compressed *(p. 145)*:
    A. 1/2 to 3 inches
    B. 1 1/2 to 2 inches
    C. 3 inches
    D. 1 inch

18. The compression rate for 1-rescuer CPR is *(p. 145)*:
    A. 80 to 100 per minute
    B. 60 to 80 per minute
    C. 30 per minute
    D. 15 per minute

19. The compression rate for 2-rescuer CPR is *(p. 152)*:
    A. 80 to 100 per minute
    B. 60 to 80 per minute
    C. 30 per minute
    D. 10 per minute

20. The rate of ventilations during 1-rescuer CPR is *(p. 145)*:
    A. 2 every 15 compressions
    B. 2 every 5 compressions
    C. 1 every 15 compressions
    D. 1 every 5 compressions

21. The rate of ventilations during 2-rescuer CPR is *(p. 152)*:
    A. 2 every 15 compressions
    B. 2 every 5 compressions
    C. 1 every 15 compressions
    D. 1 every 5 compressions

22. During CPR, the rescuer should compress the sternum of an infant *(p. 155)*:
    A. 1 to 1 1/2 inches
    B. 1/2 to 1 inch
    C. 1/4 to 1/2 inch
    D. 1 1/4 to 2 inches

23. For children, the EMT should apply compression with *(p. 155)*:
    A. Finger tips
    B. One finger
    C. Both hands
    D. The heel of one hand

24. If CPR is effective, the pupils of the eyes often *(p. 146)*:
    A. Do not change
    B. Turn gray
    C. Constrict
    D. Dilate

25. A patient is in cardiac arrest. The EMT fears he will fracture the patient's ribs during CPR. The EMT should *(p. 147)*:
    A. Continue CPR
    B. Stop CPR
    C. Use only pulmonary resuscitation
    D. Apply a precordial thump

EXERCISES

To check your answers to the Exercises, refer to *Emergency Care, 5th ed.*

1. Describe the position of the body and the hands of the EMT during CPR *(pp. 144-146)*.

2. Compare and contrast 1-rescuer and 2-rescuer CPR *(p. 157)*.

3. List 2 ways an EMT can be certain of the effectiveness of CPR *(p. 146)*.

4. Indicate whether the hand positions shown in Figure 5-3 are correct or incorrect. If a position is incorrect, describe what possible damage can be done *(p. 147)*.

5. Explain, step by step, how the switch-over is done during 2-rescuer CPR *(p. 152)*.

6. Describe the techniques used to provide CPR when moving the patient *(pp. 156-158)*.

ANSWERS

Forming Medical Terms

interventricular, pericardial

Labeling-Figure 5-1

A. Sternum B. Heart C. Xiphoid D. Lung
E. Clavicle

Completion-Figure 5-2

A. Right atrium	F. Left
B. Valve	G. Left atrium
C. Right ventricle	H. Valve
D. Valve	I. Left ventricle
E. Lungs	J. Aorta

Matching

1. B 2. F 3. A 4. E 5. C

Multiple Choice

1. B	8. D.	15. A	22. B
2. D	9. A	16. C	23. D
3. B	10. B	17. B	24. C
4. C	11. C	18. A	25. A
5. A	12. C	19. A	
6. C	13. B	20. A	
7. D	14. D	21. D	

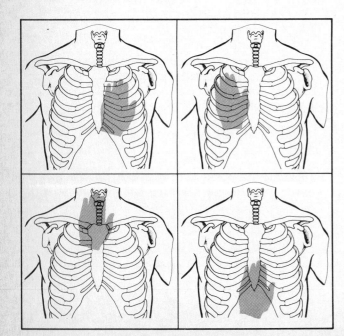

Figure 5-3

6 breathing aids and oxygen therapy

Reading Assignment: Emergency Care, 5th ed., pp. 161–189

AIDS TO BREATHING

There are many devices available to open and maintain an airway, suction a patient's mouth and throat, and supplement artificial ventilation. When using these devices, you should wear gloves to protect yourself from contact with the patient's _____ or body _____.

blood, fluids

Most of the time the head-tilt, chin-lift or jaw-thrust method can be used to open an airway. Once the airway is open, an oropharyngeal airway will keep it open.

The major function of an oropharyngeal airway is to keep the airway _____. When using the oropharyngeal airway, remember that the patient must be unconscious. Otherwise, his gag reflex will cause vomiting that may lead to aspiration.

open

To properly position an _____ airway, the EMT must select the proper airway from the possible sizes. Most kits contain 7 sizes. By holding the airway against the patient's face, the EMT can determine if the airway selected is correct.

oropharyngeal

Since there are _____ sizes of _____ airways, hold the airway selected against the patient's face to see if the correct size has been selected. The correct airway will extend from the center of the patient's mouth to the angle of his jaw (or corner of the mouth to the tip of the ear lobe on the same side). The oropharyngeal airway is inserted with the patient's neck hyperextended. This cannot be done if the patient has any injury to the _____ spine. The patient's mouth is opened by the crossed finger technique, using a scissor motion to pry open and hold the mouth.

7, oropharyngeal

cervical

The correct size oropharyngeal airway will extend from the center of the patient's _____ to the angle of his _____. To insert this airway, _____ the patient's neck and open his mouth using the _____ _____ technique. With the tip of the airway pointing toward the roof of the patient's mouth, slide the airway along the roof of the mouth until it passes the uvula (suspended from the soft palate above the back of the tongue).

mouth, jaw
hyperextend
crossed finger

During insertion, the tip of the airway points _____ the roof of the patient's mouth. Once past the _____, rotate the airway 180 degrees and hyperextend the patient's neck.

toward
uvula

After rotating the airway _____ _____, the flange should rest against the patient's lips. If it does not, the airway is not the correct size.

180 degrees

Be sure you do not force the patient's tongue back into his throat. If the

46

patient begins to gag, he is not_____ and the airway must immediately be removed.

unconscious

If there is no sign of nasal injury or cerebrospinal fluid flowing from the nose, a nasopharyngeal airway can be inserted into a patient's nostril to help keep his airway open. Unlike the oropharyngeal airway, this device does not tend to cause a conscious patient to _____.

gag
nostril

Before inserting a nasopharyngeal airway into the _____ of a patient, lubricate the tube with a water-based lubricant. Since the nasopharyngeal airway does not tend to produce a gag reflex, it can be used on _____ patients.

conscious

The bag-valve-mask ventilator and the pocket face mask with one-way valve are ventilation assist devices. The most commonly used hand-held unit is the bag-_____-mask ventilator, delivering 21% oxygen under routine operation and 50% to almost 100% oxygen when connected to an oxygen supply and O_2 reservoir.

valve

To use the bag-value-_____ ventilator, position yourself at the patient's head, _____ his neck (no spinal injuries), insert an airway, and check for proper mask size. The top (apex) of the triangular mask should be over the bridge of the nose and the base of the mask should rest between the lower lip and the projection of the chin.

mask
hyperextend

In using the _____-valve-mask ventilator, _____yourself at the patient's _____, _____ the patient's neck, insert an airway, and check to see that the apex of the mask rests on the bridge of the patient's _____and the base is between his _____ lip and the projection of his _____.

bag, position
head, hyperextend

nose, lower
chin
apex

With your thumb on the top or _____ of the mask, your forefinger on the base and the remaining fingers of your hand under the lower jaw between the patient's chin and ear, create enough pressure to form a tight seal. *Do not* push your fingers into the patient's neck. By squeezing the bag once every 5 seconds, you can introduce air into the patient's lungs. One squeeze can introduce a little over 1 liter of air.

OXYGEN THERAPY

WARNING: Oxygen is a medication. Most states have very firm laws governing oxygen therapy. Know your local laws.

The primary reason for oxygen therapy is to prevent or correct hypoxia, the condition where too little oxygen is available to the body's cells.

When using a bag-valve-mask ventilator without supplemental oxygen, you can deliver _____ oxygen to the patient. With supplemental oxygen, you can deliver almost _____. This can be critical in some cases where too little oxygen is available to the patient's cells. This condition is called _____.

21%
100%

hypoxia

Oxygen therapy equipment consists of a source of oxygen, a pressure regulator, a flowmeter, a humidifier, and a total of 5 different oxygen delivery devices.

A seamless steel or alloy cylinder filled with oxygen is the typical oxygen _____. The cylinder pressure is reduced to a safe working pressure by a pressure _____. Oxygen flow is, of course, measured by a _____. Moisture is added to the "dry" oxygen by a _____.

source
regulator
flowmeter
humidifier

There are _____ commonly used oxygen delivery devices, including

5

the simple face mask, the partial rebreathing mask, the non-rebreathing mask, the Venturi mask, and the nasal cannula.

The simple face mask is the most commonly used mask for short intervals. Since it is perforated, it will not deliver 100% oxygen. Moderate concentrations of 35 to 60% are possible. About the same percentages are possible with the partial rebreathing mask. The non-rebreathing mask can deliver 80 to 95% oxygen to a patient. Moderate concentrations can be delivered with the _____ face mask or the partial _____ mask. The Venturi mask is used for low concentrations of 24 to 40%. The nasal cannula will deliver 24 to 44% oxygen.

simple, rebreathing

If you are caring for a non-breathing patient, the _____ -_____-_____ ventilator can be connected to an oxygen supply. This device also can be used to help correct the condition of _____ in breathing patients. For patients receiving CPR, the positive pressure resuscitator can be used.

bag-valve-mask
hypoxia

WARNING: Some emergencies, such as carbon monoxide poisoning, are best cared for with oxygen. However, there are cases where supplemental oxygen can be harmful, if not fatal.

Emphysema and chronic bronchitis require special consideration in oxygen therapy. For patients with these conditions, high levels of oxygen could lead to respiratory arrest. They should be provided with only enough oxygen to correct the condition of severe _____.

hypoxia

For a patient with _____ _____ poisoning, you would deliver a _____ concentration of oxygen. In cases of emphysema or chronic _____ , deliver only enough oxygen to correct _____.

carbon monoxide
high
bronchitis,
hypoxia
chronic

Patients with emphysema or _____ bronchitis should be given no more than 24% oxygen, unless they are in respiratory arrest, cardiac arrest, shock, or are suffering respiratory distress due to a problem other than their chronic disease. Possible heart attack or stroke victims who also have chronic respiratory disease will require a high concentration of oxygen. The mask of choice for low level delivery of oxygen is the _____.

Venturi

If you are faced with the situation of a chronic obstructive pulmonary disease patient who is showing grave effects from hypoxia (severe cyanosis, disorientation, etc.) the best procedure is to call for advice from the emergency department physician. If this is not possible, begin the delivery with no more than _____% oxygen by Venturi and transport as soon as possible.

24

TERMINOLOGY

Define the following terms. Check your definitions with those in the Glossary of your textbook, or as directed.

Demand valve resuscitator—

Hypoxia—

Hypoxic drive *(p. 175)*—

Oropharyngeal airway—

Positive-pressure resuscitation—

Pressure regulator—

Venturi mask—

FORMING MEDICAL TERMS

The following elements of medical terms were used in this chapter (see the end of this chapter).

Roots and Combining Forms

oro (or-o-), *oral*: referring to the mouth
pharyngeo (fah-RIN-je-o), pharyng-, pharyngeal: referring to the throat
hemo (HE-moh-), *hemic* (HE-mik): referring to the blood

If the suffix-*itis* means an inflammation, then an inflammation of the throat (sore throat) would be called a _____itis.

Prefixes

hypo (HI-poh-): below, under, or deficient

Suffixes

-oxia (OK-se-ah): oxygen

If there is a deficiency of oxygen at the cellular level, the patient is suffering from cellular _____.

MATCHING

Match the information provided to the oxygen delivery devices listed immediately below. The answers are given at the end of this chapter. If you have problems with this section, see page 181 in your textbook.

_____ 1. Simple face mask
_____ 2. Partial rebreathing mask
_____ 3. Non-breathing mask
_____ 4. Venturi mask
_____ 5. Nasal cannula

A. 80 to 95% oxygen, long intervals

B. 24 to 44% oxygen

C. 10% oxygen

D. 24 to 40% oxygen

E. 35 to 60% oxygen, 6 to 10 LPM

F. 35 to 60% oxygen, 6 to 8 LPM

G. 65 to 80% oxygen

MULTIPLE CHOICE

Circle the letter of the correct answer for each question. The answers are given at the end of this chapter. Note page references to *Emergency Care, 5th ed*.

1. Usually, oropharyngeal airways should only be inserted in unconscious patients because *(p. 163)*:
   A. Conscious patients will be breathing
   B. They will not have a gag reflex
   C. Unconscious patients will not be breathing
   D. They will have a gag reflex

2. A patient with an oropharyngeal airway begins spontaneous breathing. You should *(p. 163)*:
   A. Remove the airway
   B. Keep the airway in and monitor respiration
   C. Keep the airway in and insert a suction device
   D. Supplement with oxygen through the airway

3. When inserting an oropharyngeal airway, point the tip toward the *(p. 165)*:
   A. Roof of the patient's mouth
   B. Patient's tongue
   C. Patient's chin
   D. Patient's uvula

4. To be the correct size, an oropharyngeal airway should extend from the center of the patient's mouth to the *(p. 164)*:
   A. Bridge of his nose
   B. Tip of his nose
   C. Full projection of his chin
   D. Angle of his chin

5. The oropharyngeal airway is rotated 180 degrees once it is *(p. 165)*:
   A. Against the roof of the patient's mouth
   B. Against the patient's tongue
   C. Inserted past the uvula
   D. Inserted past the teeth

6. The nasopharyngeal airway tube should be lubricated with *(p. 166)*:
   A. Petroleum jelly
   B. Oil-base lubricant
   C. Silicone-base lubricant
   D. Water-base lubricant

7. When applying suction to a non-breathing patient, suction for no more than _____ seconds without ventilating *(p. 168)*.
   A. 5
   B. 12
   C. 15
   D. 20

8. The apex of the mask on a bag-valve-mask ventilator should be held firmly in position by *(p. 172)*:
   A. Your thumb
   B. Your thumb and forefinger
   C. Your forefinger
   D. Velcro straps and your finger

9. Which of the following typically requires the highest possible concentration of oxygen delivered for the best of care? *(pp. 173, 175)*
   A. Emphysema
   B. Heart attack
   C. Chronic bronchitis
   D. All of the above

10. For patients with chronic obstructive pulmonary disease, deliver _____ % oxygen through a Venturi mask *(p. 175)*.
    A. 14
    B. 24
    C. 35
    D. 48

EXERCISES

To check your answers to the Exercises, refer to *Emergency Care, 5th ed.*

1. Describe the technique of mouth-to-adjunct ventilation *(p. 170)*.

2. Describe, step by step, the insertion of an oropharyngeal airway *(pp. 164–165)*.

3. Describe, step by step, the delivery of atmospheric air to a nonbreathing patient by use of a bag-valve-mask ventilator *(p. 172)*.

4. Describe the procedure of suctioning with a portable unit *(pp. 168–170)*.

50

5. Describe how to set up an oxygen delivery system, deliver oxygen to a patient, and end the administration of oxygen (pp. 184–186).

7. Describe how to use a pocket face mask to ventilate a patient (p. 170).

6. Describe how you would deliver oxygen to a nonbreathing patient using a positive pressure resuscitator (pp. 183, 187).

ANSWERS

Forming Medical Terms

pharyngitis, hypoxia

Matching

1. F   2. E   3. A   4. D   5. B

Multiple Choice

1. B	6. D
2. A	7. A
3. A	8. A
4. D	9. B
5. C	10. B

7 basic life support iii: bleeding and shock

Reading Assignment: Emergency Care, 5th ed., pp. 191-211

SECTION ONE: BASIC PROCEDURES

THE BLOOD

Blood is a mixture composed of a liquid part called plasma and microscopic solid parts called formed elements. The formed elements are the red blood cells involved with oxygen transport, the white blood cells involved with the defense of the body against disease, and the platelets involved with blood clot formation.

Blood carries out many functions. In respiration the blood will carry oxygen from the lungs to the tissues of the body and carry carbon dioxide from the tissues to the lungs. The formed elements primarily responsible for oxygen transport are the _____ _____ _____. One of **red blood cells** the body's systems of protection is in the blood. The liquid portion called the _____ contains antibodies to fight infection. The cellular por- **plasma** tion has _____ _____ _____ which can en- **white blood cells** gulf bacteria and foreign matter. In addition, the blood is also involved with nutrition by carrying food substances from the intestines to the tissues, excretion by carrying wastes from the tissues to the organs of excretion, and regulation by carrying hormones to control body functions.

Since its functions are essential to life, the loss of blood is very significant. The blood is involved with the process of respiration, as in the case of the _____ blood cells carrying _____ from the lungs. The white **red, oxygen** blood cells _____ the body by engulfing _____ and oth- **defend, bacteria** er foreign matter, while the plasma contains _____ to fight **antibodies** infection. By carrying both foods and wastes, the blood plays a key role in both _____ and _____. Also critical to life **nutrition, excretion** is the _____ of body functions by the hormones carried in **regulation** the blood.

To prevent the loss of blood, the body can form blood clots. The formed elements that will cause the blood to clot are the _____. **platelets** When there is an injury, these structures will disintegrate and release factors that combine with certain proteins in that liquid part of the blood called the _____ . The combination of _____ factors and **plasma, platelet** _____ proteins forms fibrin. The platelets do not actually form the **plasma** clot. When they _____, they release factors that combine **disintegrate** with plasma _____ to form _____. It is this substance **proteins, fibrin** that forms the tiny network of fibers that entraps blood cells to make up a blood clot.

External Bleeding

NOTE: Make certain that you avoid direct contact with the patient's blood.

Bleeding can be internal, external, or a combination of both. The danger in blood loss becomes more critical as more blood is lost. With the loss of 15% of the blood volume, or two pints in the average adult male, the body will go into a state of moderate shock. A loss of 30% of the blood volume will result in severe shock. As bleeding goes unchecked, there is a loss of
_____ _____ _____ which carry O_2 to the tissues, | **red blood cells**
the blood pressure falls as blood volume is lost, the heart rate will increase, and the force of heart contractions will be reduced.

The average adult male has about 12 pints of blood in his body. Roughly, blood volume is one-fifteenth of an individual's body weight. A man weighing 150 pounds would have _____ pints of blood in his body. Moderate shock occurs if there is a loss of _____% of the blood volume. Severe shock occurs when there is a loss of _____%.

10
15
30

When dealing with external bleeding, the EMT should check to see if the bleeding is arterial, venous, or capillary. In the case of arterial bleeding, bright red blood is given off in spurts. The body's mechanism to stop bleeding is to form a blood _____. This seldom works in serious arterial bleeding. Venous bleeding gives off a steady flow of dark maroon blood. This type of bleeding is easier to control than the spurting blood flow in _____ bleeding.

clot

arterial

The steady flow of blood in _____ bleeding usually is easier to control than the spurting blood flow in _____ bleeding. However, air bubbles forming an air embolism can be sucked into a vein, flow to the heart, and cause heart failure. Less serious than the profuse _____ of arterial blood and the profuse _____ bleeding from veins is the flow of blood coming from the microscopic vessels where exchange takes place between the blood and _____. These vessels are called _____. The flow of blood is very slow in capillary bleeding, but the threat of contamination is very serious.

venous
arterial

spurting, steady

tissues
capillaries

The slow flow of blood lost in _____ bleeding is the easiest to control. The most difficult to control is blood spurting from _____ bleeding. Bleeding can be controlled by using your gloved hand to apply direct pressure over the wound. This is the most effective method. If the bleeding is from an injured but not fractured extremity, direct pressure and elevation of the injured part will reduce blood pressure and slow bleeding. If this fails, the method of applying pressure to certain arterial pressure points can be used. A last resort is to stop the flow with a tourniquet.

capillary

arterial

The most effective way to stop bleeding is _____ _____ applied over the wound. A clean dressing, preferably sterile, can be placed over the wound and pressure applied. More dressings can be added, but none should be removed. In the case of profuse bleeding, the gloved hand can be held directly over the wound.

direct
pressure

If the _____ pressure method and elevation fail, the EMT should try to apply pressure over the correct arterial pressure _____. There are 4 major arterial pressure points on each side of the body. Of these, 2 are the most effective. They are the brachial for bleeding from the arm and the femoral for bleeding from the leg.

direct

point

If bleeding is from the arm, the fingers are used to compress the

_____ artery. If bleeding is from the leg, the heel of the hand is used to compress the _____ artery.

Even though it is the most effective method, the application of _____ _____ over a wound may fail. Elevation also may fail. If it does, the EMT should apply pressure to one of the two primary arterial _____ _____ used in field emergency care. As a last resort he can apply a _____, but only if he has the correct materials and fully understands the procedures. Once applied, the tourniquet must be left in place and not loosened. The flow of blood must be serious enough to risk the loss of limb.

Cryotherapy can be used to slow or control the loss of blood. This is the process of treating with cold, either in the form of ice, chemical cold packs, or splints inflated with cyogenic liquid. In fact, even a simple air splint, inflated just with air, will help to control some types of bleeding. This is because of the pressure it exerts. Likewise, a blood pressure cuff can be used to help control bleeding through the application of pressure. Typically, 150 mmHg pressure will stop the bleeding for a person with normal blood pressure.

Cryotherapy is _____ therapy. This type of therapy will help control bleeding. Pressure from an _____ splint or blood pressure _____ will also help to control bleeding. If the bleeding is arterial, place the splint along the limb between the heart and the wound. If the bleeding is venous, the pressure must be exerted on the other side of the wound, away from the heart.

Internal Blood Loss

The EMT should suspect internal bleeding if there are the major signs of shock, the patient is coughing up red blood, or vomiting blood that looks like coffee grounds, and/or the abdominal area is hard and stiff. Each area of bruised or contused tissue the size of a man's fist equals a blood loss of approximately 10%. If there is a 15% blood loss, the patient will be in a state of moderate _____. With the loss of _____% of blood volume, the patient will be in _____ _____. If the internal injury is in an extremity, a pressure bandage can be applied. Care must be taken not to cause any damage to fractured areas. All other areas cannot be effectively treated by the EMT, except through the application of anti-shock garments, meaning the patient should be transported quickly and safely to a hospital. With a loss of blood, the patient loses red blood cells and the _____ they carry. Therefore, the EMT should administer a high concentration of oxygen during initial care and transport.

SHOCK

When the cardiovascular system fails to provide sufficient blood to all parts of the body, the patient enters a state of shock and begins to die. The system fails if the blood vessels are widely dilated, the heart fails to provide proper circulation of the blood, or there is not enough blood to fill the vascular system.

In neurogenic shock, the blood vessels are widely _____ because of damage to the nerve pathways that control the muscles of vessel constriction and dilation. If there is a blood loss, a patient can enter the state of hemorrhagic (hypovolemic) _____. In cardiogenic shock, the _____ fails to properly _____ the blood.

Shock is usually a failure of the _____ system.

Margin answer key:

brachial
femoral

direct pressure

pressure points
tourniquet

cold
air, cuff

shock, 30
severe shock

oxygen

dilated

shock
heart, circulate
cardiovascular

Symptoms and Care for Shock

The signs and symptoms of shock are caused by inadequate blood volume and reduced circulation of blood. The eyes are dull and the pupils are dilated because of _____ circulation. Since there is an inadequate blood _____, the heart will work harder, producing a rapid and weak pulse. The loss of _____ volume will cause circulation to the extremities to be reduced, causing the skin to be cool, clammy, and pale to cyanotic. In addition to these signs, respiration is shallow and there may be nausea, vomiting, collapse, thirst, and anxiety.

reduced

volume

blood

After the EMT has corrected any breathing problems, ensured circulation, and controlled profuse bleeding, he should care for shock. Once the patient is breathing and profuse _____ has been controlled, the EMT should, as in all cases with severe blood loss, administer a _____ concentration of oxygen. Elevation of unfractured lower extremities and the proper splinting of fractures will help reduce shock. Noting the skin is _____ and clammy, the EMT should control heat loss by keeping the patient warm. The patient should be kept lying down and handled as gently as possible. The patient should not be given anything orally.

bleeding

high

cool

Anaphylactic shock is a life-threatening condition that occurs when there is an extreme allergic reaction to a substance. The EMT should transport the patient immediately, administering life-support measures. If the cause and the means of contact are known, the EMT should radio ahead. The EMT cannot treat anaphylactic shock and should transport and administer basic _____ - _____ measures.

life support

TERMINOLOGY

Define the following terms. Check your definitions with those in the Glossary at the end of your textbook.

Anaphylactic shock—

Artery—

Capillary—

Cyanosis—

Embolism—

Hypovolemic (hemorrhagic) shock—

Neurogenic shock—

Perfusion—

Plasma—

Platelets—

Shock—

Vein—

FORMING MEDICAL TERMS

The following elements of medical terms were used in this chapter (see answers at the end of the chapter).

Roots and Combining Forms

cryo- (kry–o–): cold
neuro- (NU–ro–): nerve
psycho- (SI-ko-): the mind

Prefixes

poly- (pol-i-): many

Suffixes

-genic (jen-ik): causing something to happen
-rrhage (-rej), *-rrhagic* (-RIJ-ik): an excessive flow
-uria (U-re-ah): urine

If the cause of shock is a failure of the heart, this is known as cardio_____ shock. Bleeding (the excessive flow of blood) can be called a hemo_____ . The problem of an excessive frequency of urination can be called _____.

MATCHING

Match the letter of the correct answer to each statement found immediately below. See the end of this chapter for the answers.

_____ 1. Fibrin
_____ 2. Perfusion
_____ 3. Moderate shock
_____ 4. Severe shock
_____ 5. Red blood cell
_____ 6. White blood cell

A. Engulf bacteria

B. Capillary blood flow

C. Forms the plasma

D. Blood clot formation

E. 15% blood loss

F. Carries the plasma

G. 30% blood loss

H. Oxygen transport

LABELING

Label the drawing of arterial pressure points in Figure 7-1. See the end of this chapter for the answers. If you have problems with this exercise, see page 198 in your textbook.

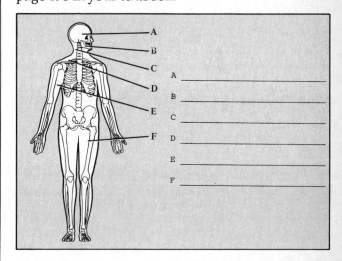

A _____
B _____
C _____
D _____
E _____
F _____

Figure 7-1

Label the blood vessels shown in Figure 7-2. Indicate the direction of flow for oxygen, carbon dioxide, food, and wastes. See page 194 in your textbook to check your answers.

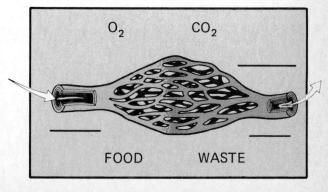

Figure 7-2

MULTIPLE CHOICE

Circle the letter of the correct answer for each question. The answers are given at the end of this chapter. Note page references to *Emergency Care, 5th ed.*

1. The formed elements in the blood that carry oxygen are the *(p. 193)*:
   A. Red blood cells
   B. White blood cells
   C. Platelets
   D. Albumins

2. Which of the following disintegrates to supply factors needed for blood clot formation? *(p. 193)*
   A. Red blood cells
   B. White blood cells
   C. Platelets
   D. Fibrocytes

3. Blood is carried from the heart to the rest of the body by way of *(p. 194)*:
   A. Arterioles
   B. Arteries
   C. Venules
   D. Veins

4. Exchange between blood and tissue takes place at the *(p. 194)*:
   A. Arteries
   B. Veins
   C. Capillaries
   D. Venules

5. Bright red blood spurting from a wound indicates *(p. 194)*:
   A. Arterial bleeding
   B. Venous bleeding
   C. Capillary bleeding
   D. Lymphatic bleeding

6. Severe bleeding from the leg can be controlled by hand pressure over the _____ artery *(p. 198)*:
   A. Femoral
   B. Brachial
   C. Celiac
   D. Iliac

7. The best method to control bleeding is *(p. 195)*:
   A. Tourniquet
   B. Direct pressure
   C. Pressure points
   D. Bandaging

8. A tourniquet should be applied *(p. 198)*:
   A. For moderate to severe bleeding
   B. For severe bleeding
   C. Only as a last resort
   D. Over contaminated wounds

9. A tourniquet should be loosened every *(p. 199)*:
   A. 10 minutes
   B. 20 minutes
   C. 30 minutes
   D. Should not be loosened

10. Which of the following can be used as a tourniquet? *(p. 199)*
    A. Rope
    B. String
    C. Wire
    D. None of the above

11. A contusion the size of a man's fist indicates a blood loss of *(p. 201)*:
    A. 5%
    B. 10%
    C. 15%
    D. 30%

12. In cases of blood loss, the EMT should administer *(p. 202)*:
    A. 25% oxygen
    B. 50% oxygen
    C. a high concentration of oxygen
    D. None, the need is for blood

13. One indication of shock is *(p. 204)*:
    A. Dilated pupils
    B. Constricted pupils
    C. Uneven pupils
    D. White pupils

14. Which of the following types of shock is primarily caused by blood loss? *(p. 203)*
    A. Anaphylactic
    B. Hemorrhagic
    C. Respiratory
    D. All of the above

15. Psychogenic shock is *(p. 203)*:
    A. Rare
    B. Corrected with 100% oxygen
    C. Usually fatal
    D. Usually self-correcting

16. Which of the following should be done first? *(p. 206)*
    A. Re-establish circulation
    B. Treat shock
    C. Correct respiration problems
    D. Control bleeding

17. Anaphylactic shock is caused by *(p. 203):*
    A. Allergic reactions
    B. Severe blood loss
    C. Burns
    D. All of the above

18. In caring for anaphylactic shock, the EMT should provide *(p. 209):*
    A. Sterile water
    B. Saline
    C. Life-support measures
    D. All of the above

EXERCISES

To check your answers to the Exercises, refer to *Emergency Care, 5th ed.*

1. List the effects of blood loss on the body *(p. 202).*

2. Describe the steps in the application of a pressure dressing *(pp. 196-197).*

3. Describe the steps in the proper application of a tourniquet *(p. 199).*

4. Describe how to use a blood pressure cuff to control serious external bleeding from the forearm *(p. 198).*

5. Describe what the EMT can do to help control internal bleeding *(p. 202).*

6. List the symptoms and signs of shock *(pp. 204-205).*

7. List 5 symptoms and 5 signs of anaphylactic shock *(p. 208).*

8. List the order in which the symptoms and signs of shock usually appear as shock develops *(p. 205).*

ANSWERS

Forming Medical Terms

-genic, -rrhagic, polyuria

Matching

1. D 2. B 3. E 4. G 5. H 6. A

Labeling—Figure 7-1

A. Brachial   B. Femorial

Multiple Choice

1. A	10. D
2. C	11. B
3. B	12. C
4. C	13. A
5. A	14. B
6. A	15. D
7. B	16. C
8. C	17. A
9. D	18. C

58

SECTION TWO: PNEUMATIC COUNTERPRESSURE DEVICES—
THE ANTI-SHOCK GARMENT

EXERCISES

1. Define "anti-shock garment" *(p. 211)*.

2. List 5 indications of when the application of an anti-shock garment should be considered *(p. 212)*.

3. Give one reason why a patient's clothing should be removed before the application of an anti-shock garment *(p. 213)*.

4. List at least four advantages associated with the use of anti-shock garments *(p. 211)*.

5. List 4 types of patients for whom an anti-shock garment should be considered *(p. 212)*.

6. Define "contraindication" *(p. 212)*.

7. What is the absolute contraindication for the application of anti-shock garments? *(p. 212)*.

8. List at least 4 conditional contraindications that may cause a physician to not order the application of an anti-shock garment *(p. 212)*.

9. Describe, step by step, the application of an anti-shock garment *(pp. 214-215)*.

10. An anti-shock garment should only be removed when a _____ is present (p. 213).

11. Describe, step by step, the removal of an anti-shock garment (p. 213).

12. Is there an indication for the prehospital removal of an anti-shock garment? If so, what is this indication? (p. 213).

8 injuries i: soft tissues and internal organs

Reading Assignment: Emergency Care, 5th ed., pp. 217-233

WOUNDS

Wounds are injuries to the soft tissues of the body. They can be closed wounds, where the skin is not broken and there is no external bleeding. They can be open wounds, where the skin is broken and there may be external bleeding.

The impact of a blunt object that does not break the skin causes a bruise or contusion. Since the skin is not broken, this is a _____ wound. Bleeding will be internal. If the _____ is the size of a man's fist, the estimated blood loss is _____%.

closed
contusion
10
open

If the skin is torn open, the injury is an _____ wound. These wounds are classified as an abrasion if the skin is scratched, an incision if the skin is cut by a sharp-edged object, a laceration if snagging and tearing leaves open jagged wounds, and a puncture wound when a sharp, pointed object passes through the skin.

When the skin is scratched, as in an _____, it is not very serious, but care must be taken to avoid contamination of the wound. If a sharp object cuts deeply, as in the case of an _____, control of bleeding can be a great problem for the EMT. There is usually less bleeding from jagged wounds, as in the case of a _____. If a sharp, pointed object breaks through the skin, it is called a penetrating _____ wound. If it breaks through the skin and has an exit wound, it is a perforating _____ wound.

abrasion

incision

laceration
puncture

puncture
closed

In addition to open and _____ wounds, the EMT also might have to treat traumatic injuries such as avulsions (tearing lacerations), traumatic amputations, and crushing injuries. In a tearing laceration, when large flaps of skin or tissues are torn loose or stripped off, the condition is called an _____ . If the extremity is torn off, this is a traumatic _____.

avulsion
amputation

Objects also can become impaled. The object should not be removed. As with any external bleeding, the most effective method of bleeding control is _____ _____. Bulky dressings should be used to stabilize the impaled object and the patient should be transported carefully.

direct pressure

When dealing with open wounds, bleeding should be stopped by direct pressure, pressure _____ , or as last resort, by a _____. Contamination should be prevented by applying a

points
tourniquet

61

sterile _____, and the injured part should be rendered immobile and elevated whenever possible.

When caring for an open wound, you should wear _____ gloves to protect yourself from contact with the patient's _____ or body fluids.

dressing

latex

blood

DRESSINGS AND BANDAGING

Dressings are applied directly to wounds to control bleeding and to protect from contamination. They should be sterile. Bandages hold dressings in place. The EMT should be familiar with all types of dressings, ranging from sterile gauze used for wounds to _____ sheets used for burns.

Bandaging is meant to hold _____ in place. The EMT must follow the general principles of bandaging. The bandage should not be too tight or it will restrict blood supply. It should not be so loose as to allow the _____ it is holding to slip. The toes and fingers should be left exposed to allow color changes to be noted. If the skin turns pale, the bandage is too right, _____ the blood supply.

sterile

dressings

dressing

restricting

TERMINOLOGY

Define the following terms. Check your definitions with those in the Glossary at the end of your textbook, or as directed.

Abrasion—

Avulsion—

Bandage—

Closed wound—

Dressing—

Epidermis—

Occlusive dressing—

Open wound—

Soft tissues—

LABELING

Identify each of the following 8 types of wounds. The answers can be found at the end of this section.

Figure 8-1

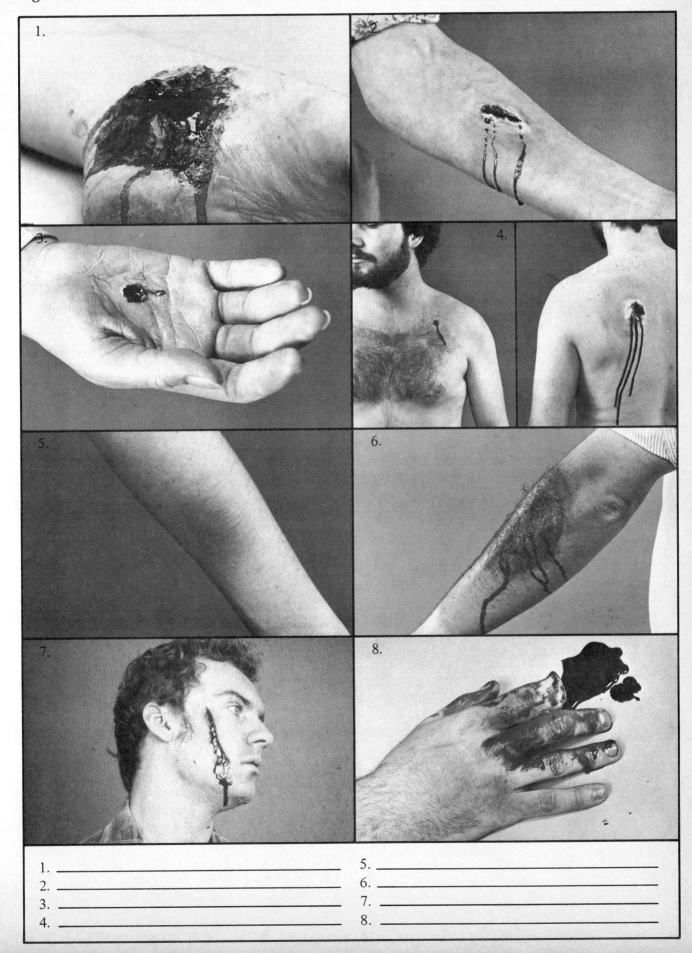

1. _____   5. _____
2. _____   6. _____
3. _____   7. _____
4. _____   8. _____

64

MULTIPLE CHOICE

Circle the letter of the correct answer for each question. The answers are given at the end of this chapter. Note page references to *Emergency Care, 5th ed.*

1. In most cases, if an in-place dressing becomes blood-soaked, it should be *(p. 226)*:
   A. Removed
   B. Left in place and more bandage should be applied
   C. Left in place and more dressing should be applied
   D. Left in place and washed free of blood with saline

2. Except for a few special cases, impaled objects should *(pp. 228-229)*:
   A. Never be removed
   B. Be removed if loose
   C. Be removed if the impalement is shallow
   D. Be removed to arrest bleeding

3. When bandaging the extremities, the fingers and toes should be *(p. 226)*:
   A. Covered loosely
   B. Covered tightly
   C. Left exposed
   D. Dressed before bandaging

4. The layers of fat and soft tissues below the dermis are called the _____ layer *(p. 219)*:
   A. Epidermis
   B. Subcutaneous
   C. Areolar
   D. Reticular

5. A bruise is known as a *(p. 220)*:
   A. Laceration
   B. Subdermal hemocorpus
   C. Avulsion
   D. Contusion

6. After exposing an open wound, you should *(p. 227)*:
   A. Clear the wound surface
   B. Clean the wound surface
   C. Irrigate the wound with distilled water
   D. Clear the wound down past the dermis

7. In cases where flaps of skin have been torn loose but not off, you should *(p. 230)*:
   A. Cut off the loose skin
   B. Gently fold the skin to its normal position
   C. Place a cold pack directly over the loose flap
   D. Clean with distilled water and dress while wet.

EXERCISES

To check your answers to the Exercises, refer to *Emergency Care, 5th ed*

1. List the 8 general principles of emergency care that apply to the majority of open wounds *(pp. 227-228)*.

2. Describe the care given in most cases of impaled objects *(pp. 228-229)*.

3. Describe the care provided for an avulsed part *(p. 230)*.

4. Describe the care provided for an abdominal evisceration *(pp. 230, 232)*.

ANSWERS

Labeling

1. Avulsion
2. Laceration
3. Penetrating puncture wound
4. Perforating puncture wound
5. Contusion
6. Abrasion
7. Incision
8. Amputation

Multiple Choice

1. C 2. A 3. C 4. B 5. D 6. A 7. B

9 injuries ii: musculoskeletal injuries —the upper extremities

Reading Assignment: Emergency Care, 5th ed., pp. 235-265

THE SKELETAL SYSTEM

The skeletal system is part of a larger system called the musculoskeletal system. This system includes the bones, muscles, ligaments, joints, and cartilage. The entire system is responsible for body shape and support, the protection of vital organs, and locomotion.

One element of the musculoskeletal system is the _____ system, or bones. There are over 206 bones in the body making up the skeleton. The skeleton is involved in body _____ and support. It helps to _____ vital organs and is involved with muscles to give _____ or movement to the body.

> skeletal
>
> shape
> protect
> locomotion
> 206

Of the more than _____ bones of the skeleton, 22 make up the cranium, face, and jaw. The cranium forms a cavity to provide _____ for the brain. The jaw consists of the maxillae, forming the upper jaw, and the mandible, the only movable bone of the skull, forming the lower jaw.

> protection

The bones of the _____ form a cavity to protect the brain. These bones are fused together and are immovable. The only movable bone in the skull is the _____ or _____ jaw.

> cranium
>
> mandible, lower

The shoulder girdle consists of the right and left clavicles (collarbones) and the right and left scapulae (shoulder blades). Each scapula forms a socket for joining with the arm bone or humerus.

The arm bone or _____ forms a ball and socket joint with the shoulder. The _____ provides the socket portion. The ulna is one of the forearm bones. It connects to (articulates) the lower end of the humerus to form the elbow.

> humerus
> scapula

There are two bones that make up the forearm. The radius, on the thumb side of the arm, is primarily involved with the rotation of the forearm. The other bone of the forearm connects with the humerus to form the _____. It is the _____.

> elbow, ulna

The upper limb is composed of three bones. The arm is the _____, connecting to the _____ at the top and the _____ and _____ in the forearm at the bottom. The radius is on the _____ side of the arm.

> humerus, scapula
> ulna, radius
> thumb

The lower limb consists of 4 bones. The thigh is the femur, forming a ball and socket joint with the pelvis. The leg is composed of the tibia, which

66

connects to the knee joint, and the fibula to the outside of the leg. The patella, or kneecap, is the fourth bone.

The pelvis joins with the thigh bone called the _____. The leg bone connecting with the knee joint is the _____. The kneecap is called the _____.

femur
tibia
patella

MUSCLES, TENDONS, LIGAMENTS, AND CARTILAGE

There are three types of muscle in the body. Most organs have smooth muscle in their walls. This is involuntary muscle. The heart is composed of a special muscle called cardiac muscle. Connecting to the bones is skeletal or voluntary muscle.

Skeletal or _____ muscle connects to bone to provide _____ or movement to the body. These muscles are connected to the bones by tendons.

voluntary
locomotion

Bones are joined to other bones by ligaments. When muscles attach to bone, they do so by _____. Cartilage can be used to attach bone to bone as in the case of the _____ attaching to the sternum. Since cartilage is a compressible tissue, it can serve as a cushion between two bones where they articulate (join).

tendons
ribs

INJURIES TO BONES AND JOINTS

Injuries to bones and joints are seldom life-threatening. Although they may appear gruesome, they should be handled after the more serious problems such as respiration, cardiac function, bleeding, shock, and serious wounds.

The primary injuries to bones are fractures. When dealing with a fracture, the EMT should prevent aggravation to the injury and provide careful transport to a proper facility for care.

The primary injury to bones, the _____, can be caused by direct violence, where the bone is broken at the point of contact with an object. Indirect violence, where forces are transmitted to the bone, is another cause of fractures. Twisting forces and other causes such as disease and aging also will be seen as the cause of fractures.

fracture

If a bone is broken at the point of contact with an object, this is an example of _____ _____. If a person lands on his leg and transfers the force to his hip, causing a fracture, this is an example of _____ _____.

direct violence

indirect violence

Fractures can be classified as transverse, oblique, spiral, greenstick, comminuted, and impacted. Even though the EMT needs only to know that there are open and closed fractures, knowledge of the types of fractures will aid in understanding the categories of accidents and the mechanisms of injuries.

The EMT should know that there are two basic types of fractures, the _____ fracture and the _____ fracture. However, he should study all classifications of fractures to better understand the categories of _____ and the mechanisms of _____.

open, closed

accidents, injuries

A fracture of the bone with no associated open wound is a closed fracture. If an open wound extends from the fractured bone to the skin surface, the injury is classified as an _____ fracture.

open

Many fractures are hard to detect. If the mechanism of the injury indicates a fracture is possible, the EMT should assume there is one. This is particularly true of the _____ fracture where there is no soft tissue damage that is visible.

Some of the signs of a fracture are exposed bone ends, deformities, pain or tenderness, swelling and discoloration, and loss of use. The EMT also can gain knowledge by asking the patient if he felt a bone break, or by noting any grating sounds (crepitus) he hears when the patient moves.

The primary injury to bone is the _____. Most injuries done solely to joints would be dislocations. In this case, injury occurs to soft tissues and the _____, which connects bone to bone.

When a joint suffers a _____ there is usually pain, deformity, and loss of movement. If the _____ joining two bones is torn, the condition is a sprain. There is usually pain, swelling and discoloration. There is no deformity as in the case of the _____ of bones and the _____ of joints. However, it is easy to confuse fractures, sprains, and dislocations.

A _____ occurs when the ligaments are torn. A strain is different. Even though there is pain and moderate swelling, the strain is not that serious since it does not involve fractures, tears, and the common joint injury, dislocation.

EMERGENCY CARE FOR INJURIES TO BONES AND JOINTS

When dealing with fractures and other bone and joint injuries, the EMT should prevent _____ of the injury by such means as splinting, and carefully transport the patient. Before treating bone and joint injuries, the EMT should handle the more serious problems of respiration, cardiac function, bleeding, shock, and open wounds.

The first step in the care of specific bone or joint injury is to check for possible circulation impairment and nerve impairment. Palpating the radial pulse can be used if the fracture or dislocation is in an _____ _____ . Palpating the posterior tibial or dorsalis pedis pulse can be used for injuries to the _____ _____.

The EMT can measure nerve impairment by having the patient attempt to move his fingers or toes. Circulation impairment to an upper extremity can be measured by palpating the _____ pulse. Lower extremity circulation impairment can be determined by palpating the _____ _____ pulse.

Without attempting to push back any bone ends, the EMT should straighten any closed angulated fractures (follow local protocol), except for fractures of the shoulder or wrist. In these areas such action could increase the chance of severe damage to nerves and large blood vessels. These areas also are primary sites of dislocations. Attempts to straighten a dislocation in these areas can cause the same damage.

Because of the high number of nerves and blood vessels present, the EMT should not try to straighten an _____ fracture or _____ in the area of the _____ or _____.

After cutting away clothing over the fracture site, the EMT should gently grasp the extremity above and below the fracture site, applying traction steadily and smoothly, and maintaining this traction during the splinting process. The EMT should not attempt to push back any bone _____.

All fractures should be splinted or immobilized in some way. While the splinting device is being applied, the EMT should maintain _____

closed

fracture

ligament
dislocation
ligament

fractures
dislocations

sprain

aggravation

upper extremity
lower extremity

radial

posterior tibial (dorsalis pedis)

angulated
dislocation, shoulder
wrist

ends

traction

while gently holding the extremity and the joints immediately _____ and _____ the fracture site.   **above, below**

All fractures should have a _____ device or some immobilizing device applied before transport. This will prevent closed fractures from become _____ fractures, reduce damage to nerves, blood vessels and soft tissue, and lessen pain.   **splinting**   **open**

The EMT should study the various types of splints that are available and consider the possible materials he can use to improve a splint. There are 3 basic types of splints, rigid, soft, and traction splints.

The rigid splint must be long enough to immobilize the entire fractured bone. The EMT should grasp the limb _____ and _____ the fracture and apply slight _____. The padded _____ splint can then be positioned and secured to the limb with bandage.   **above, below**   **traction, rigid**

If an inflatable rigid split is used, the EMT should take note of air pressure expansion due to temperature change. These types of splints are of little use on the humerus and femur, since a rigid splint must be long enough to _____ the _____ fractured bone.   **immobilize, entire**

In addition to rigid splints, there are _____ splints, such as the Hare traction splint used for fractures of the hip and femur. If the EMT has to splint a fractured femur, he would do well to use a _____ splint such as the _____ _____ splint. This would be more efficient than using a _____ splint such as the inflatable or air splint. The traction splint is dangerous to use unless the EMT has had special training to use this device.   **traction**   **traction**   **Hare traction**   **rigid**

Splints can be used to immobilize fractured limbs. Slings are another technique of immobilization. If properly used, these forms will prevent _____ of the injury.   **aggravation**

Care for the Upper Extremities

The bones of the upper extremity include the collarbone or _____, the shoulder blade or _____, and the three major upper-limb bones: the _____ of the arm, and the _____ and the _____ of the forearm. Remember, the EMT should not try to straighten fractures producing angulations of the wrists and _____.   **clavicle, scapula**   **humerus, ulna**   **radius**   **shoulders**

If the clavicle is injured, fold the arm of the injured side across the chest. Since a splint is not practical, the area can be immobilized with a _____ bound to the body with swathe.   **sling**

If the fracture is to the shoulder blade or _____, proceed as you would for a fractured clavicle. Immobilize with a _____ and _____.   **scapula**   **sling**   **swathe**

A dislocation of the shoulder joint takes place when the ball-shaped end of the _____ is displaced from the socket of the _____. Do not attempt to force the humerus back into the socket. Begin by checking for impairment to _____ and _____. Place a pad under the patient's armpit (axillary region), fold his arm across his chest, and support with a _____ and secure with a _____.   **humerus, scapula**   **circulation, nerves**   **sling, swathe**

If the arm bone, or humerus, is injured, the EMT should correct any severe _____, immobilize with a splint, and place the arm in a sling that can be bound to the body with a _____.   **angulations**   **swathe**

For fractures of the humerus, check for nerve impairment by observing for "wrist drop." Circulation impairment can be noted by _____ the _____ pulse. If the fracture is to the   **palpating, radial** proximal (upper) end of the humerus, simply immobilize by supporting with a _____ and securing with a _____. Shaft and distal end fractures are best immobilized with a _____, supported by a _____ and bound to the body by a _____. A fracture to the humerus shaft also can be cared for with support provided by a sling tied only around the wrist, secured by a wide swathe. Fractures to the distal end can be cared for by applying a sling and swathe, keeping the elbow at a 90° angle.

The same basic procedure applies to the forearm and wrist. That is, rigid splinting and placing in a sling. However, no attempt should be made to correct angulations of the _____.

The elbow must be immobilized in the same position in which it is found, unless there is no radial pulse and approval for repositioning the limb is given by the emergency department physician.

Unless angulation of a fractured or dislocated wrist is _____, attempt to immobilize with the hand placed in the position of function. A fractured or dislocated hand also should be immobilized in the position of _____. For both wrist and hand, immobilize to a padded board splint. Fractured fingers can be immobilized by taping them to uninjured adjacent fingers.

Care for the forearm is not the same as for wrist and hand. Attempt to _____ angulations. If the limb is found in a straight-out position and the elbow is fractured or dislocated, do not flex the joint. Immobilize on a _____ board splint. If the arm is flexed at the elbow, immobilize in this position. Do not attempt to straighten _____ unless there is no radial pulse (follow local protocols).

sling, swathe
splint
sling, swathe

wrists

severe

function

straighten

padded

angulations

TERMINOLOGY

Define the following terms. Check your definitions with those in the Glossary at the end of your textbook, or as directed.

Angulation—

Capillary refilling—

Closed fracture—

Crepitus—

Ligament—

Open fracture—

Sprain—

Strain—

Tendon—

LABELING

Label each bone specified in Figure 9-1 (*pp. 243-244*). See end of this chapter for answers.

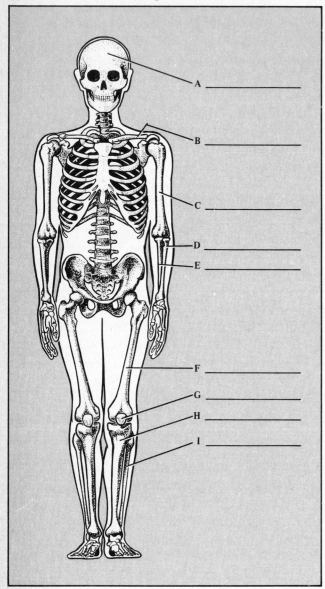

Figure 9-1

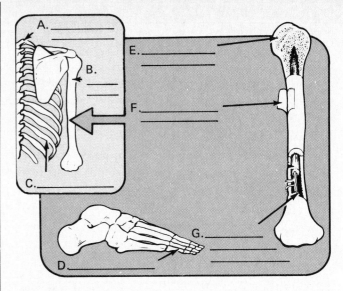

Figure 9-2

Label the parts of the bone specified in Figure 9-2. Classify these bones according to shape (*p. 239*). See the end of this chapter for answers.

MULTIPLE CHOICE

Circle the letter of the correct answer for each question. The answers are given at the end of this chapter. Note page references to *Emergency Care, 5th ed.*

1. The human skeleton is made up of approximately (*p. 239*):
   A. 206 bones
   B. 318 bones
   C. 110 bones
   D. 98 bones

2. Which of the following forms a socket for a ball and socket joint? (*p. 243*)
   A. Clavicle
   B. Patella
   C. Sternum
   D. Scapula

3. Which of the following connects (articulates) to the humerus? (*p. 243*)
   A. Patella
   B. Ulna
   C. Fibula
   D. Tibia

4. The leg bone connecting with the knee joint is the (*p. 244*):
   A. Femur
   B. Radius
   C. Humerus
   D. Tibia

5. Which of the following muscle types moves bones? *(p. 238)*
   A. Smooth
   B. Voluntary
   C. Involuntary
   D. Unstriated

6. Muscles are attached to bones by *(p. 238)*:
   A. Ligaments
   B. Cartilage
   C. Tendons
   D. Articulation cartilage

7. The first thing an EMT should attempt to treat is *(p. 250)*:
   A. Respiratory problems
   B. Severe open fractures
   C. Severe closed fractures
   D. Cardiac function

8. A person jumps from a burning building. He lands directly on his feet. His major injury is a fracture of the pelvis. This is an example of *(p. 246)*:
   A. Direct violence
   B. Twisting forces
   C. Indirect violence
   D. None of the above

9. An example of irregular bone is the *(p. 239)*:
   A. Humerus
   B. Bones of the spine
   C. Radius
   D. Sternum

10. Before an injury can be called a sprain, which of the following has to be torn? *(p. 247)*
    A. Tendons
    B. Cartilage
    C. Articulation cartilage
    D. Ligaments

11. In which of the following is there usually no deformity? *(p. 247)*
    A. Sprain
    B. Fracture
    C. Dislocation
    D. Twisting fracture

12. In which of the following should angulated fractures not be straightened? *(p. 253)*
    A. Humerus
    B. Tibia
    C. Radius
    D. Shoulder

13. After grasping the limb above and below the fracture site, the EMT should *(p. 253)*:
    A. Slip on a splint
    B. Apply steady tension
    C. Push back exposed bone ends
    D. Pull on the bone

14. The EMT should not try to straighten a dislocation. This is to prevent *(p. 253)*:
    A. Severe pain
    B. Nerve and blood vessel damage
    C. Severe bone damage
    D. The onset of shock

15. The two basic types of splints are the *(p. 254)*:
    A. Traction and multi-flex
    B. Traction and half-ring
    C. Traction and rigid
    D. Traction and molded

16. Traction is best defined as the *(p. 253)*:
    A. Stabilization of a broken bone
    B. Tension applied to a broken bone
    C. Realignment of broken bones
    D. Setting of broken bones

17. In treating a fractured clavicle, the EMT should use *(p. 257)*:
    A. An inflatable splint
    B. A traction splint
    C. A sling and swathe
    D. A rigid splint

18. When treating a fractured elbow with a radial pulse, the EMT should immobilize the bones *(p. 261)*:
    A. Only after correcting any angulations
    B. And then correct angulations
    C. After the arm has been extended
    D. In the position they are found

19. When splinting a fractured hand, the hand should *(p. 263)*:
    A. Be covered on the sides only by the splint
    B. Be maintained in the position of function
    C. Not be totally immobilized
    D. Be splinted to the elbow

20. The patient with a fractured clavicle typically sits or stands with the shoulder of the *(p. 257)*:
    A. Injured side bent backward
    B. Uninjured side bent forward
    C. Uninjured side bent backward
    D. Injured side bent forward

21. A fracture of the distal end of the humerus is best immobilized with a *(p. 260)*:
    A. Sling and swathe
    B. Wrist sling
    C. Padded board splint and sling
    D. Air-inflatable splint

22. A fractured wrist is best immobilized with a *(p. 263)*:
    A. Traction splint
    B. Padded board splint
    C. Soft splint
    D. Air-inflatable splint

23. When applying an air-inflatable splint on the patient's fractured forearm, inflate the splint until *(p. 264)*:
    A. You can make a small dent in the plastic with your finger
    B. The hand-pump offers slight resistance
    C. The splint is wrinkle-free
    D. You can no longer inflate by mouth

EXERCISES

To check your answers to the Exercises, refer to *Emergency Care, 5th ed.*

1. Describe the methods used to apply a sling and swathe *(pp. 258-259)*.

2. What are the major differences in techniques when using a sling and swathe for:
    A. Fractured humerus—proximal end:
    B. Fractured humerus—shaft:
    C. Fractured humerus—distal end:

    (see page 260)

3. List four reasons for splinting. That is, what should a splint do *(p. 254)*?

4. Explain, step by step, how you would immobilize a fractured forearm using an air-inflatable splint *(p. 264)*.

5. Explain, step by step, how you would utilize rigid splinting for a fractured humerus *(pp. 251-252, 260)*.

ANSWERS

Labeling—*Figure 9-1*

A. Cranium B. Clavicle C. Humerus
D. Radius E. Ulna F. Femur G. Patella
H. Tibia I. Fibula

Labeling—*Figure 9-2*

A. Irregular bone B. Long bone C. Flat bone
D. Short bone E. Articular cartilage
F. Periosteum G. Medullary canal

Multiple Choice

1. A	8. C	15. C	22. B
2. D	9. B	16. A	23. A
3. B	10. D	17. C	
4. D	11. A	18. D	
5. B	12. D	19. B	
6. C	13. B	20. D	
7. A	14. B	21. C	

10 injuries ii: the lower extremities

Reading Assignment: Emergency Care, 5th ed., pp. 267–293

INJURIES TO THE LOWER EXTREMITIES

CARE FOR THE LOWER EXTREMITIES

For fracture of the pelvis, dislocation of the hip, and fracture of the hip, positioning is the key element of care. The first step is still to check for _____ and _____ impairment. Be sure to monitor blood pressure since these injuries can be associated with a blood loss of 1 liter or more.

circulation, nerve

In the case of a fractured pelvis, the primary care element is the correct _____ of the patient. A folded blanket is placed between the patient's legs and then his legs are bound together at several points with wide cravats. The patient is carefully moved onto a scoop-style stretcher or long spine board. The patient is then secured to the stretcher or board.

positioning

If a patient has a dislocated hip, begin as you would for a fractured pelvis. Move the patient onto a _____-_____stretcher or _____ _____ board. The dislocation is immobilized with pillows or rolled blankets. Secure the patient to the board or stretcher. Remember to monitor for circulatory and nerve function _____.

scoop-style
long spine

impairment

Proper positioning of the patient is essential in caring for a fracture of the hip. In this case, the upper end of the thigh bone, the _____ is fractured. Before moving the patient onto a long spine board, place a folded _____ between his _____. As in the case of a fractured pelvis, _____ his legs _____. A fractured hip can be immobilized by _____ the patient's legs together, or with long padded boards. The medial board should extend from just below the groin area to just beyond the foot. The lateral board should extend from the armpit to beyond the foot.

femur

blanket, legs
bind, together
binding

Fractures of the femur should be immobilized with a traction device such as the Hare traction splint or half-ring splint. The use of such splints is a two-rescuer procedure. If need be, _____ padded boards or even binding the patient's legs together can be used. Remember to monitor circulation by taking a _____ _____ pulse. Severe angulation of a fractured femur can be corrected. Steady _____ should be applied before and during immobilization. The _____ traction splint or the _____-_____ splint are often used for immobilization.

long

posterior tibial (dorsalis pedis)
traction
Hare, half-ring
knee

As in the case of the elbow, the _____ should be immobilized in the position in which it is found unless there is no distal pulse and repositioning is approved by the emergency department physician. A pillow molded around the knee or a well-padded splint is recommended.

Injuries to the ankle and foot can be cared for by immobilizing with a soft splint made from a pillow. Do not attempt to straighten a _____ _____ fracture of the ankle. Remember to monitor for _____ and _____ _____ .

| severely angulated circulation, nerve impairment |

Terminology

Define the following terms. Check your definition with those in the Glossary at the end of your textbook, or as directed.

Iliac crest—

Ischium—

Traction splinting—

Forming Medical Terms

The following are some of the elements of medical terms used in the study of musculoskeletal injuries. Answers are at the end of the chapter.

Roots and Combining Forms

pedio- (PE-de-o-) or *paedio-*: pertaining to the child

Prefixes

ortho- (OR-tho-): to straighten or correct

Suffixes

-al, ial: pertaining to
-ic: pertaining to or related to
-ist: one who studies a given subject

The term that would mean to straighten the child is _____ (straighten) _____ (child) _____ (pertaining to) = _____ . The first _____ ists were individuals who provided care for the deformities of children.

Labeling

Label the drawing in the lettered spaces that are provided *(p. 270)*. The answers are provided at the end of this chapter.

A. _____

B. _____

C. _____

D. _____

E. _____

F. _____

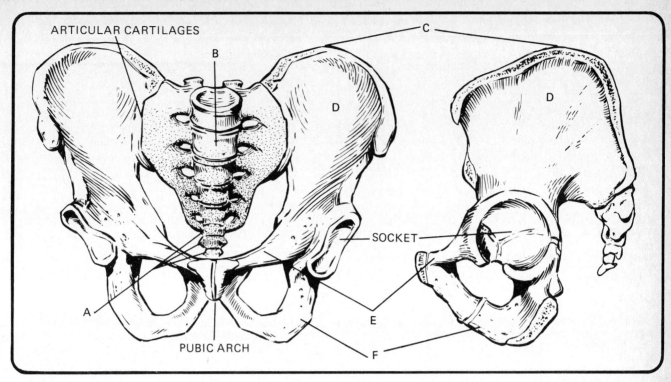

ARTICULAR CARTILAGES

B

C

D

D

SOCKET

A

E

PUBIC ARCH

F

Figure 10–1

EXERCISES

To check your answers to the Exercises, refer to *Emergency Care, 5th ed.*

1. What are the symptoms and signs commonly associated with a fractured pelvis? *(p. 273)*

2. Describe how to stabilize a patient's lower limbs in a situation where you suspect possible pelvic fractures *(p. 274)*.

3. Describe the procedures used to apply a Hare traction splint *(pp. 277-281)*.

4. Describe the procedure that is used to splint an injured knee, keeping the knee bent (*pp. 284, 285*).

6. Use Figure 10-2 to list the methods used to provide care for various skeletal injuries (*see Chapters 9 and 10*).

5. Describe an effective way to immobilize an injured ankle without using a rigid splint (*p. 293*).

Answers

Forming Medical Terms

ortho-, -ped-, -ics = orthopedics, orthopedist

Labeling

A. coccyx
B. sacrum
C. iliac crest
D. ilium
E. public bone
F. ischium

CARE FOR INJURIES TO THE EXTREMITIES

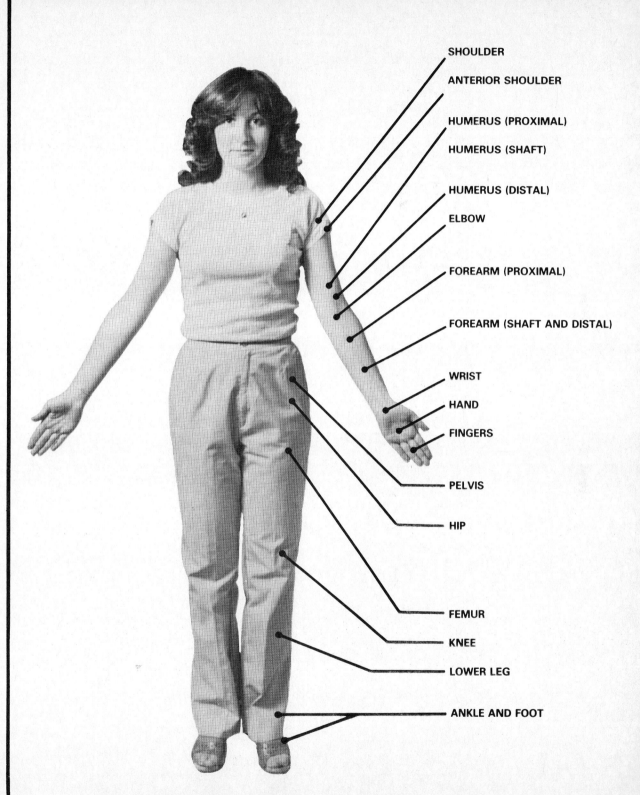

SHOULDER

ANTERIOR SHOULDER

HUMERUS (PROXIMAL)

HUMERUS (SHAFT)

HUMERUS (DISTAL)

ELBOW

FOREARM (PROXIMAL)

FOREARM (SHAFT AND DISTAL)

WRIST

HAND

FINGERS

PELVIS

HIP

FEMUR

KNEE

LOWER LEG

ANKLE AND FOOT

Anti-shock (MAST) garments are useful for fractures of the pelvis, femur, knee, and proximal tibia. They help to immobilize the injury and control the development of shock.

Figure 10-2

11 injuries iii: the skull and spine

Reading Assignment: Emergency Care, 5th ed., pp. 295-325

THE AXIAL SKELETON

Of the more than _____ bones of the skeleton, 22 make up the cranium, face, and jaw. The cranium forms a cavity to provide _____ for the brain. The jaw consists of the maxillae, forming the upper jaw, and mandible, the only movable bone of the skull, forming the lower jaw.

The bones of the _____ form a cavity to protect the brain. These bones are fused together and are immovable. The only movable bone in the skull is the _____ or _____ jaw.

The trunk of the body is made up of the thorax with its 12 pairs of ribs, and the spinal column divided into 5 regions: the neck or cervical, the upper back or thoracic, the lower back or lumbar, the rear of the pelvis or sacrum, and the end of the spine or coccyx.

The first 7 vertebrae make up the neck or _____ region. The next 12 are in the upper back or the _____ region. The _____ pairs of ribs attach to the spine in this region. The next 5 vertebrae are in the lower back or _____ region. To the rear of the pelvis are 5 bones that fuse in the adult. This is the _____. The very end of the spine is 4 to 5 bones that are fused in the adult. This is the _____.

Of the _____ pairs of ribs, only the first 7 pairs attach to the spine in the back and the sternum in the front. Each of these first 7 connect directly with the sternum by way of strips of cartilage.

The next 3 pairs of ribs attach to the spine, but not directly to the _____ in the front by way of strips of _____. Their cartilage strips unite with the cartilage of the seventh rib. The last 2 pairs of ribs attach to the spine in the back, but have no attachment in the front. All 12 pairs of ribs attach to the vertebrae in the _____ region of the spine.

206

protection

cranium

mandible, lower

cervical
thoracic, 12

lumbar
sacrum
coccyx
12

sternum, cartilage

thoracic

THE NERVOUS SYSTEM

The brain is a soft, moist organ located in the cranial cavity. The spinal cord attaches to the base of the brain. The bones of the skull protect the brain, while the bones of the vertebral column protect the spinal cord as it runs down the back. Both the brain and the spinal cord are surrounded by a 3-layered membrane called the meninges.

The brain is protected by the bones of the skull that surround the _____ cavity and a membrane called the _____. The spinal cord is protected by the bones of the _____ _____ and the meninges.

cranial, meninges
vertebral
column

INJURIES TO THE SKULL AND BRAIN

Head injuries are classified as open or closed. In open head injuries, the scalp is usually lacerated, the skull is fractured, and the membrane surrounding the brain, the _____, may be damaged. The brain can suffer contusions or lacerations.

meninges

An open head wound can cause _____ and _____ to the brain. This can occur when the scalp is _____, the bones of the skull are _____, and the meninges are _____. The protection of the brain depends on the meninges, filled with cerebrospinal fluid, and the bones forming the _____ _____.

lacerations
contusions
lacerated, fractured
lacerated

cranial cavity

In addition to open head injuries, there are _____ head injuries. The skull remains intact in a closed head wound. However, there can still be serious injury to the _____.

closed

brain

The signs of a skull fracture are unequal pupils, discoloration of tissues under the eyes, blood and/or clear fluid in the ears and nose, and deformity of the skull.

Not all skull fractures are obvious. The EMT should consider the mechanisms of the injury, and certain signs such as _____ pupils, discoloration to the soft tissues under the _____, blood and/or clear fluid in the nose and the _____, and _____ of the skull.

unequal
eyes
ear, deformities
pupils

When the brain is injured, the _____ will be unequal, the patient is often unconscious and may go into coma. There may be paralysis, vomiting, convulsions, and respiratory arrest.

With brain damage, the patient is often _____. However, many patients will remain conscious and may show a personality change. Damage can be caused by contusions, pressure, and lacerations.

unconscious

Brain damage can be caused when a blunt object strikes the skull causing a bruise or _____ of the brain. If a blood vessel ruptures and releases blood, there can be a build-up of _____ causing brain damage. When the skull is fractured, the pieces may cut into the brain tissue causing _____. If a blow to the skull causes brain damage without lacerations and bleeding, the injury is called a concussion.

contusion
pressure

lacerations

The most visible damage is done in open head wounds. However, the EMT should realize that the _____ head injury, easily overlooked, may prove to be very serious. Evaluating the patient and the _____ of the accident are very important.

closed

mechanisms

To determine if there is brain damage, the EMT should consider the mechanisms of the accident and _____ the patient for state of consciousness, awareness of surroundings, pupil condition, and possible injuries to the cervical spine.

evaluate

A patient with brain damage will usually not maintain a state of _____. If he does, his _____ of surroundings may indicate disorientation. The pupils will be _____ or nonresponsive to light. The EMT should assume that the head injury may be a sign of brain damage and a _____ injury.

consciousness, awareness
unequal

spinal

The brain-injured patient may have altered respiratory patterns. His body temperature may rise. Hearing, vision, and speech may individually or collectively become impaired. The patient with brain injury may show personality changes and an awareness of his surroundings that indicates _____ . Equilibrium disturbances may cause him to stumble or stagger. Along with personality and mental state changes, the patient with damage to the brain may show physical changes such as altered _____ patterns, impaired _____ , _____, or _____, and a _____ in body temperature. His pulse rate may start out as _____ and become _____, _____, and _____. There are similarities between brain injuries and other injuries and illness. Do not overlook the possibilities of diabetic problems, stroke, heart attack, high-fever-producing infections, convulsive disorders, and alcohol and drug abuse.

disorientation

respiratory, hearing speech, vision, rise slow, full, fast weak

EMERGENCY CARE FOR INJURIES TO THE SKULL AND BRAIN

As in the case of all injuries, the first step is to maintain an open _____. The normal method of tilting the head back cannot be employed since most head injuries can have associated _____ injuries. Use the jaw-thrust.

airway

neck

Since there may be neck injuries, an oropharyngeal airway can be used for the unconscious patient. The EMT should realize that airway obstruction, even if absent at first, may occur because of drainage from the skull, ears, and nose, and blockage from vomiting and the position of the tongue.

After considering these possibilities of airway _____ the EMT should stabilize and immobilize the _____.

obstructions

neck

Drainage of the cerebrospinal fluid should not be stopped. Impaled objects should not be removed. Dressings should not be applied with pressure. Transport should be immediate, with the greatest of care. Overheating must be avoided.

An aspirator or some form of mechanical suction will be needed during transport since the EMT should not stop the _____ of cerebrospinal fluid.

drainage

Head and brain injuries often have associated cervical spine injuries. If it can be done without aggravation of the head injury, position the patient for drainage. Carefully monitor the patient during transport, treat for shock, and provide oxygen.

INJURIES TO THE SPINE

The EMT must take great care not to overlook neck and spinal injuries. In automobile accidents, the EMT should consider that whiplash may have caused injuries to the _____ _____. Diving, skiing, and sledding accidents all have a high percentage of these types of injuries.

cervical spine

The spinal cord is protected by the bones of the _____ column. Any fractures or twist of the column can easily cause spinal injuries. Knowing the spinal cord connects to the lower part of the _____, the EMT can relate brain function to spinal function. The cord carries information to and from the brain. Any spinal cord damage will mean a loss of function, partial or full, below the injury.

vertebral

brain

Examinations for spinal injuries are easier if the patient is found on his

82

side and is conscious. Contusions and lacerations, deformities, pain, and tenderness are easier to note if the patient's back is free to examine.

There are other conditions that can be noted to support the possibility of spinal injury. Breathing without chest movements and with reduced abdominal movements indicates diaphragmatic breathing. The muscles to the chest and abdominal wall are not functioning, possibly due to the failure of motor nerves leaving a damaged spinal cord.

_____ breathing may indicate spinal damage or injury. Victims found lying with their arms above their heads may have injury in the region of the lower cervical spine. _____ nerves that extend the arm are no longer functioning. Loss of bowel and bladder function could indicate spinal injury. For male patients, priapism (the persistent erection of the penis) is a reliable sign of possible spinal injury.

Spinal injury may exist if the patient shows _____ breathing, loss of _____ and _____ control, or the characteristic positioning of the _____ above the _____. For male patients, _____ is a reliable sign.

If the patient is found on his back, the EMT will have a harder time noting any contusions and _____, any deformities, pain, and _____. The task of checking for paralysis is made easier if the patient is in the _____ state.

The EMT, when dealing with a conscious patient, should check the lower extremities for _____ or loss of feeling. He should ask the patient if he can feel touching to the feet and legs, if the patient can wiggle toes and move his feet, and if the patient can press his feet against the EMT's hand. If the patient cannot do these things, there may be injury to the spinal cord below the neck.

After checking the _____ extremities for paralysis and noting if there is any apparent spinal damage _____ the neck, the EMT should check the upper extremities. He should see if the patient can feel _____ to the hands and arms, wiggle fingers, wave his hands, and grasp the EMT's hand. If the patient can do all this, but shows indications of paralysis in the lower extremities, the damage to the cord is probably _____ the neck. If there is evidence of paralysis to the legs and the arms, the injury is probably in the area of the _____.

The unconscious patient also must be examined for signs of _____ in the upper and lower extremities. The EMT should check for muscle reactions to painful stimuli applied to the top of the feet and back of the hands.

NOTE: Consider all unconscious trauma patients to have spinal injuries.

EMERGENCY CARE FOR INJURIES TO THE SPINE

In an emergency situation, the EMT should establish an open _____. If there is evidence of neck or spinal injuries, the EMT should apply and maintain in-line stabilization of the head.

If there are neck or spinal injuries, other problems should be treated only after the EMT applies and maintains _____

Diaphragmatic

Motor

diaphragmatic
bowel, bladder
arms, head
priapism

lacerations
tenderness
conscious

paralysis

lower
below

touching

below
neck

paralysis

airway

in-line

_____ of the head. One EMT should position himself at the patient's head and apply in-line stabilization. The head and neck can then be immobilized by the second EMT using an extrication collar. Once an EMT has positioned himself at the patient's _____ and has applied _____ _____, he must remain there until the patient is completely immobilized.

Even though the neck can be stabilized with an _____ collar, the EMT applying _____ _____ at the head must remain there until the patient is _____ _____. When the patient has been immobilized, the second EMT can then return to a complete body survey.

Since the head cannot be tilted back, the jaw-thrust method may have to be used. For patients who are unconscious, an oropharyngeal airway can be inserted. To avoid fluid accumulation, manual or mechanical _____ should be used periodically. The EMT should administer a high concentration of oxygen during transport.

Once the neck is _____, _____ problems are corrected, and _____ has been controlled, one EMT can do a complete body survey while the other remains positioned at the patient's _____.

During the complete _____ _____, the EMT should check for damage along the length of the spine. This can best be done by checking for loss of sensation and _____.

If there is spinal damage, the patient must be rigidly immobilized before anything else is done (except, of course, for emergency life support measures). Regardless of the results of the survey, the patient suspected of having neck and spinal injuries should be rigidly _____ before transport. A long spine board should be used.

The short wooden spine board is an excellent device used to rigidly immobilize both conscious and unconscious patients with suspected spinal injuries. The recommended procedure for the use of the short spine board calls for eventual securing to the long spine board.

If the patient has a spinal injury, correctly apply an _____ collar and secure the patient's torso and then his head to a _____ spine board.

WARNING: *Do not* use chin straps or chin cups to immobilize the patient's head. Once the patient is properly packaged on the short spine board, he should be moved, remaining secured to the short spine board, and secured as a unit to a long spine board.

The 4-rescuer log roll requires 1 EMT to be the head-end EMT. His job is to apply in-line stabilization to the head and neck and to direct the other rescuers. This EMT continues to apply in-line stabilization even after an _____ collar is in place.

Once _____ _____ has been applied to the patient's head and neck and an extrication collar is in place, the other members of the _____-rescuer log roll team can position themselves at the patient's shoulders, waist, and knees. When the patient is rolled onto his side, the waist-level rescuer pulls the spine board into position against the patient's back. The patient is then rolled onto the board. Remember, the _____-level EMT coordinates all activities.

Answer column:

stabilization

head
in-line stabilization

extrication
in-line stabilization
completely
immobilized

suction

immobilized, respiratory
bleeding

head
body survey

paralysis

immobilized

extrication
short

extrication
in-line stabilization

4

head

TERMINOLOGY

Define the following terms. Check your definitions with those in the Glossary at the end of your textbook, or as directed.

Cerebrospinal fluid—

Cranial cavity—

Diaphragmatic breathing—

Meninges—

Subdural hematoma *(p. 299)*—

FORMING MEDICAL TERMS

The following are some of the elements of medical terms used in this chapter. Answers are at the end of the chapter.

Root and Combining Forms

capito (KAP-i-to-): in reference to the entire head, as in decapitate.

cephalo (se-FAL-o-), *cephalic* (se-FAL-ik): pertaining to the head, but often limited to the cranium.

cerebro (SER-e-bro-): the cerebrum of the brain. Sometimes used to mean the entire brain.

cranio (KRAY-ne-o-): pertaining to the skull, but usually without reference to the face.

duro (DU-ro-), *dural* (DU-ral): tough, as in durable. Used in reference to the outer layer of the meninges, the _____ mater.

neuro (NU-ro-): in reference to the nerves, as in _____ logic assessment.

Prefixes

auto (aw-toh-): self, as in auto _____ nervous system (a self-governing system).

en (en-): in or on. An inflammation in the head would be an en_____itis.

intra (in-trah): in, inside of. The pooling of blood inside the cerebrum is an intra _____ hematoma.

inter (in-ter-): between. The fluid between the cells in inter _____ fluid.

sub (sub-): below, under. A hematoma formed below the outer layer of the meninges is a _____ _____.

LABELING

Label the 5 divisions of the verebral column and state the number of vertebrae in each division. The answers are given at the end of this chapter. If you have problems labeling this illustration, see page

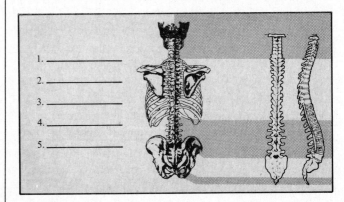

1._____
2._____
3._____
4._____
5._____

Figure 11-1

MULTIPLE CHOICE

Circle the letter of the correct answer for each question. The answers are given at the end of this chapter. Note page references to *Emergency Care, 5th ed.*

1. The membrane surrounding the brain and spinal cord is the *(p. 299)*:
   A. Pleura
   B. Peritoneum
   C. Meninges
   D. Mesentery

2. The area of the spinal column that receives added bony support other than the vertebrae is in the _____ region *(p. 308)*.
   A. Cervical
   B. Thoracic
   C. Lumbar
   D. Coronal

3. A patient with head injury has profuse arterial bleeding that flows blood to an area between the meninges and the cranial bones. The patient is said to have a (p. 300):
   A. Intracerebral hematoma
   B. Subdural hematoma
   C. Epidural hematoma
   D. Subarachnoid space hematoma

4. The EMT can suspect brain damage if there is a head injury and the pupils of the eyes are (p. 300):
   A. Dilated
   B. Constricted
   C. Pale orange
   D. Unequal

5. The EMT usually can suspect a skull fracture if he observes (p. 300):
   A. Unequal pupils
   B. Blood and clear fluids in the ears and nose
   C. Bleeding from the ears
   D. Any of the above

6. When the tissues of the brain are damaged, new cells (p. 298):
   A. Will not be produced
   B. Replace scar tissue
   C. Grow after drug treatment
   D. Grow back, but very slowly

7. A patient with a closed head injury has a contusion of the brain. Disruption of normal brain function occurs because of (pp. 299-300):
   A. Pain
   B. Skull fragments
   C. Pressure
   D. Loss of CSF

8. A blow to the head causing momentary loss of consciousness without lacerations and bleeding in the brain is called a (p. 299):
   A. Cerebrovascular accident
   B. Compression
   C. Convulsion
   D. Concussion

9. If a patient has a head injury, the EMT must suspect _____ injuries (p. 299):
   A. Spinal
   B. Eye
   C. Ear
   D. Nasal

10. If a patient has a head injury, but no indication of spinal injury, the first step in treatment is to (p. 302):
    A. Rigidly stabilize the entire body
    B. Establish and maintain an open airway
    C. Rigidly stabilize the neck
    D. Complete body survey

11. Which of the following should be used on a patient who is unconscious and has a head injury? (p. 302)
    A. Head-tilt, chin-lift method
    B. Chin-lift method
    C. Jaw-thrust method
    D. Head-tilt, neck-lift method

12. If cerebrospinal fluid loss is noted, the EMT should (p. 302):
    A. Apply pressure dressings
    B. Pack the ears and nose
    C. Cover with a loose dressing
    D. Inject saline

13. If a patient has a bleeding open head wound, the EMT should apply (p. 302):
    A. Aluminum foil seal
    B. Sterile pressure dressings
    C. Loose sterile dressings
    D. Plastic seal

14. If an object is impaled in the skull, the EMT should (p. 305):
    A. Remove the object
    B. Remove the object and apply loose dressings
    C. Remove the object and apply pressure dressings
    D. Not remove the object, but stabilize it

15. Which of the following can cause a severe spinal injury? (p. 308):
    A. Whiplash
    B. Diving accidents
    C. Sledding accidents
    D. All of the above

16. The task of examining a patient for spinal injuries is made easier if the patient is (pp. 308-309):
    A. Conscious and on his back
    B. Conscious and on his side
    C. Unconscious and on his side
    D. Unconscious and on his back

17. The most reliable sign of spinal injury is (p. 309):
    A. Paralysis
    B. Cuts and bruises
    C. Deformity
    D. Pain

18. If the mechanism of the injury and observations indicate a neck or spinal injury, the first step of care after ensuring an open airway is (p. 312):
    A. Survey the entire spine
    B. Immobilize the entire body

C. Apply and maintain in-line stabilization of the head
D. Make a complete body survey

19. The first step in the survey for paralysis is *(p. 310)*:
   A. Touch feet and legs for feeling
   B. Have patient lift legs
   C. Have patient grasp hand
   D. Have patient lift arms

20. Paralysis in the upper extremities may indicate spinal cord damage in the *(p. 311)*:
   A. Lower back
   B. Upper back
   C. Neck
   D. Entire back, below the neck

21. Paralysis limited to the lower extremities may indicate spinal cord damage in the *(p. 311)*:
   A. Neck
   B. Entire length below the neck
   C. Lower back only
   D. Upper back only

22. Diaphragmatic breathing usually indicates *(p. 309)*:
   A. Normal breathing
   B. Airway obstruction
   C. Paralysis of chest muscles
   D. Paralysis of abdominal muscles

23. A vehicle accident victim is still seated in the vehicle. Your survey indicates an injury to the cervical spine. You should first *(p. 312)*:
   A. Secure the patient to a short spine board
   B. Apply an extrication collar
   C. Reposition the patient and secure him to a long spine board
   D. Reposition the patient and use a scoop-style stretcher

EXERCISES

To check your answers to the Exercises, refer to *Emergency Care, 5th ed.*

1. List the signs of possible skull fracture *(pp. 300-301)*.

2. Describe the emergency care for a patient with possible trauma-induced injury to the brain *(pp. 302-303)*.

3. Describe the survey of a conscious patient for signs of possible spinal injury *(pp. 310-311)*.

4. Describe the application of an extrication collar *(pp. 313-316)*.

5. Describe how to use the 4-rescuer log roll to move a patient onto a long spine board *(pp. 317-319)*.

If your EMS system has approved any other technique for moving a patient onto a long board, describe this method in the space provided.

6. Describe, step by step, the use of the short spine board for a vehicle accident victim with a cervical spinal injury. Assume that the patient is still seated *(pp. 322-324)*.

7. What problems can be eliminated by using an extrication vest (e.g., K.E.D.) *(p. 324)*?

ANSWERS

Forming Medical Terms

dura, neurologic, autonomic, encephalitis, intracerebral, intercellular, subdural hematoma

Labeling—*Figure 11–1*

From superior to inferior:
1. Cervical (7)
2. Thoracic (12)
3. Lumbar (5)
4. Sacral (5-fused)
5. Coccyx (4-fused)

Multiple Choice

1. C	7. C	13. C	19. A
2. B	8. D	14. D	20. C
3. C	9. A	15. D	21. B
4. D	10. B	16. B	22. C
5. D	11. C	17. A	23. B
6. A	12. C	18. C	

12 injuries iii: soft tissue injuries of the head and neck

Reading Assignment: Emergency Care, 5th ed., pp. 327–347

INJURIES TO THE SOFT TISSUES OF THE HEAD

INJURIES TO THE SCALP AND FACE

When dealing with facial injuries, the EMT should carefully determine the extent of all emergency problems. The grotesque appearance of facial injuries and profuse superficial bleeding are often given false priority over more serious injuries. As in all primary surveys, the first priority should be given to the detection and correction of breathing problems.

Facial injuries are often given false priority over _____ problems associated with the wound. The force of the accident also may produce neck injuries, including spinal cord damage. If there is a neck injury, or if the mechanism of the injury indicates such damage, the head and neck must be immobilized during examination and care.

breathing

In addition to breathing problems, _____ injuries often are associated with facial injuries. To prevent aggravation of these injuries, the EMT should _____ the patient's head and neck.

neck

immobilize

An open airway is essential. Obstructions can take the form of blood clots, broken teeth and dentures, the tongue forced back into the throat, or severe mouth and nose injuries. Even if there are no airway _____ there may still be a _____ problem because of brain damage that can prevent stimuli being sent from the respiratory center.

obstructions, breathing

The EMT should sweep the inside of the patient's mouth clean of such obstructions as blood _____, broken _____, and dentures. Use gloves to protect yourself from contact with the patient's blood or body fluids. Taking care not to aggravate _____ injuries, the head should be positioned to free the _____, which may have been forced back into the throat.

clots, teeth

neck

tongue

While clearing the patient's _____, the EMT should also check for soft tissue damage such as perforation of the cheek wall. At the same time observations should be made for profuse bleeding.

mouth

If _____ bleeding is noted, the patient should be positioned so he is resting on his side with the head tilted back and the face down. This will provide for drainage away from the throat. Care should be taken to avoid any aggravation to _____ injuries. Remember, if there are neck injuries, there also may be injuries to the _____ _____.

profuse

neck

spinal cord

When the EMT finds profuse bleeding in the mouth or nose, he should position the patient to provide ________________ away from the throat. The patient should be positioned on his ______, his head tilted ______ and the face placed ______. Blood may also have to be removed from the mouth and throat by suction.

drainage
side, back
down

When the patient is not breathing, artificial ventilation (or CPR if there is cardiac arrest) should be given, once an ______ airway is established. If facial injuries are slight, mouth-to-mouth (nose) methods may be used or a bag-valve-mask ventilator can be used for ventilation. The EMT may find that an artificial airway can be useful as long as the patient is unconscious.

open

When dealing with facial injuries, ________________ problems are to be corrected. In the case of neck injuries, the head and the neck are to be ________________. After these procedures are done, the EMT can turn his attention to ______ tissue injuries.

breathing
immobilized
soft

Facial soft tissue injuries can be blunt injuries (primarily contusions to the mouth and nose) or sharp injuries. These blunt injuries are not usually serious, and most bleeding may be no more than an annoyance.

Nasal bleeding indicates a soft tissue injury that is usually not ____________. In most cases it can be stopped by lightly pinching the nostrils together.

serious

There are blunt injuries to soft tissues and also ____________ injuries. These often take the form of lacerations, while blunt injuries are primarily ____________. The face and scalp have many blood vessels and are therefore highly vascular areas; lacerations can produce profuse bleeding.

sharp
contusions

A sharp injury to the scalp or face, such as a ________________, can cause profuse bleeding because the area is highly ____________. Bleeding can be controlled by the direct pressure method, or if that fails, the pressure point method can be utilized. Since facial skin and scalp are ______ tissues, avulsions are possible and should be properly wrapped and transported.

laceration
vascular
soft

Unlike most other cases, objects impaled in the cheek can be removed and the area between the cheek wall and teeth can be packed. The object, if it will easily come loose, has to be ____________ because the ____________ pressure method applied to the outside of the wound will not control bleeding.

removed, direct

Fractures and blood clots from tissues lacerated by broken bones can obstruct the ____________ to cause breathing problems. The EMT must keep the airway open, control bleeding, and transport the patient. Bleeding in the mouth and nose may require manual or mechanical ____________. The patient should be transported on his ______ with the head positioned to facilitate drainage.

airway
suction
side

Injuries to the Eyes

The EMT should know the classification and causes of eye injuries. Eye injuries can be caused by foreign objects, lacerations and contusions, and burns from chemicals, heat and light. All eye injuries have the potential of becoming major injuries. The EMT should transport all patients with eye injuries so that they may be examined by a physician.

Foreign objects, ________________, lacerations, and chemical, heat, and light ____________ can cause eye injuries. The most common injuries are caused by flying particles. These can lodge under the eyelid or in the outer surface of the eyeball.

contusions
burns

Great care should be taken when removing ____________ lodged in the outer surface of the eyeball or under the ____________. Fold the upper

particles
eyelid

lid over an applicator and wash the eye clean with sterile (if available) water, having the patient look down to ensure reaching the extensive area under the lid.

The EMT should wash foreign particles from the eye by using _____ _____. If this fails, a cotton swab or the corner of a clean handkerchief can be used.

Even though flying _____ are the most common source of eye injuries, the EMT may find and have to treat impaled objects. The EMT should never remove impaled objects from the eye.

Large foreign objects _____ in the eye should never be removed. The EMT should protect the object from accidental movement or removal. The eye with an impaled object must be given rigid protection by a thick sterile dressing.

Impaled objects must be given _____ protection from accidental movement or removal. The EMT should apply a _____ sterile dressing, such as several layers of sterile gauze pads or a multi-trauma dressing. A hole, the size of the eye opening, can be cut into the center of the thick _____. Next, the dressing may be placed over the center of the injury site. For protection, a cup or cone of cardboard should be bandaged over the pad with a self-adherent roller bandage.

After protecting the injury site dressing with a cardboard _____ or cone, and fastening it with a self-adherent _____ _____, the EMT should securely bandage the good eye. This is done to prevent sympathetic eye movement. (This is the bad eye duplicating the movements of the good eye.)

Since both eyes are bandaged to prevent _____ eye movements, the patient will not be able to see, thus increasing his fear. The EMT should calm the patient and explain why he is bandaging both eyes.

Eye injuries can be from foreign objects, burns, _____ and _____ . When the eyelid has been lacerated, it may appear to be very serious. This is because the eyelid, like other facial skin, is highly _____ and will bleed profusely. As long as the globe of the eye is not injured, a direct pressure dressing will stop most bleeding.

When the globe of the eye is lacerated, the EMT should not use _____ _____ dressings. Vitreous humor will be forced out of the eye with pressure. This cannot be replaced by the body and will lead to blindness.

To prevent the loss of _____ humor by pressure, a loose dressing should be applied when the _____ of the eye has been lacerated. Remember, the loss of vitreous humor can cause _____ .

Avulsed eyes should be given rigid protection dressings using the same procedure followed for _____ objects.

Chemicals, heat, and light can cause _____ to the eyes. In the case of burns from light, transport the patient after applying dark patches. For burns from heat, loosely dress the eyes and transport. When the burns are caused by _____ , immediately flush the eye with running water and continue to flush during _____.

Injuries to the Ears

Most wounds to the outer ear take the form of _____ or cuts and _____ or scratches. They should be treated the same as similar wounds found elsewhere on the body. Apply a _____

---

sterile
water

particles

impaled

rigid
thick

dressing

cup
roller bandage

sympathetic

lacerations
contusions

vascular

direct pressure

vitreous
globe

blindness

impaled
burns

chemicals
transport

lacerations
abrasions
sterile

dressing to the site. Should the ear be severely torn, a bulky dressing should be applied with the ear resting between several layers.

A perforated ear drum (tympanic membrane), severe pressure due to middle ear infections, and pressure from water can all cause great pain and at least some temporary hearing loss. Emergency care is limited to placing gauze against the ear canal and instructing the patient not to attempt to release pressure or regain hearing by striking his head with his hands. Transport the patient.

A wound to the outer ear is usually cared for with a sterile _____. Severe wounds may require a _____ dressing. *(dressing / bulky)*

Should the patient have a foreign object in his ear, do not try probing to dislodge the object. Even dislodging with a jet of water can be dangerous in some cases. Transport the patient.

In case of an avulsed external ear, care for the injury site as if it were a laceration; apply a _____ _____. If the avulsed part can be retrieved, transport it in a plastic bag or wrap, keeping the wrapped part moist (follow local protocol) and cool. Do not freeze the avulsed part. *(sterile dressing)*

The EMT should keep in mind that an injury to the skull may have taken place if there is bleeding from the ears. An almost certain indication is _____ watery cerebrospinal fluid in the ear. *(clear)*

Injuries to the Nose

As stated before, nasal bleeding usually indicates a _____ tissue injury that can be cared for by _____ the nostrils. However, fractures, foreign object injuries, and avulsion can occur to the nose. Nasal fractures often mean a partial obstruction to the _____. The EMT should ensure an open airway. For nasal avulsion, apply a sterile pressure _____ and recover the avulsed part. A moist (follow local protocol) sterile dressing kept cool should be used to transport the avulsed part. *(soft / pinching / airway / dressing)*

In addition to nasal bleeding, fractures, and avulsed parts, the EMT also may have to care for _____ _____ injuries to the nose. As with the ear, do not attempt to pull the object from the nose or to dislodge by _____. Often, objects can be dislodged by having the patient gently blow his nose, keeping both nostrils open. Do not have the patient blow his nose if he is bleeding from the nostrils or has had a recently controlled nosebleed. *(foreign object / probing)*

Injuries to the Mouth

Bleeding due to injury to the mouth requires positioning to allow for proper _____ to avoid _____ of blood into the lungs. Do not pack the patient's mouth. Pain or convulsions could cause the patient to attempt to swallow the packing and cause airway obstruction. Injury to the lips can be controlled with rolled or folded _____ between the lip and gum. *(drainage, aspiration / dressings)*

Injuries to the mouth also may involve the teeth. Any dislodged teeth should be removed. Do not attempt to pull loosened teeth. Transport any dislodged teeth wrapped in moistened dressing. Control bleeding from the tooth socket with gauze. *Do not* use cotton or cotton-filled gauze.

Often, injuries to the teeth are associated with injuries to the gums and lips. These can usually be controlled with _____ or folded _____ placed between the lip and gum. Bleeding from the tooth socket can be controlled by _____. Remember to remove and _____ any dislodged teeth. *(rolled / dressings / gauze / transport)*

INJURIES TO THE NECK

Neck injuries can be classified the same way as facial soft tissue injuries, that is, _____ injuries and also _____ injuries. Blood vessels going to and from the brain, the cervical spinal cord, and the airway all pass through the neck. Therefore, any injury to the neck can be very serious. In order to prevent aggravation to injuries of the neck, the EMT should _____ the patient's head and neck.

blunt, sharp

immobilize

Blunt injuries to the neck can often cause the trachea or the larynx to collapse. If this has occurred, the patient must be transported without delay, receiving forced mouth-to-mouth resuscitation or, preferably, a high concentration of oxygen from a bag-valve-mask resuscitator or positive pressure resuscitator should be administered.

A blunt injury to the neck can cause the collapse of the _____ or the _____ requiring a _____ concentration of oxygen from a _____ - _____ -mask. The other classification of neck injuries, _____ injuries, can have profuse bleeding as their most serious problem.

trachea
larynx, high
bag-valve-
sharp

Sharp injuries to the neck can cause _____ _____ . Venous bleeding can be stopped by direct pressure dressing. Remember, bandaging too tightly will interfere with breathing or arterial blood flow to the brain.

profuse bleeding

_____ bleeding can be controlled by direct pressure dressing. This method can be used for arterial bleeding, but great care must be taken since it may stop the flow of blood to the _____ . The EMT should use a dressing and direct pressure to control arterial bleeding (the same technique as used for venous bleeding can be applied).

Venous

brain

If a large neck vein has been severed, bleeding may not be controlled by a direct _____ dressing. Use plastic wrap to make an occlusive dressing. Apply this to the wound, place a roll of gauze over the top of the occlusive dressing, and secure both in place using a figure-eight dressing. The methods to stop the bleeding from severed neck blood vessels include _____ _____ dressings for small veins and arteries, _____ dressings for large veins.

pressure

direct pressure
occlusive

Terminology

Define the following terms. Check your definitions with those in the Glossary of your textbook or as directed.

Epistaxis—

Jugular vein—

Sympathetic eye movements—

Vitreous fluid (humor)—

Multiple Choice

Circle the letter of the correct answer for each question. The answers are given at the end of this chapter. Note page references to *Emergency Care, 5th ed.*

1. When there is profuse bleeding in the mouth and nose, the patient should be positioned *(p. 332)*:
   A. Lying on back, head straight, face up
   B. Lying on side, head back, face to side
   C. Lying on stomach, head back, face to side
   D. Lying on back, head back, face to side

2. Nasal bleeding can usually be controlled by *(p. 342)*:
   A. Pinching the nostrils together
   B. Facial pressure points
   C. Tilting the head forward
   D. Tilting the head to one side

3. Profuse bleeding can occur from wounds of the facial skin and scalp because the area is very *(p. 328)*:
   A. Spongy
   B. Vascular
   C. Compact
   D. Muscular

4. In certain cases, an impaled object can be removed from the *(p. 331)*:
   A. Eye
   B. Chest
   C. Cheek
   D. Pelvis

5. Direct pressure should not be applied to a lacerated eye to avoid *(p. 334)*
   A. Changing the shape of the lens
   B. Aqueous fluid loss
   C. Vitreous fluid loss
   D. Detachment of the retina

6. Which of the following is the thin membrane covering the sclera? *(p. 332)*
   A. Renal capsule
   B. Conjunctiva
   C. Glisson's capsule
   D. Bowman's capsule

7. Which of the following best describes eye movement? *(p. 334)*
   A. Paradoxical
   B. Antagonistic
   C. Dorsolateral
   D. Sympathetic

8. The clear structure of the eye in front of the iris is the *(p. 332)*:
   A. Cornea
   B. Lens
   C. Ciliary
   D. Sclera

9. Which of the following is the best method to care for the eyes of an unconscious patient? *(pp. 332–333)*
   A. Cover with multi-trauma dressings
   B. Cover with loose dressings
   C. Wash before transport
   D. Keep the eyelids closed

10. Which of the following would be most likely to cause the larynx to collapse? *(p. 343)*
    A. Blunt injury to the sternum
    B. Sharp injury to the face
    C. Blunt injury to the neck
    D. Sharp injury to the neck

11. Which of the following are basically treated the same? *(p. 337)*
    A. Avulsed eye, protruding intestine
    B. Avulsed eye, object impaled in eye
    C. Object impaled in eye, chemical burns to eye
    D. Object impaled in eye, object impaled in cheek

12. Which of the following is recommended to control bleeding from the socket of a dislodged tooth? *(p. 343)*
    A. Gauze
    B. Cotton-filled gauze
    C. Cotton packets
    D. All are recommended

13. The injury site of an ear avulsion should be cared for with *(p. 340)*:
    A. A bulky dressing
    B. A simple folded pad of gauze
    C. A cotton pressure dressing
    D. An ice pack

14. Which of the following is used to control severe bleeding from a severed large neck vein and may prevent an air embolism? *(p. 345)*
    A. Sterile pressure dressing
    B. Trauma dressing
    C. Sanitary napkin
    D. Occlusive dressing

Exercises

To check your answers to the Exercises, refer to *Emergency Care, 5th ed.*

1. List the steps in the care procedure used to treat a patient with an object impaled in the eye *(p. 336)*.

2. Describe how to transport an avulsed ear *(p. 340)*.

3. Describe, step by step, the application of a bandage in the care of a scalp wound *(pp. 328–329)*.

4. Describe how to control bleeding from a neck vein *(pp. 346–347)*.

Answers

Multiple Choice

1. B
2. A
3. B
4. C
5. C
6. B
7. D
8. A
9. D
10. C
11. B
12. A
13. A
14. D

13 injuries iv: the chest, abdomen, and genitalia

Reading Assignment: Emergency Care, 5th ed., pp. 349-367

INJURIES TO THE CHEST

Chest injuries can be open wounds that allow air into the chest cavity, or closed wounds. Shortness of breath, failure of the chest to expand, coughing up blood, and shock all can indicate chest injuries.

Chest injuries can be open or _____ wounds. One of the most common closed wounds is a fractured rib. This is usually the result of direct blows or compression to the ribs. The fifth through the tenth sets of ribs are most often involved.

closed

Direct blows or compression to the ribs may cause _____. Local pain, tenderness and crackling sensations are all signs of rib fractures. The crackling sensation indicates that the lung has been punctured, releasing air into surrounding tissues. This is called subcutaneous emphysema.

fractures

The emergency care of rib fractures involves supporting the arm on the injured side with a sling. Of the _____ sets of ribs, the EMT should pay particular attention to the _____ through _____ sets.

12
fifth, tenth

Flail chest is a condition that results from many rib fractures loosening a large segment of the chest wall and/or separation of the sternum. The loose segment will move in the opposite direction of the chest wall during breathing. This is called paradoxical motion.

Paradoxical motion is an indication of _____ chest. Treatment requires the application of bulky pressure dressings or a small pillow held in place by tape to correct _____ respiration. Positive pressure resuscitation with 100% oxygen may be recommended. Transport the patient on his injured side.

flail

paradoxical

A true emergency requiring immediate transport is traumatic asphyxia. This is caused by the sternum and sections of the ribs being broken off and forced inward. As the blood is forced from the heart into the veins of the neck, the skin of the shoulders, head, and neck will turn blue. The patient is usually in severe shock. As with all serious respiratory problems, _____% _____ should be given.

100
oxygen

Injuries to the chest can be closed or _____ wounds. When the pleural sac has been punctured, _____ is able to enter the cavity. This condition is called pneumothorax. Because of the pressure change in the thoracic cavity, this condition is often called a "sucking chest wound."

open
air

To prevent air from entering and causing a serious pressure change in the _____ cavity, the EMT should seal off all open chest wounds with an occlusive dressing, securing all but one edge of the seal with tape (some protocols allow all four edges to be sealed). The patient should be transported lying on his _____ _____.

thoracic

Penetration of the _____ sac allowing air to enter the thoracic cavity will lead to the condition of _____. This condition requires the wound to be _____ off. If the lungs are penetrated, often indicated by bright red frothy blood at the mouth, pressure will build up inside a fully sealed open chest wound, creating a condition called tension pneumothorax. If a patient with a fully sealed open chest wound begins to decline, it is possible that pressure is building up, indicating the condition of _____ _____. This will require that the seal be opened.

injured side
pleural
pneumothorax
sealed

tension pneumothorax

The EMT will have to treat pneumothorax, tension pneumothorax, and impaled objects in the chest. As with all impaled objects, except for those in the _____, the object should not be removed. The object should be stabilized with _____ dressings.

check
bulky

INJURIES TO THE ABDOMEN

The cavity below the diaphragm, lined with a membrane called the peritoneum, is called the abdominal cavity. The EMT should realize that there are organs in the abdominal region and the pelvic region. Actually, he is dealing with the abdominopelvic cavity. This cavity contains both solid and hollow organs.

Below the diaphragm is the _____ cavity containing both _____ and hollow organs. The liver, spleen, and pancreas are solid organs. Just behind the cavity are the kidneys. These are also solid organs.

abdominopelvic
solid

The liver, kidneys, and pancreas are vital _____ organs. The spleen is not considered to be vital. However, injury to any of these organs is serious.

solid

Besides the solid organs there are the _____ organs, such as the stomach, small intestine, large intestine, gallbladder, and urinary bladder. When injured, these organs can dump their contents into the _____ cavity.

hollow

abdominopelvic

The EMT should check for sharp and blunt injuries. He should look for impaled objects, remembering not to remove them, but to _____ them with _____ dressings. The EMT should check for the symptoms and signs of abdominal injury such as vomiting, pain, tenderness, muscle spasms, or stiffening of abdominal muscles, shock, and any bruise or abrasion over the injury site.

stabilize, bulky

When the EMT sees an abdominal wound or impaled object, or notes the _____ and signs of an abdominal injury, he should transport the patient. When possible, the patient should be placed lying on his back with the legs flexed to relieve abdominal tension. No attempt should be made to replace protruding (eviscerated) organs. They should be held in place with an occlusive dressing.

symptoms

The patient with an abdominal injury should be transported lying on his _____, with the legs _____. As with all cases of blood loss, _____ should be given. The EMT should not try to replace _____ organs.

back, flexed
oxygen
protruding

INJURIES TO THE GENITALIA

Bleeding from the genitalia can be controlled by the standard method of _____ pressure. For the male, this may require direct pressure applied to the veins of the penis. A diaper style pressure dressing held in place by a 4-tailed bandage works best to control bleeding of the penis.

direct

A sanitary napkin can be used to maintain pressure to the injured female genitalia. As with the male, the best bandage to hold the dressing is a _____-_____ bandage.

4 tailed
moist

Any avulsed parts should be transported, wrapped in a _____ sterile dressing (follow local protocols). As in most cases, impalements should _____ be _____. An ice pack can be applied to any blunt injuries to the penis or scrotum.

not, removed

TERMINOLOGY

Define the following terms. Check your definitions with those in the Glossary of your textbook, or as directed.

Flail chest—

Inguinal hernia—

Paradoxical movement—

Pneumothorax—

LABELING

Label the following illustration in the spaces provided. The answers are given at the end of this chapter. If you have trouble labeling this illustration, see pages 40 and 351 in your textbook.

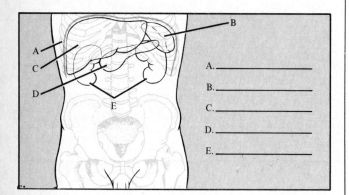

A._____

B._____

C._____

D._____

E._____

Figure 13-1

MULTIPLE CHOICE

Circle the letter of the correct answer for each question. The answers are given at the end of this chapter. Note that page references to *Emergency Care, 5th ed.,* are given.

1. Bright red frothy blood from the mouth indicates *(p. 352)*:
   A. Punctured lung
   B. Fractured ribs
   C. Flail chest
   D. Punctured pleura

2. The ribs most frequently fractured are the *(p. 355)*:
   A. Second through fourth
   B. First through fifth
   C. Fifth through tenth
   D. Eleventh and twelfth

3. When a section of a flail chest moves in the opposite direction of breathing movements, this is called *(p. 357)*:
   A. Traumatic pneumothorax
   B. Subcutaneous emphysema
   C. Traumatic asphyxia
   D. Paradoxical motion

4. The condition of the heart bleeding into its own protective sac is *(p. 358)*:
   A. Cardiac emphysema
   B. Cardiac tamponade
   C. Pericardiopneumothorax
   D. Cardiac asphyxia

5. Which of the following methods can be used to stabilize a flail chest? *(p. 357)*
   A. An occlusive dressing
   B. A four-tailed bandage
   C. Multi-trauma dressings
   D. All of the above

6. An accident victim has suffered a severe compression injury to the chest, breaking away the sternum and pushing it inward. The shoulders, neck, and face turn a deep blue. This indicates *(p. 359)*:
   A. Subcutaneous emphysema
   B. Traumatic asphyxia
   C. Tension pneumothorax
   D. Traumatic pneumothorax

7. During tension pneumothorax, the pressure will usually interfere with the lung and the *(p. 354)*:
   A. Heart
   B. Brain
   C. Esophagus
   D. Neck arteries

8. Which of the following is the dressing of choice for an open abdominal wound with a protruding intestine? *(p. 362)*
   A. Sterile moist gauze
   B. Dry sterile gauze
   C. Occlusive dressing or plastic wrap
   D. Wet sterile plastic wrap

9. Which of the following is a pelvic organ? *(p. 363)*
   A. Pancreas
   B. Gallbladder
   C. Urinary bladder
   D. All of the above

EXERCISES

To check your answers to the Exercises, refer to *Emergency Care, 5th ed.*

1. Describe the initial emergency care for fractured ribs *(p. 356)*.

2. Describe how to apply an occlusive dressing (flutter valve) for an open chest wound *(pp. 352-354)*.

3. Describe how to stabilize a flailed section of the chest wall *(p. 357-358)*.

4. Describe how to apply an occlusive dressing to an open abdominal wound *(p. 362)*.

5. Classify each of the following as a solid (S) or hollow (H) organ *(p. 360)*:
   Stomach _____
   Gallbladder _____
   Spleen _____
   Small intestine _____
   Liver _____ Pancreas _____
   Urinary bladder _____
   Large intestine _____

ANSWERS

Labeling

A. Diaphragm
B. Spleen
C. Liver
D. Pancreas
E. Kidneys

Multiple Choice

1. A
2. C
3. D
4. B
5. C
6. B
7. A
8. C (in some systems, A is also correct.)
9. C

14 *medical emergencies*

Reading Assignment: Emergency Care, 5th ed., pp. 369-401

SECTION ONE

POISONING

A poison is any chemical that can cause harm when it is ingested, inhaled, absorbed, or injected into the body. Associated with the harm done by the chemical are symptoms and signs that indicate that the patient is having a _____ emergency.

Any chemical that can harm the body is a potential _____. This chemical may find its way into the body by being _____ through the mouth, _____, _____ through the skin, or _____ through the tissues and into the bloodstream. The venom from spiders, insects, snakes, and certain marine life forms are examples of _____ poisons.

When possible, you should contact your local poison control center, physician, or emergency department physician as the first step in caring for a poisoning after providing basic life support. If the poison was ingested, you may be directed to dilute the poison by giving the conscious patient water or milk, then induce vomiting with syrup of ipecac (if allowed in your EMS system).

Before diluting an _____ poison with _____ or _____, you should contact your local _____ _____ _____ physician or emergency department physician for specific care directions. You may be directed to _____ _____ by having the conscious patient drink 2 tablespoons of _____ of _____ in no less than 8 ounces of water. Make certain to position the patient so that he does not aspirate any vomitus.

If you are called upon to induce vomiting, you will probably do so after _____ the poison. Vomiting is usually induced by having the _____ patient drink _____ tablespoons of syrup of ipecac in no less than _____ ounces of _____. In some cases, you may be directed to give the patient charcoal, or to induce vomiting and then provide charcoal.

Some poisons are inhaled. You must safely remove the patient from the source of the poison, maintain an open airway, provide basic life support, and administer oxygen. The patient may have chemical burns requiring care. Ensure an open airway and keep the patient in a lateral recumbent position in case he _____.

A poison may be _____, inhaled, absorbed through the _____, or injected into the body. Absorbed poisons usually irritate or damage the skin. You should use water to immediately flood the patient's

medical
poison
ingested
inhaled, absorbed
injected

injected

ingested, water
milk, poison control
center
induce vomiting
syrup
ipecac

diluting
conscious, 2
8, water

vomits
ingested
skin

skin to wash away the poison. After washing, remove all contaminated clothing and jewelry and wash the patient again. You may have to follow the same procedure for patients who have _____ a poison and have chemical burns to their skin.

inhaled

The venom from insect, spiders, and snakes are _____ poisons. Always treat the patient with an injected poison as if shock is about to occur. Scrape away stingers and venom sacs. Except for cases of snakebite, apply a cold pack or covered ice bag over the site of _____. Keep the limb immobilized.

injected

injection

In the case of snakebite, keep the patient calm, treat for shock, and conserve body heat. One light constricting band should be placed above and another below the wound. Do NOT place a _____ pack on the site.

It is very important in cases of snakebite to keep patients _____. You should always treat for _____, conserving body heat. You should place _____ _____ _____ above and below the wound, about 2 inches from the site, but never one band on each side of a joint.

cold
calm
shock
light constricting bands

DISORDERS OF THE CARDIOVASCULAR SYSTEM

Disorders of the Heart

Nearly 1.2 million cases of acute myocardial infarction (AMI) are reported in the United States each year. Approximately 400,000 people die suddenly from cardiac arrest before they reach a medical facility.

Heart attacks can be brought about by a variety of factors. However, most attacks can be traced back to changes in, or blockage of, the coronary arteries supplying the myocardium (heart muscle) with blood. This is true for most AMIs, or _____ _____ _____.

acute myocardial
infarctions

Most heart attacks are caused by changes in, or blockage of, the _____ arteries. Such changes and blockages are termed *coronary artery disease* (CAD).

coronary

One form of CAD or _____ _____ disease is arteriosclerosis or *hardening of the arteries*. Another form is atherosclerosis, where fatty deposits and, eventually, calcification combine to narrow the inner diameter of the coronary _____ and reduce the flow of blood to the _____.

coronary artery

arteries
myocardium

The symptoms of heart attack will vary greatly according to type and severity of attack. The EMT should consider any chest pain as a possible heart attack. This is particularly true for patients suffering from angina pectoris, a condition in which chest pains result from a decreased flow of blood through the _____ _____ and thus a decreased supply of oxygen reaching the _____.

coronary arteries
myocardium

A patient having, or about to have, a heart attack will often have _____ pains. This is true of patients with _____ _____ attacks caused by the decreased blood and oxygen supply reaching the heart _____.

chest, angina
pectoris
muscle (myocardium)

Quite often the early stages of coronary _____ disease will be accompanied by pains in the chest called _____ _____. The nature of the disease could be hardening of the arteries, which is also called _____. Perhaps fatty deposits are building

artery
angina pectoris

arteriosclerosis

up on the inner surface of the artery walls to cause _____.

atherosclerosis

Angina attacks usually cause unremitting pain throughout the 3-5 minute attack. Stress often sets off these attacks. As the attacks worsen, pain originating behind the breastbone or _____ will radiate down either of the upper extremities.

sternum

Angina attacks, usually lasting _____ to _____ minutes, are often brought about by _____. In addition to pain originating behind the _____ and pains that radiate down either _____ _____, pain may also occur in the neck, jaw, teeth, upper back, or even the epigastric region of the abdomen.

3, 5
stress
sternum, upper extremity

Along with severe _____, the EMT may observe shortness of breath, apprehension, restlessness, sweating, nausea, and in some cases, shock and unconsciousness all associated with angina attacks.

pain

Never assume the patient has "merely" had a "simple" angina attack. If the patient is under care for angina and has been told to take nitroglycerine for attacks, help the patient take his medication and place him in a restful position. If the patient's systolic blood pressure is below 90 mmHg, call the emergency department physician before nitroglycerine is taken. *Be certain* to check vital signs after the attack. Transport all patients who may have suffered an angina attack.

Many pending severe heart attacks given little warning. If the patient has chest pains, *transport*. Be sure to maintain an open airway and provide for adequate air exchange. Reduce stress on the patient as much as possible. Provide oxygen.

AMI stands for _____ _____ _____. In this case, a portion of the heart muscle or _____ dies due to oxygen starvation. This is caused by a narrowing or occlusion (blockage) of the _____ artery that supplies blood to that region of the heart.

acute myocardial infarction
myocardium

coronary

If the coronary artery supplying blood to a region of the myocardium undergoes _____ or _____, the muscle will die of _____ starvation. This condition is called _____ _____ _____ and can be caused by CAD, blood clots, shock, diseases of the myocardium, pulmonary embolism, or other factors such as stress and unrelieved fatigue.

narrowing, occlusion
oxygen
acute myocardial infarction

An arrhythmia is a disturbance of heart rate and rhythm. AMI victims usually experience severe chest _____, and about 85% to 90% experience arrhythmias. Those arrhythmias can be either lethal or nonlethal.

pain

Asystole is cardiac standstill. This is a lethal _____. If the lower chambers of the heart begin to have unsymmetrical beating of the heart muscle, the condition is an arrhythmia called _____ fibrillation.

arrhythmia

ventricular

Ventricular _____ and _____ are both lethal arrhythmias. Bradycardia is a slow heart rate, below 60 beats per minute. Tachycardia is too fast a heart beat, above 100 beats per minute. Both of these can be lethal _____.

fibrillation, asystole

arrhythmias

Some arrhythmias are cardiac standstill or _____, ventricular fibrillation, or the _____ beating of the heart muscle, heart rates above 100 beats per minute or _____, and heart rates below 60 beats per minute or _____.

asystole
unsymmetrical
tachycardia
bradycardia

Two other factors can be seen in cases of AMI: mechanical pump failure and cardiac rupture. When the heart fails to produce adequate circulation due to myocardial damage, mechanical pump failure occurs. This can lead to congestive heart failure, cardiogenic shock, or ventricular aneurysm, a condition where a thin-walled bulge forms in the dead myocardial tissue.

When the heart can no longer carry out its normal work load due to myocardial damage, the patient may suffer _____ _____ _____. Another complication of AMI, one almost certainly lethal, is the rupturing of the heart wall. This is cardiac rupture.

mechanical pump failure

A patient about to have an AMI will usually suffer chest pains. During an AMI, even if the patient is at rest, he will have chest pains that originate in the same area as an angina attack, that is, below the _____. The pain will not be short and sharp, but constant and compressing.

sternum

The signs and symptoms of an AMI are often very similar to those of an angina attack, although they tend to be more pronounced. The patient will usually experience _____ of breath and difficulty in breathing, termed *dyspnea*. Sweating, nausea, restlessness, and _____ can all be observed. Expect to see signs of shock. The patient may become unconscious.

shortness

apprehension

For the unconscious AMI victim, as with all unconscious patients, establish and maintain an _____ _____. If respiration stops, provide _____ resuscitation. CPR should be initiated if the patient goes into _____ _____.

open airway
pulmonary
cardiac arrest

After considering the reasons why the AMI probably occurred, the EMT usually provides a _____ concentration of _____.

high, oxygen

The conscious patient will be both _____ and _____. The EMTs should talk to the patient to reassure him and keep him at ease. Transfer the patient directly to the stretcher and carry or roll the stretcher and patient to the ambulance. Transport should be in the position most comfortable for the patient, usually seated. Body heat should be conserved. Provide oxygen.

restless
apprehensive

Congestive heart failure occurs when the heart can no longer carry out its normal work load due to pulmonary or venous congestion. This condition can be brought on by an AMI, diseased heart valves, hypertension, and a variety of respiratory diseases.

Pulmonary congestion and venous congestion can bring about _____ _____ _____. When the left ventricle of the heart is damaged and can no longer function properly, blood backs up in the pulmonary veins. Serum is then forced from the blood into the airsacs of the lungs, called _____, and pulmonary edema results that prevents proper CO_2 and O_2 exchange. All this is _____ congestion and is called left heart failure.

congestive heart failure

alveoli

pulmonary

Pulmonary congestion is associated with right heart failure. As the right ventricle fails, blood backs up the systemic venous system, and blood serum escapes into the tissues, causing massive edema.

The primary symptom of left heart failure is difficult breathing called _____. Cyanosis, tachycardia (a heart rate above _____ per minute) and rapid, noisy, and labored breathing all occur with left heart failure.

dyspnea, 100

In cases of left heart failure, the primary symptom is _____. Respirations will be _____, noisy, and _____. Rales and coughing usually are present, with many patients producing blood-tinged sputum. Left heart failure also can cause right heart failure to occur.

dyspnea
rapid, labored

Associated with right heart failure is _____ congestion lead-

venous

ing to massive _____ caused when blood _____ escapes into the tissues. Expect to see the swelling of tissues, neck vein distention, and in some cases, a general bloating of the lower or entire body. **edema, serum**

When venous congestion occurs due to _____ heart failure, expect also to find a rapid pulse rate or _____, high blood pressure or _____, and possibly chest pains. As with left heart failure, respirations will be _____ , _____ , _____, and usually shallow. The patient will show some level of apprehension and agitation. **right tachycardia hypertension rapid, noisy labored**

NOTE: When both left and right heart failure occur together, expect to observe the signs and symptoms of both.

Keep the patient with congestive heart failure as quiet as possible. Carry the stretcher to the patient. As with angina victims, the best positioning will be a _____ position. **sitting**

Since congestive heart failure reduces the efficiency of circulation, the patient's cells will be starved for _____. Administer a high concentration of supplemental oxygen. **oxygen**

CAUTION: If the congestive heart failure is associated with a respiratory disease such as emphysema or other chronic obstructive pulmonic diseases, oxygen may worsen the patient's condition. One hundred percent oxygen can kill these patients. The EMT should call or radio for guidance from the emergency department or the patient's physician. Many squads now use 24% oxygen through a Venturi mask for hypoxic emphysema patients in congestive heart failure. This procedure is not agreed upon by all emergency care professionals. If other problems exist that require the delivery of a higher concentration of oxygen, do not withhold the needed oxygen.

Stroke

The stroke or cerebrovascular accident (CVA) occurs when part of the brain is cut off from its blood supply through artery obstruction or rupturing. Respiration is slow, the pupils are uneven and paralysis to one side only may be noticed.

Since _____ is slow, the EMT should ensure an open airway and oxygen should be administered. The patient also may go into cardiac arrest, requiring CPR. Even though CPR is not very effective on many stroke victims, the EMT should use the procedure. **respiration**

During a CVA, blood vessels may _____ and release blood that will cause great pressure. Transport the conscious patient lying down with his head raised to relieve some of this pressure. Do not give anything by mouth. Transport the unconscious victim in the lateral recumbent position. Administer oxygen to CVA patients. If respiration is of the slow, snoring type, the pupils are _____ , and there is a weakness or _____ to _____ side, the EMT can assume the patient has had a CVA or _____. **rupture** **uneven paralysis, one stroke**

RESPIRATORY SYSTEM DISORDERS

Dyspnea

When a patient displays labored or difficult breathing, he has dyspnea. Dyspnea is one stage of respiratory distress, following an increase in the rate and depth of respirations.

A patient in respiratory distress will usually begin by having an increase in the _____ and _____ of respirations. He will then experience difficult or labored breathing. This is _____. Hypoxia will result from a decreased supply of oxygen to the tissues.

rate, depth
dyspnea

Dyspnea is difficult or _____ breathing that may lead to _____. If the distress continues, the patient may have periods of temporary cessation of breathing known as apnea. If uncorrected, dyspnea may lead to respiratory arrest and death. Death by suffocation is known as asphyxia.

labored
hypoxia

The condition where a patient with dyspnea experiences temporary cessation of breathing is known as _____ . If the respiratory _____ continues, he may die of _____.

apnea
distress, asphyxia

Try to find out the cause of the respiratory distress. Since the patient is _____ , provide a _____ concentration of _____. This may have to be modified if the patient suffers from a chronic obstructive pulmonary disease such as _____.

hypoxic, high
oxygen
emphysema (or chronic bronchitis)

Chronic Obstructive Pulmonary Disease

The chronic obstructive pulmonary disease (COPD) patient usually is an older person suffering from chronic bronchitis, _____, miner's black lung, or some undetermined respiratory illness. Cough, shortness of breath, and tightness in the chest are common complaints.

emphysema

The chronic _____ pulmonary disease patient may suffer from _____ bronchitis, emphysema, or miner's _____ _____.

obstructive
chronic
black, lung

Cyanosis and edema in the lower extremities are warnings of possible serious problems.

COPD patients can be oxygen-sensitive. As with all such patients, the current recommendation is _____% oxygen delivered by _____ mask.

24, Venturi

TERMINOLOGY

Define the following terms. Check your definitions with those in the Glossary of your textbook.

Acute myocardial infarction—

Cerebrovascular accident—

Chronic obstructive pulmonary disease—

Dyspnea—

Edema—

Hyperventilation—

Poison—

FORMING MEDICAL TERMS

The following elements of medical terms were used in this section. Answers are at the end of the chapter.

Roots and Combining Forms

athero- (ath-er-o-): exhaustion. The breakdown (exhaustion) of arterial linings is called _____sclerosis

arterio- (ar-te-re-o-): in reference to the arteries.

corono- (KOR-o-no-): referring to the arteries that supply the myocardium; the coronary arteries.

sclero- (skle-RO-): hardening. Hardening of the arteries is called _____ sclerosis.

Prefixes

Brady- (brae-de): slow. A slow heart rate is called _____ cardia.

Dys- (dis-): difficult

tachy- (tack-e-): fast, rapid. A rapid heart rate is called tachy_____.

Suffixes

-pnea (-p-NE-ah): breathing. Difficult breathing is called _____pnea.

MULTIPLE CHOICE

Circle the letter of the correct answer to each question. Note the page references to the textbook.

1. Most acute heart attacks are caused by the blockage of _____ arteries. *(p. 388)*
   A. Cephalic
   B. Coronal
   C. Coronary
   D. Carotid

2. Which of the following is a case of chest pains caused by a decreased blood supply to the heart muscle? *(p. 388)*
   A. CVA
   B. Arrhythmia
   C. Congestive heart failure
   D. Angina pectoris

3. Which of the following is the condition caused when the heart can no longer carry its normal load? *(pp. 392-393)*
   A. Congestive heart failure
   B. Acute heart failure

   C. Acute myocardial infarction
   D. Chronic myocardial infarction

4. A man in his early 50s suddenly has pains in his chest that radiate down his left arm. He quickly becomes short of breath and very apprehensive and restless. He goes into shock. He is probably having *(pp. 390-391)*:
   A. An angina attack
   B. Congestive heart attack
   C. A stroke
   D. An AMI

5. A 65-year-old woman with a history of emphysema is found suffering from severe fatigue. She is short of breath, cyanotic, and exhibits swelling of the feet and hands. She has prob-ably suffered *(p. 393)*:
   A. An angina attack
   B. Congestive heart failure
   C. A stroke
   D. An AMI

6. Which of the following terms applies to a heart rate below 60 beats per minute? *(p. 392)*
   A. Bradycardia
   B. Ventricular fibrillation
   C. Tachycardia
   D. Atrial fibrillation

7. An at rest heart beat above 100 beats per minute is *(p. 392)*:
   A. Bradycardia
   B. Ventricular fibrillation
   C. Tachycardia
   D. Atrial fibrillation

8. A disturbance of heart rate and rhythm is defined as *(p. 392)*:
   A. Mechanical pump failure
   B. An arrhythmia
   C. Cardiogenic shock
   D. Congestive heart failure

9. Which of the following should not be eliminated by induced vomiting? *(p. 376)*
   A. Poisonous berries
   B. Acid drain cleaner
   C. Sleeping pills
   D. Aspirin

10. You should remove the stinger of a honeybee by *(p. 380)*:
    A. Grasping it with your fingers
    B. Grasping it with tweezers
    C. Gently scraping it with a blade
    D. Rubbing with adhesive tape

11. You have administered two tablespoons of syrup of ipecac followed by a full glass of water. The patient does not vomit in 20 minutes. You should *(p. 377)*:
    A. Administer charcoal and water
    B. Contact medical command and the poison control center for further instructions
    C. Wait until the patient vomits and give charcoal and water
    D. Administer mineral oil

12. A 70-year old man is found with slow, snoring respiration. His face is flushed and warm. The pupils of his eyes are uneven. He probably has had *(p. 395)*:
    A. A CVA
    B. Chronic heart failure
    C. A heart attack
    D. An angina attack

EXERCISES

To check your answers, refer to *Emergency Care, 5th ed.*

1. List the symptoms and signs of an AMI. Next to each, indicate the care (if any) that applies to that particular symptom or sign *(pp. 390-391)*.

2. Describe the basic care for an unconscious patient who has probably suffered a stroke *(p. 395)*.

3. Describe, step by step, the emergency care for snakebite *(p. 381)*.

4. List 4 ways by which a poison can enter the body and some typical reactions seen in each case *(p. 374)*.

5. Describe, step by step, the emergency care for a patient who has ingested a poisonous substance that allows for the induction of vomiting *(pp. 376-377)*.

6. Describe how you would care for a hyperventilating patient, when there are no other signs of a medical problem *(p. 399)*.

ANSWERS

Forming Medical Terms

atherosclerosis, arteriosclerosis, bradycardia, tachycardia, dyspnea.

Multiple Choice

1. C	4. D	7. C	10. C
2. D	5. B	8. B	11. B
3. A	6. A	9. B	12. A

Reading Assignment: Emergency Care, 5th ed., pp. 401-415

SECTION TWO

DIABETIC STATES

The body's cells need glucose. Before glucose can enter the cells, insulin must be present. If there is not enough insulin, the cells will starve for glucose and the patient will go into diabetic coma. If there is too much insulin, the blood glucose will be used too quickly by all the body cells and starve the brain cells. This is insulin shock, often caused when a diabetic takes too much insulin.

When insulin levels are too low, the patient will go into _____ _____ . This is true of the diabetic, a person with insufficient _____ production. The patient in diabetic coma will have deep, rapid respiration. The skin will be dry. In Caucasians, the skin may turn red. Acetone breath or fruity breath odor is common. The patient should be transported immediately. **diabetic coma insulin**

If there is too much insulin in the blood, _____ _____ will occur. The patient's pulse will be rapid and weak. His skin will be cold and clammy. He may show convulsions, unconsciousness or coma, and general muscular weakness. Trembling and hunger pains are common. The EMT can help by giving the conscious patient sugar, such as candy or orange juice. **insulin shock**

The patient in _____ _____ must be transported without delay. The patient with insulin shock can be given _____ and transported. The skin of the patient in diabetic coma is _____ and _____, while the skin of the patient in insulin shock is _____ and _____. **diabetic coma sugar (glucose) red, dry cold, clammy**

When you cannot determine if the patient is in a diabetic _____ or in insulin _____ , treat as if there is insulin shock and give _____. For unconscious patients, do not administer the sugar in liquid form, and observe all granulated sugar until it fully dissolves in the patient's mouth (follow local protocols). **coma shock sugar (glucose)**

CONVULSIVE DISORDERS

Convulsive disorders usually involve uncontrolled muscular contractions. This is often true for epilepsy. However, not all epileptic seizures will bring on convulsions. The petit mal seizure may produce no more than brief moments of altered consciousness. The patient with a grand mal seizure will have violent muscular contractions.

If a patient with epilepsy is having uncontrolled muscle contractions or _____, the condition is called a _____ _____ seizure. Care consists of protecting the patient from injury and embarassment and transport to a medical facility. **convulsions, grand mal**

Since seizures involve _____ muscle contractions, the patient may injure himself during his fall to the ground or on nearby objects. The EMT should have objects near the patient moved away. He should not try to restrain the patient during the _____ or try to move him. The patient should be transported after the seizure. **uncontrolled seizure**

As well as protecting the patient from injury, the EMT should control onlookers to protect the patient from _____. **embarrassment**

When irregular, uncontrolled muscle contractions occur, the condition is called a convulsion. The first phase of a convulsion or convulsive seizure

112

is the tonic phase where the body becomes rigid, usually for no more than 30 seconds. Respirations may stop and bowel and bladder control can be lost.

A convulsion occurs when the patient has irregular, uncontrolled _____ _____ . The first phase is the _____ phase indicated by the body becoming _____ for up to _____ seconds. This is followed by the second phase, the clonic phase, noted for violent body jerks lasting usually no more than 1 or 2 minutes. Foaming at the mouth, drooling, and facial cyanosis are often seen. After the _____ phase and the _____ phase comes the postictal phase where the convulsions stop. The _____ at the mouth, drooling, and facial _____ seen during the _____ phase disappear. Depending on the cause of the seizure, the patient may immediately regain consciousness and be in a mild state of confusion and drowsiness, or he may remain deeply unconscious for several hours.

muscle contractions
tonic, rigid
30

tonic, clonic
foaming
cyanosis, clonic

ACUTE ABDOMEN

Many different illnesses and internal injuries can lead to acute abdominal distress. NEVER assume the patient has a "simple bellyache." These patients almost always will have pain that will be constantly severe or occurring as quick shooting pains. The abdomen can be rigid or soft, usually with local or diffuse tenderness. Nausea and vomiting are common.

Take care in transporting patients with _____ abdominal _____ . Most of these patients are more comfortable on their backs. However, _____ and _____ are common. Monitor continuously for adequate drainage, and be ready to suction vomitus.

acute
distress
nausea, vomiting

COMMUNICABLE DISEASES

As an EMT, you will be expected to care for and transport some patients with communicable diseases. The main concern is viral diseases carried in blood, body _____, and wastes. You can protect yourself from communicable diseases by avoiding direct contact with _____, body fluids, and _____. Use latex gloves that are free of holes, tears, and breaks. Wear goggles if there is a chance of eye contamination. When necessary, you should wear a gown and mask. For delivering artificial ventilations, a pocket face mask with one-way valve or bag-valve-mask unit will also protect you from _____ disease.

fluids

blood, wastes

You are not expected to diagnose communicable diseases. You must depend on the emergency department staff to inform you if you will be or have been in contact with pathogenic organisms. Be suspicious of contact if you transport patients with high fever, sore throats, stiff necks, or skin rashes. Communicable disease contact is also possible if the patient is coughing, sneezing, vomiting, or suffering from diarrhea.

communicable

Be suspicious of communicable disease contact if the patient has high _____, a sore _____, a stiff _____ or _____ of the skin. In addition to sneezing and coughing, consider possible contamination from patients _____ or suffering from _____.

fever, throat, neck, rashes

vomiting, diarrhea

The key points to reducing risks to yourself and to others are to use _____ gloves and other protective equipment, use disposable items whenever possible, dispose of all items as directed, wash your hands and other exposed skin areas, dispose of soiled items, and clean the ambulance interior. Avoid contact with the patient's body fluids and wastes.

latex

When practical to do so, wear gloves while providing care and during cleaning of the ambulance.

ALCOHOL AND DRUG ABUSE

As an EMT, you will probably come into contact with patients who have abused alcohol or some other drug. Remember that these patients may not act rationally and that they may quickly change moods and behavior patterns. There are cases of EMTs being injured by blows to the head because they thought an alcohol abuser was placid. Recently, injuries and one death have been reported, caused by a "very gentle young man" on PCP.

Remember, patients suffering from alcohol and drug abuse may not act _____ . They may quickly change _____ and _____ patterns.

rationally, moods
behavior

As an EMT you should realize that alcohol and other drugs may mask the symptoms of injuries and illnesses. You may also confuse diabetic problems, head injuries, stroke, and high fever with drug and alcohol abuse. Remember, you must survey and care for the patient.

If the patient is conscious, talk to him and try to gain his confidence. It may take 15 to 20 minutes to "talk down" a drug abuser. Treat the unconscious drug abuser and alcohol abuser as you would someone who has been poisoned. Ensure an _____ _____ and adequate air exchange. Be prepared for cardiac _____ . Contact medical control or your nearest _____ _____ or drug abuse center physician.

open airway
arrest
poison control

If the patient is unconscious, proceed as you would with all unconscious patients and ensure an _____ _____ . Do not give fluids or attempt to induce vomiting. Since there may be a chance of the patient vomiting, transport in the _____ _____ position. Transport the patient immediately along with any vomitus, containers, or suspect poisons.

open airway

lateral recumbent

TERMINOLOGY

Define the following terms. Check your definitions with those on page 402 of your textbook.

Acute abdomen—

Diabetic coma—

Delirium tremens—

Downer—

Hallucinogen—

Insulin shock—

Narcotic—

Upper—

Withdrawal—

FORMING MEDICAL TERMS

The following are some of the elements of medical terms used in this section.

glyco- (gli-ko-): sweet, sugar

Prefixes

hyper- (hi-per-): above, too much
hypo- (hi-po-): below, not enough

Suffixes

-emia (-E-me-ah): blood, in the blood.

A condition where there is too much sugar in the blood is called _____ (too much) _____ (sugar) _____ (in the blood) = _____. Too little sugar in the blood is called _____.

MATCHING

Match the types of drugs to the typical signs of drug abuse listed below.

_____ 1. Swollen oral membranes
_____ 2. Increased pulse, dry mouth
_____ 3. Low pulse, sluggish behavior
_____ 4. Low pulse, constricted pupils
_____ 5. Fast pulse, dilated pupils

A. Uppers

B. Downers

C. Hallucinogens

D. Narcotics

E. Volatile chemicals

MULTIPLE CHOICE

Circle the letter of the correct answer to each question. The answers are given at the end of this chapter. Note the references to the textbook.

1. In which of the following conditions will the patients have "acetone breath"? *(p. 405)*
   A. Stroke
   B. Diabetic coma
   C. Ulcers
   D. Insulin shock

2. A diabetic is found with a full, rapid pulse, cold clammy skin, and complains of hunger pangs. He is suffering from *(p. 405)*:
   A. Insulin shock (hypoglycemia)
   B. Cardiogenic shock
   C. Diabetic coma (hyperglycemia)
   D. Ulcers

3. To care for the condition described in question 2, the EMT should *(p. 404)*:
   A. Give sugar
   B. Give insulin
   C. Give adrenalin
   D. Transport immediately

4. If you cannot decide whether a problem is diabetic coma or insulin shock *(p. 404)*:
   A. Give sugar
   B. Give insulin
   C. Give sugar and insulin
   D. Do nothing, but transport

5. Which of the following can produce symptoms that resemble alcohol intoxication? *(p. 404)*
   A. Diabetes
   B. Emphysema
   C. Congestive heart failure
   D. All of the above

6. Which of the following is the course of initial action for dealing with a patient having a grand mal seizure? *(p. 406)*
   A. Transport at once
   B. Give 100% oxygen
   C. Protect from injury
   D. Induce vomiting

7. Which of the following may produce signs that are similar to alcohol abuse? *(p. 411)*
   A. Head injury
   B. Diabetes
   C. Epilepsy
   D. All of the above

8. Most patients in acute abdominal distress will lie perfectly still in an effort to *(p. 408)*:
   A. Prevent vomiting
   B. Prevent shallow breathing
   C. Hold the abdomen rigid
   D. Alleviate pain by guarding the abdomen

EXERCISES

Complete the following exercises and check your answers with the information presented in your textbook. Note the page references to *Emergency Care, 5th ed.*

1. List the 11 steps to the care for a drug abuse patient *(p. 414)*.

2. Describe the signs and symptoms collected in the case of a typical drug withdrawal patient *(p. 414)*.

3. Compare and contrast the symptoms and signs of diabetic coma with those of insulin shock, then write down how you can usually tell one from the other *(pp. 403-404, 405)*.

4. You have just transported a patient with a highly communicable disease. What should you do for yourself and for the ambulance? *(p. 409)*

5. List the major signs of acute abdominal distress *(p. 408)*.

ANSWERS

Forming Medical Terms

hyper-, glyc-, emia = hyperglycemia (HI-per-gli-SE-me-ah), hypoglycemia (HI-po-gli-SE-me-ah)

MATCHING

1. E 2. A 3. B 4. D 5. C

MULTIPLE CHOICE

1. B 2. A 3. A 4. A 5. D 6. C 7. D 8. D

15 *pediatric emergencies*

Reading Assignment: Emergency Care, 5th ed., pp. 417-433

INFANTS AND CHILDREN

BASIC LIFE SUPPORT

Many of the life support techniques you have learned apply to the treatment of children. However, there are special techniques that must be learned for some of the illnesses and injuries of childhood and some special considerations given due to physical size and emotional maturity.

Respiration

If a child's airway is obstructed, head positioning is critical. As with the adult procedures, the simple _____-tilt, chin-lift maneuver will correct most problems.   **head**

The head-tilt _____ maneuver is very effective on children, but for infants and children under the age of 8 years, head tilting may actually obstruct the _____ if the head is tilted back too far. To avoid blocking the airway of _____   and children _____ 8 years of age, never hyperextend the neck during the head-tilt. You need to make certain that you have tilted the head back far enough to open the airway.   **chin-lift** **airway** **infants** **under**

A complete airway obstruction in an infant can often be dislodged by cradling the infant face down on your forearm and delivering sharp blows to the spinal area between the _____ _____.   **shoulder blades**

If manual thrusts are used on the infant, they should be chest thrusts applied mid-sternum one finger-width below the intermammary line. The rescuer can remove visible objects, but blind finger sweeps are not to be done on the infant.

For children, the procedures used include attempts at ventilating (unresponsive patient), the delivery of _____ to _____ abdominal thrusts, and finger sweeps. As with infants, _____ finger sweeps should not be done.   **8, 10** **blind**

If partial dislodging is the best you can do, discontinue removal attempts and attempt to force air or oxygen past the partial obstruction by mouth-to-mouth, bag-valve-mask, etc. Administer pulmonary resuscitation and CPR as required. Transport to a medical facility is essential.

When administering mouth-to-mouth resuscitation to a child, care must be taken with the head-tilt to avoid _____ that can actually obstruct the airway. Remember to cover both the child's _____ and _____ with your mouth. Use smaller breaths than those for the adult.   **hyperextension** **mouth, nose**

117

118

For infants, ventilations should be provided at the rate of one every _____ seconds. For children, the rate is one every _____ seconds. Great care must be exercised to avoid _____ distention.

The Use of CPR

When compressing the sternum of a small child, use only the _____ of one hand. For infants, use only the tips of the _____ and _____ fingers. The compression site is over the _____, _____ finger-width below the intermammary line. Compress the _____ of an infant 1/2 to 1 inch. For a small child, the compression should be 1 inch to 1 1/2 inches. These compressions are done over the _____ of the child, at the CPR compression site.

For the infant, compressions must be delivered at a rate of at least _____ per minute. The compression rate for children is _____ to _____ per minute. For both types of patients, one ventilation is provided every _____ compressions. Remember, for an infant, compressions of the sternum are _____ to _____ inch, while for the child _____ inch to _____ inches are the limits for compression.

Control of Bleeding

Use the same methods to control bleeding in a child as you would in an adult. The first procedure recommended is _____ pressure. Next, attempt elevation. The third procedure is that of _____ points. Your last resort is that of the _____. Pediatric anti-shock garments can be used to help control internal bleeding and the development of shock.

Treatment for Shock

The most common type of shock found in children is hemorrhagic shock, caused by _____ loss. Children also will show the signs and symptoms of shock when they are severely dehydrated. Systolic blood pressure readings will help you determine if the patient is in shock.

You can determine if an adult is in shock if his _____ blood pressure falls to less than 2/3 its normal measurement or less than _____ mmHg. For teenagers and young adults, this figure is 70 mmHg. Children from age 6 to 12 should have readings above 60 mmHg or they are to be considered in shock. Preschoolers should normally have readings above 50 mmHg. Be sure to use the correct size blood pressure cuff for the patient. If a child has a bleeding wound, he may be in _____ shock. This can be quickly determined if his _____ blood pressure is below _____ _____. The care for a child in shock is basically the same as for an adult.

INJURIES COMMON TO CHILDREN

Children can suffer the same injuries as adults. However, EMTs have reported one injury that is fairly common to children: bike fork compression injury.

A bike _____ compression injury occurs when the child's foot becomes caught in the wheel spokes and is then jammed against the wheel fork. Be certain to survey the patient. Be sure there are no neck, spine, or hip injuries. Check for possible fractures to the leg and ankle bones. Care for this injury as you would a broken ankle. _____ the foot in a folded _____ and transport.

Immobilize
pillow

MEDICAL PROBLEMS COMMON TO CHILDREN

Most medical problems seen with adults also can occur with children. The emergency care procedures are essentially the same. However, fever, seizures, and intussusception deserve special consideration.

Along with seizures and intussusception, _____ in children deserves special consideration. Before transporting a child with fever, remove the child's clothing and cover him with a towel that has been saturated with tepid water.

fever

Do not use alcohol or ice water to reduce the temperature of fever. Such procedures constrict skin and superficial blood vessels, driving the blood deep into muscle and other body tissues, thus, increasing core temperature. Soak the towel with _____ water.

tepid
convulsions

Fever, intussusception, and _____ deserve special attention when caring for children. Emergency care is basically the same for a child with convulsions as for the adult with convulsions. Lower the child to the floor or ground. Loosen any restrictive clothing. Your primary action during the convulsion will be to _____ the child from _____.

protect
injury

When the convulsions stop, place the child in the _____ position and ensure an _____ _____ until consciousness returns. Transport as soon as possible. Along with the patient, transport patient _____. In other words, observe and remember the activities of the convulsion.

coma (lateral recumbent), open
airway
information

Fever, seizures and _____ are medical problems common to children that deserve special consideration. Intussusception, when a portion of the intestine telescopes into an adjoining portion, will cause acute abdominal distress. Care is the same as for an adult in abdominal pain. Remember, the most comfortable position for people with abdominal pain is the _____ position with the _____ flexed.

intussusception

supine, knees

SUDDEN INFANT DEATH SYNDROME

SIDS is often associated with respiratory arrest. You cannot pronounce the child to be dead. Since there will be no heartbeat or breathing, initiate and continue _____. Transport, continuing resuscitative procedures. Be sure the parents know that everything possible has been done for the child.

CPR

THE BATTERED CHILD SYNDROME AND SEXUAL ASSAULT

There is no standard appearance, behavior pattern, or "look" to the abused child. During the _____ examination, look for injuries indicative of battering, including healing wounds and scars. Note the child's surroundings and any "odd" mechanism of injury. Note whether accounts of how the accident happened are conflicting or suspicious. Remember, you not only transport and hand over the patient, but also patient _____. It is your *professional responsibility* to discuss your observations with the emergency department physician.

objective

information

In cases of sexual assault, protect the child from onlookers. Conduct patient evaluation procedures and care in the presence of parents, and, if at all possible, a police officer. As with all patients, do not examine the genital region unless there is _____ injury.

obvious

NOTE: In all cases of rape and sexual assault, it is important not to break the "chain of evidence." Do not have the child change clothing. Do not wash the child. Discourage defecation or urination. If at all possible, do not administer anything by mouth.

TERMINOLOGY

Define the following terms. Check your definitions with those in the Glossary at the end of your textbook or as directed.

Child abuse—

Croup—

Epiglottitis—

Intussusception—

Sudden infant death syndrome—

FORMING MEDICAL TERMS

Answers can be found at the end of the chapter.

Roots and Combining Forms

pedia- (PE-de-ah-): child
pepsia- (PEP-se-ah-): digestion
entero- (en-ter-o-): intestine

Prefixes

dia- (di-ah-): through, to pass through
dys- (dis-): difficult or bad. A patient having difficulties with digestion may have _____.

Suffixes

-atrics (-at-riks): to cure. The term that means to cure the child is _____.
-itis (-I-tis): inflammation. An inflammation of the intestine is _____.
-rrhea (-RE-ah): discharge or flow. To flow through would be _____ rrhea.

MULTIPLE CHOICE

Circle the letter of the best answer to each question. The answers are given at the end of this chapter. Note page references to *Emergency Care, 5th ed.*

1. How many back blows and manual thrusts should you deliver in rapid succession to correct a complete airway obstruction in an infant? *(pp. 420-421)*
   A. 4 and 2
   B. 4 and 4
   C. 4 and 8 to 10
   D. 2 and 4

2. When providing ventilations to an infant or child, you should take _____ to _____ seconds per ventilation *(pp. 420-421)*.
   A. .5 to 1
   B. 1 to 1.5
   C. 1.5 to 2
   D. 2 to 2.5

3. The pulse site for CPR for the infant is the _____ pulse *(p. 420)*.
   A. Carotid
   B. Femoral
   C. Apical
   D. Brachial

4. When ventilating infants and newborns, ventilate with (p. 420):
   A. Adequate ventilations
   B. Half-sized breaths
   C. Full-sized breaths
   D. Double-sized breaths

5. CPR sternum compressions for an infant should be between (p. 420):
   A. 1/2 and 1 inch
   B. 1/4 and 1/2 inch
   C. 3/4 and 1 1/2 inches
   D. 1 1/2 and 2 inches

6. The best method to control bleeding in infants and small children is (pp. 420-421):
   A. Tourniquet
   B. Indirect pressure
   C. Pressure point
   D. Direct pressure

7. A preschool child is probably in shock if his systolic blood pressure is below (p. 421):
   A. 70 mmHg
   B. 50 mmHg
   C. 90 mmHg
   D. 60 mmHg

8. If a child has a high fever, remove the child's clothing and cover him with a towel that has been soaked with (p. 428):
   A. Ice water
   B. Tepid water
   C. Rubbing alcohol
   D. Cold water

9. When a child has had a seizure and the convulsions have stopped, ease the child into the _____ position (pp. 406, 429).
   A. Prone
   B. Supine
   C. Lateral recumbent
   D. Seated

10. Transport a child with abdominal pain (pp. 408, 430):
    A. On his back
    B. On his back, knees flexed
    C. On his side
    D. On his side, knees flexed

11. Care for the typical bike fork compression injury as you would a fractured (p. 425):
    A. Ankle
    B. Leg
    C. Wrist
    D. Arm

12. In cases of Sudden Infant Death Syndrome, you should (pp. 431-432):
    A. Not deliver care, but still transport
    B. Declare the infant to be dead
    C. Hunt for evidence of child neglect
    D. Initiate CPR and transport

EXERCISES

To check your answers to the Exercises, refer to *Emergency Care, 5th ed.*

1. List the emergency care procedures for a child in shock (p. 421).

2. List 5 common injuries of the battered child (pp. 426-427).

3. Describe the care given to a child you suspect has been sexually abused recently (p. 428).

4. Describe how you would interview a child patient (pp. 419, 422).

5. List five special cases of poisoning that are problems with children *(pp. 430-431)*.

6. Describe the care provided in cases of probable epiglottitis *(p. 429)*.

ANSWERS

Forming Medical Terms

dyspepsia, pediatrics, enteritis, dia-

Multiple Choice

1. B	7. B
2. B	8. B
3. D	9. C
4. A	10. B
5. A	11. A
6. D	12. D

16 childbirth

Reading Assignment: Emergency Care, 5th ed., pp. 434–457

CHILDBIRTH

ANATOMY AND PHYSIOLOGY OF CHILDBIRTH

The developing baby growing in its mother's uterus is called a fetus. As well as providing a place for development, the uterus is made of muscle that will contract during labor to move the baby into the vagina or birth canal. While in the uterus, the fetus is surrounded by a sac of fluids called the amniotic sac. This sac will break during labor.

The fetus develops in the mother's _____. The lower portion of this organ is called the cervix. It leads into the birth canal or _____. | **uterus**
| **vagina**

While it is developing inside the uterus, the _____ is surrounded by a sac of fluids called the _____ sac. During development the fetus obtains oxygen and nourishment from its mother's blood. The blood of the mother and the blood of the fetus do not mix. Exchange takes place through a special organ of pregnancy called the placenta. | **fetus**
| **amniotic**

The fetus receives oxygen and nourishment by way of exchange that takes place between its blood and the blood of the mother. This exchange takes place in the _____. The umbilical cord connects the fetus with this organ. | **placenta**

To deliver the baby, the mother goes through 3 stages of labor. The first stage of labor is when the muscles of the _____ contract to push the baby toward the birth canal. Frequently, at the end of the first stage of labor, the amniotic sac ruptures. The lower end of the uterus, the _____, dilates during this stage. | **uterus**

| **cervix**

The first stage of labor ends when the _____ is fully dilated. The second stage begins when the baby enters the birth canal and ends when the baby is born. The third stage begins when the baby is born and ends when the special organ of pregnancy, the _____, is expelled. | **cervix**

| **placenta**

PREPARING FOR DELIVERY

The first step in preparing for delivery is to evaluate the mother. If the EMT believes that the mother may deliver during transport, he should prepare the mother to give birth before transport.

In order to _____ the mother, the EMT needs to know if this is her first baby, how long she has been in labor, if she feels as though she has to strain or move her bowels, and if there is crowning or the presenting part of the baby has begun to bulge out of the vaginal opening. | **evaluate**

The EMT needs to know if this is the mother's _____ baby. Labor usually lasts 16 hours for the first baby and is considerably shorter for each subsequent baby. For this to be of any value, the EMT must know how long the mother had been in _____. Straining and the feeling that the mother has to move her _____ usually means the baby has started to move through the _____ into the birth canal. The EMT should examine the vaginal opening for _____. | **first**

| **labor**
| **bowels**
| **cervix**
| **crowning**

If the EMT believes the mother will deliver in transport, he should prepare to assist the mother to give birth _____ transport. To aid the EMT, there should be a sterile delivery pack (obsteric pack) as part of the ambulance supplies.

before

NORMAL DELIVERY

To assist in delivery away from the hospital, the EMT must prepare the mother-to-be, the delivery room, and himself. The mother is placed in delivery position, on her back with a sheet under her lower back and buttocks. The EMT should ask her to bend her knees and spread her legs to allow clear access to the vaginal opening. After the mother is placed in the _____ position, a second EMT or someone who will assist, is placed at the mother's head to aid her in case of vomiting.

delivery

A second person is useful during delivery to be positioned at the mother's head. This person will help prevent the possibility of the mother aspirating _____.

vomitus

The EMT should prepare himself by putting on any protective items and clothing. He should then open the _____ delivery pack and put on a pair of sterile gloves.

sterile

Since the items of the delivery pack are sterile, the EMT should not touch any of these items until he has put on _____ _____. The mother is draped with towels or sheets, taken one at a time from the pack. One towel is placed under her perineum, the area between the vaginal opening and the anus. She is also draped on the abdomen and each thigh. Only the vaginal opening is left fully exposed.

sterile gloves

Childbirth is a normal function for women. The EMT is to help her and guide the baby. He is not to force delivery of pull on the baby. The greater pain during the second stage of labor when the cervix is fully _____ and the baby moves into the _____. The mother may feel she has to strain or have a _____ movement. The EMT can help her by telling her this is normal and encourage her to relax between contractions.

dilated
vagina
bowel

The baby will move down the birth canal as the _____ contracts. Normally the head will be presented first through the _____ opening. This is a head-first or cephalic delivery. Slight tearing of the tissues at the vaginal opening may occur. This is of little consequence, at this time.

uterus
vaginal

During a normal presentation or _____ delivery, the head will appear first. The EMT should place one hand between the mother's vaginal opening and anus. This area is called the _____. The hand in this position will give some support to the baby's head and avoid contact with the anal area. The second hand is used to guide and support the baby's head. The fingers of this hand are spread evenly around the baby's head. Care should be taken to avoid pressure on the soft areas of the baby's skull.

cephalic

perineum

During cephalic delivery, the baby's _____ appears first. The EMT should be positioned with one hand over the mother's _____ and the other hand placed to support the baby's head with the fingers _____ _____ around the baby's head. If the connection between the baby and the placenta, the _____ cord, is wrapped around the baby's neck, it should be gently loosened.

head
perineum

spread evenly
umbilical

The EMT should continue to support the baby's _____ during delivery. If it is practical to do so and the speed of delivery allows, the EMT should suction the baby's mouth and nose. The shoulders may cause some problems. The upper shoulder should deliver first. The EMT can help both mother and child by gently guiding the baby's head downward.

head

After gently guiding the baby's head _____ to assist with the delivery of the _____ shoulder, the EMT should support the head and shoulders of the baby. When delivery of the baby is finished, it should be laid on its side with the head downward to drain blood and mucus. Be sure to note the time of delivery.

> downward
> upper

To ensure spontaneous breathing, the EMT should place the baby on its _____, with the head _____ for drainage from the mouth and nose. The EMT can wipe blood and mucus from the baby's mouth and nose using sterile gauze. A rubber bulb syringe can be used to gently suction the baby's mouth and nostrils. The bulb must be squeezed *before* inserting. When practical, this can be done during delivery.

> side downward

After ensuring _____ breathing, the EMT should tie (with umbilical tape) or clamp the umbilical cord about 10 inches from the baby. A second clamp is placed 3 inches closer to the baby.

> spontaneous

After clamping off the umbilical cord _____ inches and _____ from the baby, it can be cut between 2 clamps using sterile scissors. If bleeding continues after cutting, the old ties and clamps should be left in place and new ties or clamps should be placed close to the originals.

> 10, 7

After delivery, ensuring spontaneous _____ , and cutting the _____ _____, the EMT should wrap the baby in a blanket and place it with the mother. He should record the time of delivery and tape the name of the parents loosely around the baby's wrist.

> breathing
> umbilical cord

Transport of the mother and child, if the delivery was normal and both appear healthy, should be delayed to allow for completion of the third stage of labor, the delivery of the _____. Wrap the placenta in a towel or plastic bag and transport to be examined by a physician. The EMT should wait not more than 20 minutes from the baby's birth for the placenta to be delivered. If it is not delivered after this length of time, the EMT should transport both mother and child.

> placenta

After the placenta is delivered, the end of the _____ stage of labor, there is always bleeding. The EMT should place a sanitary napkin over the _____ opening and lower the mother's legs.

> third
> vaginal

He should direct her to hold her legs together during transport; however, she need not "squeeze" them together. If possible, you should replace blood-soaked sheets and dressings before transport and wipe and dry the mother's face and hands. If circumstances permit, it would also be considerate to clean up any disorder you created in the room.

To control bleeding, a _____ _____ can be placed over the vaginal opening. Position the mother's legs down and together. Massaging the uterus will help to control bleeding. The EMT should look for a grapefruit-sized protrusion on the mother's lower abdomen and massage this area without pushing it down toward the vagina.

> sanitary napkin

COMPLICATIONS OF DELIVERY

Otherwise normal deliveries can have such complications as an unbroken amniotic sac, failure of the infant to begin spontaneous breathing, prolonged delivery time, and excessive bleeding. The EMT is trained to handle these problems. However, it should be noted that improper handling can cause death to the child and perhaps the mother.

If the _____ _____ does not break, it can be punctured with a finger and carefully removed from around the baby's mouth and nose.

> amniotic sac

When a normal delivery is expected and the mother is having contractions every 2 to 3 minutes, yet delivery does not occur in 20 minutes, a

126

_____ delivery is indicated. The mother should be transported without delay.

prolonged

If the baby does not begin _____ breathing in 30 seconds after delivery, resuscitative measures are needed. The EMT should again suction the infant's mouth and nose with a rubber bulb _____.

spontaneous

syringe

If spontaneous breathing does not begin after the application of _____, the EMT should hold the baby and gently, but rigorously rub the baby's back. If this fails, the EMT can snap his forefinger against the soles of the baby's feet. Should this method fail, mouth-to-mouth and nose resuscitation should be started, utilizing the techniques for infants.

suction

A pediatric bag-valve-mask ventilator or a pocket face mask can be used to protect yourself from contact with _____ or body fluids, if your system allows and you are trained to use this adjunctive equipment.

blood

Once spontaneous breathing begins using the _____ -to- _____ and nose or mask method, oxygen can be given by holding the mask in an aluminum foil tent placed over the baby's head.

mouth

mouth

If spontaneous breathing does not begin and there is no pulse, the EMT should begin CPR, after clamping and cutting the cord. Remember to use only one or two fingers on the sternum and apply very little pressure. The mother and child should be transported immediately. Resuscitation should be continued during transport. Since part of the cord is still attached and the _____ is not yet delivered, great care should be exercised during transfer and transport. The infant should be kept warm, but not hot. The EMT should reassure the mother that he is doing all that is possible and that the child does have a chance to survive.

placenta

PREDELIVERY COMPLICATIONS AND ABNORMAL DELIVERIES

Certain pre-delivery emergencies can arise. One example is eclampsia, or toxemia of pregnancy. It is accompanied by apparent obesity and swelling of the face, hands, and feet. The patient may have severe headaches, visual difficulties, and pain in the upper abdomen, and will become convulsive. If she does not have seizures, the condition is known as pre-eclampsia.

A patient with severe toxemia of pregnancy, or _____, may become apprehensive, begin to shake, and go into _____. The EMTs should protect her and place her on her side. When the seizure is over, she should be transported immediately, repositioned onto her back with head and shoulders elevated.

eclampsia

convulsions

Ectopic pregnancy occurs when the site of egg implantation is not the uterus lining (endometrium). The most common ectopic site is the fallopian tube. Eventually, the tube will rupture and hemmorhage will occur.

If the site of implantation is not the _____ , an _____ pregnancy occurs. Frequently, the ectopic site is the _____ _____. Signs and symptoms include acute abdominal pain, vomiting, near collapse, and shock. Immediate transport is needed, treating for shock and providing oxygen.

endometrium

ectopic

fallopian tube

The 3 major abnormal deliveries that are considered to be true emergencies are the breech presentation or buttocks-first presentation, the prolapsed umbilical cord where the cord is presented first, and the arm or leg presentation.

If the buttocks are presented first, this is a _____ presentation. Early warning signs include close uterine contractions, straining, and the mother having the sensation of an impending bowel movement. Allow the

breech

baby's buttocks and trunk to deliver spontaneously, supporting them as the emerge. As the legs deliver, support the baby in the palm of your hand, allowing the legs to dangle astride your arms.

In a breech birth, the _____ are delivered first and the _____ last. A serious problem can occur if the head does not deliver on its own within 3 minutes. The EMT can place his gloved hand into the mother's vagina with his palm toward the baby's face. By pushing away the vaginal wall with a finger to each side of the baby's nose, the EMT will create an open airway and may reduce pressure on the umbilical cord.

buttocks
head

The head of the baby can be controlled as in a normal birth. If the head does not deliver in _____ minutes, the EMT must maintain the open _____ and immediately transport, with great care, the mother and baby. Maintain the air passage during transport.

3
airway

If the cord is presented first, this is known as a _____ umbilical cord. Elevate the mother's hips (exaggerated shock position), administer oxygen, and keep her warm. The prolapsed _____ _____ should not be pushed back; however, it should be wrapped to conserve heat. Gently push up on the baby's head to keep pressure off the cord.

prolapsed
umbilical
cord

Another type of abnormal delivery is shoulder dystocia. As in the case of normal childbirth, a head first, or _____, delivery is initiated. However, in shoulder _____, the baby has large shoulders which will not pass through the area between the pubic symphysis and the hollow of the sacrum. Suction the baby's mouth and nose and transport mother and baby immediately.

cephalic
dystocia

In the case of an arm and leg presentation, a normal delivery is not possible and the EMT should transport. No attempt should be made to place a gloved hand into the mother's vagina as in the case of the _____ cord or the _____ presentation. The same applies to compound presentations, where an arm and a foot or a shoulder and an arm become the presenting parts. Do NOT place your hands into the vagina unless there is a prolapsed cord.

prolapsed, breech

OTHER CHILDBIRTH SITUATIONS

The EMT may be confronted with other childbirth situations such as multiple births, abortions (miscarriages), premature births, and stillborn (dead) infants.

If there is to be a multiple delivery, contractions of the _____ will continue after the delivery of the first child. These will not be mild contractions, but very similar to those encountered during the delivery of the first child. To prevent hemorrhaging, the EMT should tie or clamp the _____ _____ of the breathing first child before the second is delivered.

uterus

umbilical cord

In the case of miscarriage or _____, be it spontaneous or induced, the main problems will be excessive bleeding and the mental state of the mother.

abortion

Your main concerns should be excessive _____ and the patient's emotional state. A sanitary napkin can be used to absorb blood. The EMT should not put his hand into the vagina or push and pull on the fetus or umbilical cord. All tissues passed should be saved.

bleeding

If a baby weighs under 5 1/2 pounds, or it is born before the thirty-seventh week of pregnancy, it can be definitely classified as being premature. Information gathered from the mother and observations of the baby's size will aid the EMT in deciding if the baby is premature.

128

When a baby is born before the _____ week of pregnancy, it is premature. The EMT should wrap the baby in a blanket and then aluminum foil or plastic wrap to ensure its warmth. (Be sure to keep plastic wrap away from the baby's face.) Special care should be taken in the winter to be certain that the patient compartment of the ambulance is warm. The EMT should keep the mouth and nose clear of blood and mucus, prevent bleeding from the cord and gently administer oxygen.

thirty-seventh

To maintain an open airway, the EMT should keep the mouth and nose clear of _____ and _____ by suction. He should administer _____ into an aluminum foil tent above the baby's head.

blood, mucus
oxygen

Resuscitation measures should be continued until the baby is turned over to the hospital staff. Should the baby be dead at delivery (or stillborn), or if it is apparent that the baby is dying, the EMT must do all he can to comfort the parents. At the request of the parents, the EMT may baptize the newborn.

TERMINOLOGY

Define the following terms. Check your definitions with those in the Glossary of your textbook or as directed.

Abortion—

Amniotic sac—

Cephalic delivery—

Eclampsia—

Ectopic pregnancy—

Labor—

Perineum—

Placenta—

Pre-eclampsia—

Prolapsed umbilical cord—

FORMING MEDICAL TERMS

The following are some of the elements of medical terms used in this chapter.

Roots and Combining Forms

cephalo- (se-Fal-o-): the head
nato- (NA-to-), *natal* (NA-tal): related to birth
topo- (top-o): a place. The study of the surface features (places) of the body is _____graphy.
toxo- (TOK-o-): a poison

Prefixes

ante- (an-te-): after
ec- (ek-): out, away from the normal
neo- (ne-o-): new
pre- (pre-): before

Care provided before birth is neo-_____ care. The time prior to birth is the _____partum period. After the delivery of the baby, the _____ partum period begins.

Suffixes

-emia (-em-e-ah): pertaining to the blood
-ic (ik): pertaining to or connected with

Blood poisoning is _____ . A head-first delivery is a _____ic delivery. A pregnancy in which the embryo attaches to the wrong place is an _____ (away from the normal) _____ (place) _____ (pertaining to) = _____ pregnancy.

LABELING

A. _____
B. _____
C. _____
D. _____
E. _____
F. _____
G. _____

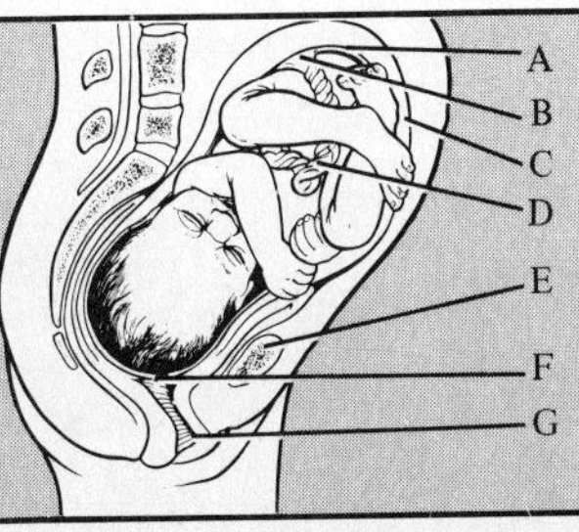

Figure 16-1

MATCHING

Match the letter of the correct answer to each item. The answers are provided at the end of this chapter.

_____ 1. Stage one
_____ 2. Stage two
_____ 3. Stage three
_____ 4. Normal
_____ 5. Abnormal

A. Breech

B. Birth

C. Crowning

D. Cervical dilation

E. Cephalic

F. Uterine massage

G. Placenta

MULTIPLE CHOICE

Circle the letter of the correct answer to each question. The answers are given at the end of this chapter. Note page references to *Emergency Care, 5th ed.*

1. The organ for exchange between the mother's blood and that of the developing unborn baby is the (p. 438):
   A. Omentum
   B. Placenta
   C. Cervix
   D. Foramen ovale

2. The developing unborn baby is called a (p. 437):
   A. Meatus
   B. Rete
   C. Ampulla
   D. Fetus

3. The muscular organ that protects the unborn infant is the (p. 437):
   A. Umbilicus
   B. Placenta
   C. Uterus
   D. Fundus

4. While developing, the unborn is protected by a bag of fluids called the _____ sac (p. 438):
   A. Uterine
   B. Placental
   C. Perineal
   D. Amniotic

5. The area between the vaginal opening and the anus is the *(p. 448)*:
   A. Fimbra
   B. Perineum
   C. Infundibulum
   D. Ampulla

6. When the typical presenting part of the baby first bulges out the vaginal opening, this is called *(p. 438)*:
   A. Crowning
   B. Dilating
   C. Labor
   D. Prolapsing

7. The first stage of labor begins with *(p. 438)*:
   A. Cervical dilation
   B. Perineum
   C. Uterine contractions
   D. Vaginal contractions

8. The second stage of labor ends with *(p. 438)*:
   A. Cervical dilation
   B. Infant delivery
   C. Placental delivery
   D. Uterine contractions

9. The third stage of labor is the *(p. 438)*:
   A. Full cervical dilation
   B. Perineum tearing
   C. Delivery of placenta
   D. Delivery of infant

10. During the most active stage of labor, the uterus usually contracts every *(p. 439)*:
    A. Minute
    B. 10 minutes
    C. 5 minutes
    D. 3 minutes

11. If a woman is having her first baby, labor will usually last *(p. 439)*:
    A. 16 hours
    B. 5 hours
    C. 2 hours
    D. 1 hour

12. To make a final decision about transporting the expectant mother, the EMT should *(p. 440)*:
    A. Time the mother's pains
    B. Feel the abdomen for movement
    C. Check for bleeding
    D. Examine for crowning

13. In a normal delivery, the baby's face is turned *(p. 442)*:
    A. Up
    B. To the right
    C. Down
    D. To the left

14. If difficulties arise during the delivery of the upper shoulder, the EMT can assist by *(p. 442)*:
    A. Gently pulling at the baby's shoulders
    B. Gently guiding the baby's head downward
    C. Gently guiding the baby's head upward
    D. Gently pushing his gloved hand into the vagina

15. Which of the following should be done first? *(p. 442)*:
    A. Clamp and cut the cord
    B. Clear the baby's nose and mouth
    C. Lay the baby on its back
    D. Lift the baby by the feet and slap its buttocks

16. The first clamp placed on the umbilical cord should be _____ inches from the baby *(p. 446)*:
    A. 2
    B. 5
    C. 10
    D. 12

17. If bleeding continues from the umbilical cord after clamping and cutting, the EMT should *(p. 446)*:
    A. Clamp the cord again, close to the original clamp
    B. Unclamp the cord and tie
    C. Apply a sterile dressing
    D. Transport the baby immediately

18. Which of the following is the maximum amount of time the EMT should wait for the placenta to be delivered before transporting the mother and child? *(p. 447)*
    A. 2 hours
    B. 1 hour
    C. 45 minutes
    D. 20 minutes

19. An expectant mother is having contractions every 3 minutes. A prolonged delivery is indicated if she does not deliver within *(p. 450)*:
    A. 2 hours
    B. 1 hour
    C. 45 minutes
    D. 20 minutes

20. Delivery of the placenta is accompanied by the loss of _____ blood *(p. 447)*.
    A. 1/2 pint
    B. 1 pint
    C. 2 pints
    D. 3 pints

21. The first step to control maternal bleeding is to (p. 447):
    A. Apply a pressure dressing
    B. Place a sanitary napkin over the vaginal opening
    C. Massage the uterus
    D. Pack the vagina with sterile gauze

22. If the amniotic sac does not break during delivery, the EMT should (p. 442):
    A. Do nothing, it will burst after birth
    B. Wait until after delivery and strip with sterile scissors
    C. Puncture it with his finger and remove the membrane from the baby's nose and mouth
    D. Transport immediately

23. Spontaneous respiration should begin within _____ after delivery (p. 445):
    A. 2 minutes
    B. 1 minute
    C. 45 seconds
    D. 30 seconds

24. If spontaneous respiration does not begin after clearing the baby's mouth and nose, the EMT should (p. 445):
    A. Begin mouth-to-mouth and nose resuscitation
    B. Apply mechanical resuscitation with 100% O_2
    C. Hold the baby and rigorously rub its back
    D. Transport immediately, administering 100% O_2

25. The presented part of the baby in a breech birth is the (p. 453):
    A. Arms
    B. Buttocks
    C. Legs
    D. Head

26. If the head does not deliver in _____ minutes after establishing an open airway, the EMT should transport (p. 453):
    A. 3
    B. 5
    C. 9
    D. 15

27. When transporting an expectant mother who has begun a prolapsed cord delivery, the EMT should (pp. 454):
    A. Push the cord back
    B. Gently push the baby's head off of the cord
    C. Administer oxygen to the mother by Venturi mask
    D. All of the above

28. If an arm presentation without a prolapsed cord is noted, the EMT should (p. 454):
    A. Reach up the vagina and turn the baby
    B. Do nothing, the delivery will be normal
    C. Transport immediately, providing oxygen
    D. Insert his gloved hand and push back the vaginal wall

29. Spontaneous abortion (miscarriage) describes a delivery before _____ weeks of pregnancy (p. 452):
    A. 20
    B. 28
    C. 32
    D. 26

30. A baby is considered premature if the baby weighs less than 5 1/2 pounds or is born before the _____ month (p. 455):
    A. 7th
    B. 8th
    C. 9th
    D. None of the above

EXERCISES

To check your answers to the Exercises, refer to *Emergency Care, 5th ed.*

1. List and describe the use of the major items found in a sterile emergency childbirth pack (p. 437).

2. Describe how you would evaluate an expecting mother before deciding if you should transport before or after delivery (pp. 439–440).

3. Describe the resuscitation procedures used for a newborn who has not begun spontaneous respiration (pp. 449–450).

4. In step-by-step fashion, describe how you would handle a breech delivery (*pp. 453–454*).

5. List five factors that may place an expectant mother at high risk (*p. 448*).

6. What is the Apgar Score for a newborn who has a pulse over 100, normal crying, some flexion, some motion to irritation, and blue hands and feet (*p. 444*)?

ANSWERS

Forming Medical Terms

topography, neonatal, prepartum, antepartum, toxemia, cephalic, ec-top-ic = ectopic

Labeling—Figure 16-1

A. Amniotic sac
B. Placenta
C. Uterus
D. Umbilical cord
E. Pubic bone
F. Cervix
G. Vagina

Matching

1. D   2. B   3. G   4. E   5. A

Multiple Choice

1. B	9. C	17. A	24. C
2. D	10. D	18. D	25. B
3. C	11. A	19. D	26. A
4. D	12. D	20. A	27. B
5. B	13. C	21. B	28. C
6. A	14. B	22. C	29. B
7. C	15. B	23. D	30. A
8. B	16. C		

17 burns and hazardous materials

Reading Assignment: Emergency Care, 5th ed., pp. 458–477

CARE FOR BURNS

BURNS

Burns can be thermal (due to intense heat), chemical, or electrical. They can be classified as partial (burning part of the skin) and full thickness. The most common system of classification is according to degree.

Using the most common system of classification allows burns to be identified as first through third _____. A burn that is superficial, causing a reddening of the skin, is a first degree burn. It involves only the epidermis or outer layer of skin. | **degree**

A second degree burn extends beyond the outer layer of skin or the _____ into the second layer called the dermis. Unlike the epidermis, the dermis contains blood vessels. Plasma is released and forms blisters. Second degree burns are considered to be critical if they involve more than 30% of the body surface. | **epidermis**

A more severe form of burn is the third degree burn. This is a full _____ burn involving the epidermis, the _____, and the underlying fat layer called the subcutaneous layer. This burn cannot heal by itself. Infection can cause death. If 10% of the body receives third degree burns, the patient's condition is critical. | **thickness, dermis**

Burns may be classified from first to _____ degree. A third degree burn involves the fatty layer, the _____ layer. In some cases, underlying muscles and bones may be damaged. | **third** / **subcutaneous**

The most severe burns are _____ degree burns. Such burns to the hands, face, and feet are always considered critical. If _____% of the body surface has third degree burns, the condition is critical. | **third** / **10**

For a second degree burn to be critical, more than _____% of the body surface has to be burned. If 15 to 30% received second degree burns, the condition is said to be moderate. Less than 15% of the body area receiving second degree burns is classified as minor. | **30**

Burns can be critical, _____, or minor. Since first degree burns involve only the _____, they are minor, except when they involve more than 75% of the body surface. | **moderate** / **epidermis**

The amount of skin surface burned can be estimated by the "rule of nines" method. This assigns a value of 9% to each of the major body areas, and 1% to the genital region. The major areas are the head and neck, each arm, the chest, the abdomen, the upper back, the lower back and buttocks, the front of each leg, and the back of each leg. Each of these 11 major areas is given a value of _____%. The groin is given a value of 1%. | **9**

If an adult has a burn covering both arms and his head and neck, _____% of his body is burned using the "rule of _____" method. When evaluating children and infants, the head is given a value of 18% since it is proportionately larger.

27 (3 x 9), nines

Never apply ointments or sprays to a burn. If the burn is a minor one to the outer layer of skin, the _____, the burned part can be covered with a sterile burn dressing and moistened. Moist dressing can be applied to partial-thickness burns that involve 9% or less of the body (follow local protocols).

epidermis

When the dermis is involved, use dry sterile dressings. For minor burns, apply a _____ sterile dressing.

moist

For intensive first and second degree burns and all _____ degree burns, first consider whether the patient may be having respiratory problems. A swelling of the voicebox, or _____ , can develop quickly. This is laryngeal edema and may even require an oropharyngeal airway. Immediate transport is required.

third

larynx

Burns caused by heat are _____ burns. The EMT should make sure that there is an open airway and the patient is breathing. Injuries, including fractures and lacerations, are treated before burns. Since contamination is a serious problem, burns should be covered with _____ dressings. Sterile gauze pads should be used to cover burns to the eyes and to dress between fingers and toes.

thermal

sterile

Burns can be thermal, electrical, or _____. Acids and alkalis are the general groups of corrosive chemicals that cause serious burns. Alkali burns are usually more serious.

chemical

If a chemical burn is caused by an _____ or _____ contaminated articles of clothing or jewelry should be removed and the burned area flushed clean of the chemical with water. It is recommended that removal of all clothing, shoes, and jewelry be done during the washing process. If the alkali is dry lime, it should be brushed from the skin and clothing. Phenol (carbolic acid) burns should be washed with ethyl alcohol and then washed again with water.

acid, alkali

After washing, the EMT should follow the same course of action used for thermal burns. He should apply _____ dressings.

sterile

Chemical burns to the eyes should be flooded and washed with water. Contact lenses must be removed. A 20-minute wash, (or until arrival at the medical facility) is recommended by EMS Systems for all chemical burns of the eye.

Burns should be cared for after the EMT has established an open _____, respiration and cardiac function are stabilized, and he has treated other injuries such as serious laceration and _____.

airway

fractures

HAZARDOUS MATERIALS

RADIATION ACCIDENTS

Ionizing radiation can take three basic forms: alpha, beta, and gamma. Alpha radiation can be stopped by protective clothing. Beta and gamma radiation can penetrate both clothing and the body.

_____ radiation is the most dangerous. However, the EMT should not underestimate the danger of _____ radiation, even if it can be stopped by protective clothing. Before attempting to assist in or control a radiation accident, he should be trained to do so.

Gamma

alpha

Danger from radiation increases as a person comes closer to the source. Since the EMT is to treat the victims, he must be certain that he does not place himself in danger from overexposure.

As the EMT approaches a radiation source, his chances of overexposure _____.

> increase

The EMT will encounter 4 types of patients in radiation accidents. Patients receiving whole or partial body external radiation and those who have inhaled or ingested radioactive materials are of no danger to the EMT, unless the material is an extreme gamma source.

Patients with external contamination and those with open wounds can represent various degrees of danger to the EMT. He should wear protective clothing and have on a protective breathing apparatus. Usually, no danger to the EMT exists if the patient has suffered whole or partial body _____ radiation, or the patient has _____ or _____ radioactive materials.

> external, inhaled, ingested

The EMT should guard his own safety with protective clothing and a protective _____ _____ . He should follow strict decontamination procedures.

> breathing apparatus

TERMINOLOGY

Define the following terms. Check your definitions with those given in the Glossary of your textbook or as directed.

CHEMTREC *(p. 472)*—

First-degree burn—

Second-degree burn—

Third-degree burn—

MULTIPLE CHOICE

Circle the letter of the correct answer for each question. The answers are given at the end of this chapter. Note page references to *Emergency Care, 5th ed.*

1. A burn that involves all three layers of the skin is a _____ degree burn *(p. 461)*:
   A. First
   B. Second
   C. Third
   D. None of the above

2. A patient has burns covering both arms, his neck and head, and his chest. What percentage of his body is burned? *(pp. 462–463)*
   A. 21%
   B. 36%
   C. 18%
   D. 27%

3. Which of the following chemicals should be brushed off rather than washed off? *(p. 468)*
   A. Hydrochloric acid
   B. Acetic acid
   C. Sodium hydroxide
   D. Dry lime

4. Acid burns to the eyes should be flooded with water for at least _____ minutes *(p. 468)*:
   A. 20
   B. 5
   C. 10
   D. 30

5. Which of the following types of radiation cannot easily penetrate clothing? *(p. 474)*
   A. Alpha
   B. Beta
   C. Gamma
   D. All of the above

6. A patient has ingested some mild gamma radioactive material. He is *(p. 476):*
   A. Dangerous to anyone nearby
   B. Dangerous to those close enough to treat him
   C. Only a moderate hazard
   D. No danger to those around him after external cleansing

EXERCISES

To check your answers to the Exercises, refer to *Emergency Care, 5th ed.*

1. Distinguish between a critical and a moderate third degree burn *(p. 463)*.

2. Outline the care of severe third degree burns to the skin from scene to emergency department *(pp. 464–467)*.

3. Describe the field decontamination procedures for the EMT and the patient during a radiation accident *(p. 476)*.

4. Your ambulance is first to arrive at the scene of a traffic accident involving a chemical tank truck. There is no fire, but the scene is hazardous because of fluids and colored vapors leaking from the tank. Describe your initial actions and list what information you would provide to the dispatcher *(pp. 471–473)*.

5. Complete the following chart *(p. 467)*.

TYPE OF BURN	TISSUE BURNED		TISSUES BELOW SKIN	COLOR CHANGES	PAIN	BLISTERS
	OUTER LAYER OF SKIN	2nd LAYER OF SKIN				
1st Degree						
2nd Degree						
3rd Degree						

6. Fill in the values for the "Rule of Nines" *(p. 463)*.

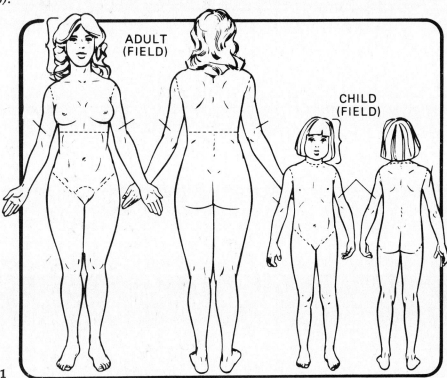

Figure 17-1

ANSWERS

Multiple Choice

1. C
2. B
3. D
4. A
5. A
6. D

18 *environmental emergencies*

Reading Assignment: Emergency Care, 5th ed., pp. 478–497

SECTION ONE: HEAT- AND COLD-RELATED EMERGENCIES

HEAT-RELATED DISORDERS

Emergencies due to heat can be classified as heat cramps, usually caused by loss of body fluids and salts; heat exhaustion, caused by fluid and salt loss and the pooling of blood in the skin as the body tries to release heat; and heatstroke, caused by a disturbance of the heat-regulating mechanisms of the body.

Long exposure to heat and heavy sweating may bring on muscle _____ . Leg muscle cramps, pain, fatigue, faintness, and profuse perspiration are all signs of heat cramps. Care requires moving the patient to a cool area, giving him sips of plain water or half-strength commercial electrolyte fluids (depending on local protocols) and applying manual massage to the cramped muscles. Be observant for more serious problems.

cramps

A person suffering from heat cramps will usually have _____ _____ cramps, pain, _____ , faintness, and profuse _____ . Remove the patient to a _____ area and give him sips of regular drinking water or half-strength electrolyte fluids. Apply _____ massage to cramped muscles.

leg
muscle, fatigue
perspiration, cool

If the return of blood to the heart is inadequate because the blood is pooled in the skin to release body heat, the patient will suffer heat _____ . His pulse is weak, breathing is rapid and shallow, the skin is clammy and perspiration is profuse. The patient is very weak and may become dizzy and collapse, or suffer a loss of consciousness.

manual

exhaustion

Care for heat exhaustion resembles the care for heat cramps. The patient should be moved to a _____ area and be given large volumes of drinking water or _____ -strength commercial _____ fluids. The patient should be fanned, but not be allowed to become chilled. Treatment for shock may be necessary. Transport is recommended for cases of heat exhaustion.

cool
half, electrolyte

The disturbance of the heat-regulating mechanisms of the body is called _____ . It is a serious threat to life. The skin is dry and hot, with the body temperature reaching 105°F or higher. The pupils are dilated and the pulse is full and fast. Breathing will be deep at first and then decline to become very shallow. Muscular twitching may be present that develops into convulsions. Remove as much of the patient's clothing as possible. Immediate transport with cold packs is recommended. The patient should be protected in case of convulsions.

heatstroke

A true life-threatening emergency due to heat is _____ .

EMERGENCIES DUE TO COLD

The entire body can be affected by cold, as in general cooling. This is called systemic hypothermia. Local cooling will affect only parts of the body, as in frostbite and freezing.

When the entire body, including core temperature, is affected by cold, as in _____ cooling, a true emergency exists. No artificial heat should be placed next to bare skin. The EMT should provide external heat by way of heating pads, hot water bottles, etc. Respiratory and cardiac arrest is possible.

WARNING: DO NOT WARM THE MILD HYPOTHERMIA PATIENT TOO QUICKLY. If the core temperature is below 80°F, there is serious difficult breathing, the pulse rate is very slow, or if the patient is unconscious, do NOT try to rewarm the patient. In cases of severe hypothermia, rewarming in the field may lead to lethal ventricular fibrillation.

Local cooling can be either _____ or _____. Warm water, held between 100° and 105°F, can be used effectively to immerse the frostbitten parts when transport is delayed. Freezing is a true emergency that requires _____ transport. The frozen part should be kept dry and warm.

Local cooling can be freezing or _____. Incipient, superficial, and deep frostbite are all possible. The mildest is incipient (frostnip), followed in severity by superficial, and _____.

The mildest form of frostbite, _____, results in the affected part turning white and becoming numb. All that is needed for care is simple rewarming.

If incipient frostbite goes untreated, _____ frostbite may occur. The affected part takes on a white or waxy appearance. The area will feel frozen to the touch, but pliable tissue will be felt below the frozen layer.

If superficial frostbite goes untreated, _____ frostbite occurs. Consider this form of frostbite and freezing to be the same thing. There will be no noticeable _____ tissue below the frozen area as in _____ frostbite. The affected area in deep frostbite appears mottled or blotchy blue or gray.

If transport is immediate, cover the frozen areas lightly, avoid rubbing affected areas. For delayed transport, use _____ water immersion. Do not thaw a frozen limb if there is any chance that it will be refrozen.

heatstroke

general

frostbite, freezing

immediate

frostbite

deep
incipient

superficial

deep

pliable
superficial

TERMINOLOGY

Define the following terms. Check your definitions with those given in the Glossary of your textbook or as directed.

Deep frostbite—

Incipient frostbite—

Superficial frostbite—

Systemic hypothermia—

MULTIPLE CHOICE

Circle the letter of the correct answer for each question. The answers are given at the end of this chapter. Note page references to *Emergency Care, 5th ed.*

1. Which of the following requires rapid cooling and immediate transport? *(p. 481)*:
   A. Heat cramp
   B. Heatstroke
   C. Heat exhaustion
   D. All of the above

2. An EMT finds a 30-year-old man collapsed in a field. He smells alcohol on the man's breath. The pupils are dilated, the skin is hot and dry. The pulse is full and fast. These indicate *(p. 482)*:
   A. Heatstroke
   B. Shock
   C. Delirium tremens
   D. Diabetic coma

3. Which of the following would be an effective water temperature for treating frostbite? *(p. 485)*
   A. 70°F
   B. 98.6°F
   C. 104°F
   D. 110°F

4. In frostbite the skin first turns red. As exposure continues it will turn *(p. 484)*:
   A. Gray or white in certain areas, such as the tip of the nose
   B. Cherry red, except for the extremities
   C. Deep blue at the nose and cheeks
   D. Completely white, except for the tip of the nose and the cheeks

5. If deep freezing of the body tissues occurs, and transport is immediate, the best course of action is *(p. 484)*:
   A. Immerse in 100° water and transport
   B. Keep area wet, warm and transport
   C. Keep area dry, cold and transport
   D. Keep area dry, warm and transport

EXERCISES

To check your answers to the Exercises, refer to *Emergency Care, 5th ed.*

1. List the symptoms and signs of heatstroke *(p. 482)*.

2. How might you cool the heatstroke patient? *(p. 482)*

3. List three signs of mild to moderate hypothermia *(pp 485–486)*.

4. List three signs of severe hypothermia *(p. 486)*.

5. Describe the care that you should provide for a patient who is suffering from mild hypothermia *(p. 486)*.

6. Complete the following chart *(p. 484)*.

CONDITION	SKIN SURFACE	TISSUE UNDER SKIN	SKIN COLOR
Frostnip			
Frostbite			
Freezing			

142

7. Complete the following chart *(p. 482)*.

CONDITION	MUSCLE CRAMPS	BREATHING	PULSE	WEAKNESS	SKIN	PERSPIRATION	LOSS OF CONSCIOUS-NESS
Heat Cramps							
Heat Exhaustion							
Heat-Stroke							

Reading Assignment: Emergency Care, 5th ed., pp. 488–497

SECTION TWO: WATER- AND ICE-RELATED ACCIDENTS

REACHING PERSONS WHO ARE IN WATER

If the victims are inside submerged vehicles, or in water and free of the vehicle, your last effort should be to go in after them. If you cannot safely reach the victims, attempt to throw them objects that float. Remember, the spare tire wheel of the ambulance will float.

The last thing and EMT should do to rescue victims in water is to _____ _____. First, _____ them objects that _____. If **go in, throw, float** none is available, see if you can get a line to the victims and attempt to tow them in. If possible, approach one victim at a time with the line and tow him in before attempting to rescue the next. If towing fails and a boat is available, try to row to the victims (swimmers only with PFDs).

For victims in water, try to safely reach for them, or _____ **throw** objects that float. Next, try to get a line to them and _____ the victims. If a **tow** boat is available, _____ to the victims. If you go to the victims by boat, **row** *always* wear a personal flotation device. Your last effort should be to _____ **go** _____. **in**

If the victim is in the water and is out of reach, first _____, then **throw** _____, then _____, and finally _____. *Do not* go into the water unless **tow, row, go** you are a capable swimmer and are trained in water lifesaving techniques.

NEAR-DROWNING PATIENTS

There should be no delay in the treatment of near-drowning victims. Do not waste time trying to expel water from the lungs. Establish an airway and begin pulmonary resuscitation. For in-water care, mouth-to-mouth resuscitation will probably be necessary. This places the EMT at risk for certain _____ diseases. Follow your EMS System's guidelines. **infectious**

The first steps in treating a near-drowning victim are to establish an _____ **open** _____ and begin _____-to-_____ resuscitation. If **airway, mouth, mouth** there is no heart action, _____ should be started as soon as possible. **CPR**

Oxygen should be administered under positive pressure and continued during transport. Keep the patient warm and treat for shock.

If spontaneous breathing does not occur, administer _____ **oxygen** under _____ _____. If you revive the patient, you must **positive pressure** still transport.

REACHING PERSONS WHO HAVE FALLEN THROUGH ICE

For victims who have fallen through ice, your first effort should be the same as for victims in water: _____ them objects that _____. **throw, float** Next, try to pull them out with looped ropes placed around their chests. If you must go out on the ice after them, spread your weight out on a spine board or basket stretcher. A small aluminum boat tied with a piece of rope for pulling also can be used. A ladder can be extended to the victim. As with the aluminum boat, the ladder should have a _____ for _____. **rope, pulling**

CAUTION: If you work as an EMT in areas where ice accidents are possible, even remotely, know self-rescue techniques and carry protected ice-picks or long nails for such purposes.

TERMINOLOGY

Define the following terms. Check your definitions with those given on page 489 of your textbook.

Air embolism—

Asphyxia—

Decompression sickness—

Laryngospasm—

EXERCISES

Complete the following exercises. Note references to *Emergency Care, 5th ed.*

1. Describe the care you should provide for the breathing, near-drowning patient who has been rescued by others *(p. 491)*.

2. State how you would determine if a patient was suffering from possible air emboli related to a SCUBA diving accident *(pp. 496–497)*.

3. Assume that you and you and your partner are good swimmers, trained in water rescue. What should you do in the initial steps of care for a breathing patient with possible spinal injury who is in the water when you arrive at the scent? *(p. 494)*

4. Explain why you should attempt to resuscitate a patient who is the victim of a cold water drowning, even though the patient may have been in arrest for one hour *(p. 491)*.

19 special patients and behavioral problems

Reading Assignment: Emergency Care, 5th ed., pp. 499-513

MANAGEMENT OF SPECIAL PATIENTS

SPECIAL PATIENTS AND SITUATIONS

The Concept of Crisis

The patient, his family and friends, and bystanders may consider an emergency to be a crisis—a crucial moment or turning point in life. Whether the crisis is real or imagined, it must be managed. The important initial steps of crisis management are often the responsibility of the EMT.

A crucial moment or turning point in life can be considered to be a _____ . When the EMT begins crisis _____, he should keep in mind that a person in a crisis is upset. The emotional stress may be a significant factor in the physical and mental stability of the patient.

crisis, management

A patient in a crisis may be under great emotional _____ . This can cause a deterioration of the patient's _____ and _____ stability. The EMT will have to initiate _____ _____ techniques as part of patient care.

stress
physical
mental, crisis
management

In a crisis situation, the EMT must look and act like a professional, exhibiting a calm professional manner. He needs to talk with the patient, indicating he is listening to what the patient says and avoiding improper conversation. When possible, the EMT must do something for the patient, even if the action taken is as simple as dressing a minor wound.

During a crisis, the EMT must act in a _____ _____ manner. Appropriate conversational techniques include letting the patient know that you are _____ to what he is saying.

calm professional

listening

BEHAVIORAL PROBLEMS

Stress Reactions

At the scene of accident or illness, the EMT may have to provide care for stress reactions, emotional emergencies, and psychiatric emergencies. Remember that an emergency is a stressful situation that may be viewed by the patient as being a _____ . The distressed patient will display emotions that are typical for the emergency scene. This display is a stress reaction.

crisis

In any stressful situation, the EMT may have to initiate the techniques of _____ _____. This will help patients who are displaying emotions that are expected at the emergency scene. Patients who show such _____ _____ need support provided in a _____ professional manner. The key element of this support is personal

crisis management

stress reactions
calm

interaction, or calmly talking with the patient using appropriate language, and letting him know that someone is listening to what he is saying.

In addition to stress reactions, the EMT may have to face psychiatric and _____ emergencies. For all these patients, the primary methods of care will have to include _____ _____ .

emotional

personal interaction

EMOTIONAL AND MENTAL HEALTH PROBLEMS

The EMT always should consider the emotional and mental health of the patient, his friends and family, and the bystander affected by the emergency situation. Any crisis can cause a change in emotional state brought about by increased internal and/or external stress.

Accidents, severe injury or illness, and natural disasters often bring about a change in _____ state. The EMT should remember that excessive internal and/or external _____ can affect the patient, his friends and family, and any _____. When there is more than a simple loss of emotional control, the EMT may be faced with a psychiatric emergency.

emotional

stress

bystanders

A loss of emotional control that causes a person to behave in a manner that is threatening to his own well-being and the well-being of others is a _____ emergency. Not all emotional displays, including such behavior as hysterical excitement, are true emergencies. The EMT should look for loss of _____ _____ and behavior that is threatening to the _____ and to _____. Obviously, if the EMT is to evaluate the behavior of others, he must be calm and totally professional in his actions.

psychiatric

emotional control
patient, others

After observing the _____ of the patient and finding an emotional or psychiatric _____, the EMT should attempt to apply his first line of action, personal interaction. The patient is anxious and is usually trying to maintain emotional stability. Reassurance and awareness that help has arrived will not only help the true psychiatric emergency patient, but anyone who has lost a degree of his _____ control.

behavior
emergency

emotional

The EMT should observe the patient and the situation and gain any information he can from bystanders. He should remember that atypical behavior might be the result of a head injury, brain tumor, CVA, insulin shock, etc.

The EMT should _____ the patient. While doing so he should apply his first line of care, _____ interaction. Simple conversation works best of all.

observe
personal

The EMT should attempt, through observations and gaining information from bystanders, to classify the situation and see if it is a true psychiatric emergency. He should look for acute anxiety or panic; aggressive, bizarre, or antisocial behavior; impaired consciousness; and suicidal or homicidal threats or attempts. He should also be aware that alcohol, drugs, and acute physical illness or injuries may cause the observed behavior.

Any real emergency can cause people to lose emotional control. The EMT should be _____ and act in a professional manner. Personal interaction, usually through simple _____ works best. This is very important when dealing with children who have their normal childhood fears and sensitivities heightened in a crisis. Remember, most children and some adults have a great fear of strangers. _____ conversation is the best approach.

calm
conversation

Simple

If a patient is violent, the EMT should wait for police assistance. Force will often intensify the patient's abnormal behavior. If a patient's behavior is a threat to _____ or to _____, and he will not respond to simple _____, the EMT, with police assistance, should apply restraint with a minimum of aggressive moves and force.

himself, others
conversation

Aggressive Patients

There are some rules to follow when transferring a violent patient. First of all, do not restrain a patient without police or physician's approval. If you are acting without the support of the police or a physician, and you feel the patient or others are in danger, never attempt restraint without at least 3 helpers.

Patient restraint requires the approval of the _____ or a _____. If you have to act on your own, have at least _____ helpers. Simple Velcro straps should be used to secure the patient's hands, then his ankles.

police
physician, three

Place the violent patient in a horizontal position. Place _____ restraints on his _____ and then his _____. Position the patient on a wheeled stretcher for transfer to the ambulance. Do not "spread eagle" the patient to the stretcher. Chest, hip, and leg belts may be used if necessary. Do not be fooled by your patient telling you he can be freed from restraints. Once a patient is restrained, keep the restraints in place. Transport and hand over the patient still in restraints.

Velcro
hands, ankles

Attempted Suicide

As an EMT you may be called upon to administer care to someone who has attempted suicide or is threatening suicide. For these patients, try to establish visual and verbal contact as soon as possible.

Gaining access to the patient may be difficult. However, even while you are trying to gain access, establish _____ or _____ contact with the patient. If you can start the potential suicide victim talking, keep him talking.

visual, verbal

Remember to keep your own safety in mind. A potential suicide victim may be homicidal as well as suicidal. Be careful–your patient may still be holding a weapon or have one nearby.

In cases of attempted suicide and in all cases of abnormal behavior, don't hurry yourself or the patient. Evaluate the situation while keeping your own emotions under control. The thing that you should do quickly is to establish _____ or _____ contact with the patient and try to keep him _____. Be honest in your conversation with the patient, taking care not to make any threats. Do not criticize the patient or challenge him. Do not joke about the situation. Avoid force. Rely on police assistance whenever possible.

visual, verbal
talking

TERMINOLOGY

Define the following terms. Check your definitions with those found on page 500 of your textbook or as directed.

Crisis—

Emotional emergency—

Personal interaction—

Psychiatric emergency (p. 508)—

Stress reaction (pp. 505-506)—

FORMING MEDICAL TERMS

The following elements of medical terms were used in this chapter.

Roots and Combining Forms

psycho- (si-KO-): the mind. The study of diseases of the mind is psychiatry. A major disorder of the mind is a _____ sis.

Prefixes

a-: without, not. You can consider behavior that is not what is expected to be _____ typical.

ab-: away from, not. A physician may consider someone's behavior to be _____ normal.

MULTIPLE CHOICE

Circle the letter of the correct answer to each of the following questions. The answers are given at the end of this chapter. Note page references to *Emergency Care, 5th ed.*

1. Older patients are usually slower in conversations because they (p. 503):
   A. Have arteriosclerosis
   B. Give more importance to words
   C. Think more slowly
   D. Have atherosclerosis

2. Should you have to move a blind patient who is able to walk, you should (p 504):
   A. Stand behind him and guide his way by pushing on his shoulders
   B. Stand directly in front of the patient, letting him hold your shoulders

   C. Stand to one side slightly ahead of the patient and let him hold your arm
   D. Always move the patient by wheeled stretcher or chair

3. Your first step in trying to care for an attempted suicide victim is to (p. 510):
   A. Gain access to the patient
   B. Wait for police assistance
   C. Survey for behavioral changes
   D. Ensure your own safety

4. The EMT can usually avoid having to restrain a patient having a psychiatric emergency by (p. 509):
   A. Representing authority
   B. Acting with a police officer present
   C. Taking time to reassure the patient
   D. Acting quickly at the scene

5. The EMT's first priority at the safe crime scene is to (p. 510):
   A. Provide needed emergency care
   B. Preserve the chain of evidence
   C. Help control bystanders
   D. Gain information about the crime from the victim

EXERCISES

Complete the following exercises. Note that page references to the textbook have ben provided.

1. Describe 3 patients so that another EMT would be able to tell which one was having a stress reaction, an emotional emergency, or a possible psychiatric emergency (pp. 505-510).

2. List the various methods you can use to communicate with a deaf patient (pp. 503-504).

3. Describe how you would deal with an aggressive patient (p. 509).

4. Describe the special care you should render to a patient who is a victim of rape *(p. 511)*.

5. List five signs of the post-traumatic stress disorder know as EMT *stress syndrome (p. 511)*.

6. State three ways in which the EMT can deal with EMT stress syndrome *(pp. 511-512)*.

ANSWERS

Forming Medical Terms

psychosis, atypical, abnormal

Multiple Choice

1. B   2. C   3. D   4. C   5. A

149

20 triage and disaster management

Reading Assignment: Emergency Care, 5th ed., pp. 515-525

MULTIPLE-PATIENT SITUATIONS

At an emergency scene where many people have been injured, the EMS unit that arrives first is initially responsible for beginning to organize the scene. Effective organization is essential to giving the best chance of survival to as many victims as possible. The task of organizing the scene includes controlling hazards, setting priorities for patient care (triage), establishing a command post, establishing staging areas for vehicles, equipment, and personnel, initiating communications that will be needed to coordinate activities at the scene, and controlling hazards.

If your unit is the first to arrive at a multi-patient accident, your unit will become the initial _____ post for the emergency scene. After controlling _____ , one partner should begin the task of _____ patients. The second partner should begin to establish _____ areas for vehicles, equipment, and personnel. At the same time, you will have to set up _____ with your dispatcher to coordinate activities at the scene. If these functions are carried out well, confusion can be avoided as new units and equipment begin arriving on the scene.

command
hazards
triaging
staging
communications

In some cases, your unit may be the first to respond to a scene that has already been identified as a disaster. In other cases, you may be responding to an emergency that has not yet been identified as a disaster. In both cases, your description of the scene and your assessment of needs will be essential to an effective EMS response.

If you are the first-arriving unit at a disaster scene, the key to doing your job effectively will be your understanding of your EMS system's disaster plan.

TRIAGE

Triage is the sorting of patients into categories for receiving care and transport. Patients are sorted based on the severity of their injuries or illnesses.

_____ is used to determine who will have priority for receiving care and _____. There are several different triage systems for assigning priorities. You should be familiar with the triage protocols used by your EMS system. However, most triage systems have certain elements in common.

Triage
transport

The highest priority patients are the first to be treated. Conditions that are often included in this category are breathing emergencies, unconsciousness, open chest and abdominal wounds, severe shock, burns involving the

152

respiratory tract, severe medical problems (including heart attack and stroke), and joint fractures with no distal pulse.

Secondary priorities generally include severe burns, injuries to the spine other than the cervical spine, moderate bleeding, conscious patients with head injuries, multiple fractures, and back injuries. These patients would be treated after the _____ priority patients.

When assigning a triage priority to patients, a patient who was unconscious would generally be assigned _____ priority. A patient with a suspected back injury would probably be assigned _____ priority. Low priority conditions generally include minor bleeding, minor fractures and soft tissue injuries, moderate and minor burns, and obviously mortal wounds.

During triage for a multiple-patient accident, a patient with obviously mortal wounds would generally be assigned _____ priority.

highest

high
secondary

low

TERMINOLOGY

Define the following terms. Check your definitions with those on page 515 of your textbook.

Disaster—

Disaster Plan—

Triage—

EXERCISES

Complete the following exercises. Note page references to *Emergency Care, 5th ed.*

1. You are performing triage at the site of an industrial accident. Assign a priority (high, secondary, low) to each of these patients (*pp. 516-517*).
   a. A patient with a severe burn on his right leg _____
   b. A patient who may be having a heart attack _____
   c. A patient with burns on his face who is having difficulty breathing_____
   d. An unconscious patient who may have a neck injury _____
   e. A conscious patient with a head injury _____
   f. A patient in respiratory arrest _____
   g. A patient with minor burns on his chest _____
   h. A patient with abrasions and contusions on both arms _____

2. If your ambulance is the first to arrive at a disaster, describe what you and the other members of the crew must do (*pp. 523-524*).

3. List the specific activities that must have designated areas set up at a disaster scene *(p. 524)*.

4. List three things that can be done help reduce stress on disaster personnel during a disaster *(p. 523)*.

ANSWERS: Exercise 1

a. secondary
b. high
c. high
d. high
e. secondary
f. high
g. low
h. low

21 preparing for the ambulance run

Reading Assignment: Emergency Care, 5th ed., pp. 527-535

PREPARATION

THE AMBULANCE

An ambulance is a special vehicle. It must always be ready to respond for service and ready to be operated by many different individuals. A preventive maintenance program is required. This program should include periodic inspections and servicing.

So that it is always ready to respond, an ambulance requires a _____ _____ program, including periodic _____ and servicing. Fuel, oil, battery, tires, radiator, lights, warning devices, and mirrors should be inspected and _____ as needed. The best policy is to refill the ambulance gas tank after each run. All mechanical, hydraulic, and electrical equipment is best checked after each run, or according to a set schedule.

As a part of every_____ maintenance inspection, include: fuel, _____ , battery, _____ , radiator, lights, _____ devices, and mirrors. All major mechanical, _____, and electrical devices should be checked. The time to refuel the ambulance is after _____ _____.

preventive maintenance
inspections

serviced

preventive
oil, tires
warning
hydraulic
each run

EXERCISES

1. State at least three reasons why basic supplies must be carried on an ambulance *(p. 528)*.

2. List at least three patient-carrying devices that should be part of an ambulance equipment inventory *(pp. 528-529)*.

3. List at least two devices that should be carried for providing artificial ventilations *(p. 529)*.

4. In general, what two types of suction equipment should be carried on an ambulance *(p. 529)*?

5. Describe the steps in inspecting an ambulance prior to any inspections that would require its engine to be started *(p. 532-534)*.

22 responding to a call for help

Reading Assignment: Emergency Care, 5th ed., pp. 537-561

RECEIVING THE CALL FOR HELP

ACTIVATING THE SYSTEM

Ideally, everyone in the United States should have immediate, unlimited access to the nearest emergency medical services through a system called *one-number calling*. The universal number, 911, would allow anyone to call for help, toll-free, even in the most remote areas.

The telephone number _____ is used as the emergency number in a system called _____ - _____ calling. Not all areas have adopted this system. In some communities there are small dispatch centers, often requiring redialing between agencies. Many communities have a system less efficient than one-number calling but better than small dispatch centers. They use two dispatch centers, one for police and one for fire, rescue, and ambulance services. Such a system has cross-communication capabilities in case the caller needing medical services dials the police instead.

911
one, number

Communities may have any one of three systems to allow a caller entry into the emergency medical system. The most basic of these systems is the small dispatch center. A better method is a two-dispatch-center system with _____ - communication capabilities. Many professionals now believe the most efficient system is the one using the 911 number, known as the _____ - _____ _____ system.

cross

one number calling

Information Obtained by the Dispatcher

The first thing a dispatcher should do when answering a call for help is to identify the agency. After this, there are 7 pieces of information he should obtain to pass on to the ambulance crew assigned to the run. Even more information will be needed in the case of a traffic accident, fire or disaster.

Upon answering a call for help, the dispatcher should _____ the agency and then obtain a minimum of _____ pieces of information to pass on to the ambulance crew. The first bit of information is whether this is to be an emergency or routine transport.

identify
7

The dispatcher should ask, "Do you have an emergency?" If the answer is "yes," he should then ask, "What is the exact location of the sick/injured person?" This information may include the address, direction designator (north, south, east, west), and the name of the community or development. When this information is given to the ambulance crew, the dispatcher will provide them with a cross street to allow for a quicker response.

The third question the dispatcher should ask is, "What is the nature of

157

158

the emergency?" The answers obtained from these first 3 questions will tell the dispatcher whether the call should be treated as an _____ or _____ transport, and which emergency services need to respond.

The question, "What is the _____ of the emergency?" will gain the information: which _____ _____ need to respond based on what is apparently wrong with the patient.

When determining the exact location of a patient, the dispatcher must find out the exact address, name of community or development, and the _____ _____. Remember that apartment buildings have a street address and also a number and/or letter for each unit in the building. The dispatcher will give the ambulance crew the name of the nearest _____ street to improve response time.

By now, the dispatcher has 3 essential pieces of information: whether or not it is an _____ call, what emergency _____ are needed based on what is wrong with the patient, and the _____ _____ of the patient. Next he must find out the patient's name and age.

After determining the exact _____ of the patient and the nature of the emergency, the dispatcher should find out both the _____ and _____ of the patient. Next, the dispatcher should ask for the name and telephone number of the caller. The next piece of information is whether or not the caller will be at that telephone if more information is needed.

The procedure for gathering information becomes more complex in the case of traffic accidents. The dispatcher also must obtain information about the accident scene. This knowledge can be gained by securing 4 additional pieces of information.

Along with the information needed for all runs, the name of the caller and his _____ _____, the dispatcher must secure more bits of information if the response is to the scene of a _____ accident. He must ask for the exact location of the accident, how many and what kinds of vehicles are involved, how many people are injured and how seriously, if any of the victims appear to be trapped and, finally, whether there are any apparent hazards.

In the case of a traffic accident, more information is needed to help describe the accident _____. The dispatcher needs to know the exact _____ of the accident, how many and what kinds of vehicles are involved, how many people are injured and how _____ and whether there are any apparent _____.

Word bank (margin):
- emergency, routine
- nature
- emergency services
- direction designator
- cross
- emergency, services
- exact location
- location
- name
- age
- telephone number
- traffic
- scene
- location
- seriously
- hazards

DRIVING THE AMBULANCE TO THE SCENE

UNDERSTANDING THE LAW

Each state has its own statutes regulating the operations of emergency vehicles. Even though wording may vary from state to state, the intent of the laws is the same. These statutes usually grant privileges relating to speed, passage through traffic signals, direction of travel, and parking. However, with these privileges also come penalties for driving without regard for others. *You are responsible for knowing the laws of the state in which you drive.*

THE DRIVING TASK

The driver, vehicle, road, and other drivers make up the components of the driving task.

The Driver

The driving task has 4 components: the driver, the _____, the _____, and other _____.

An ambulance driver should be physically capable, not hindered by uncorrected defective vision, physical impairments, or physical disabilities (including temporary injuries). He should not attempt to drive when taking certain medications or drugs, including alcohol.

Not only should the ambulance driver be _____ capable, he also must be mentally capable. He should be able to fully concentrate on his driving and have a healthy attitude toward his own abilities and all other drivers.

A healthy attitude toward his own abilities and toward others is one of the _____ capabilities required of the ambulance driver. It is very important for him to have a cooperative attitude.

The Vehicle

STOPPING DISTANCES. As noted, preventive maintenance and inspection of the vehicle are important. However, even an ambulance in optimum operating condition has limitations. Quite often the stopping characteristics of the ambulance are forgotten by the inexperienced ambulance driver.

The ambulance driver needs to know the _____ characteristics of his vehicle. The technique of bringing a vehicle to a stop depends on speed, vehicle condition, road condition, and the alertness of the driver. The stopping distance is the total number of feet a vehicle travels from the time the driver decides to stop until the vehicle has come to a full stop.

The distance traveled from the time you decide to stop until you actually bring the vehicle to a full stop is called the _____ _____. It is the total of the reaction distance and the breaking distance. The reaction distance is the distance covered between your decision to stop and the time your foot applies pressure to the brake pedal. This distance added to the _____ _____ equals the stopping distance.

Braking distance is the distance covered from the time you begin to apply pressure on the brake pedal until the vehicle comes to a full stop. The number of feet traveled from the decision to stop until pressure is applied to the brake pedal is the _____ _____. To determine stopping distance, add the _____ distance and the _____ distance.

REMEMBER: As the speed increases so does stopping distance. You must consider whether the speed required for a slight gain in arrival time is worth the tremendous increase in _____ distance that will result from this increased speed.

The Road

The most common road problems are caused by weather. These problems, along with types of road surface and curves, can create unfavorable road conditions.

---

vehicle
road, drivers

physically

mental

stopping

stopping
distance

braking distance

reaction distance
reaction, braking

stopping

Most road problems are caused by _____ . Ice, snow, rain, and high winds require special driving techniques. The hazards of ice and snow can be reduced if the ambulance has been equipped with studded snow tires. Even with these special tires, you should travel at reduced speeds and avoid locking the wheels (caused by jamming on the brakes). When stopping, pump the brakes. Learn to steer in the direction needed to return a skidding ambulance to a straight course. These skills and _____ snow tires will reduce the hazards of driving on ice or snow.

Wet roads, especially during the first few minutes of rainfall, are dangerous. As on ice and snow, _____ your brakes to stop, and steer in the direction needed to regain control during skids. _____ speed is called for.

Hydroplaning can occur on wet roads. Reduce speed and gradually slow down during hydroplaning. If braking is necessary, _____ the brakes.

In addition to the weather, the type of road _____ and _____ can present hazardous conditions. A thorough knowledge of how to handle these road problems is required of the ambulance driver.

THE USE OF WARNING DEVICES

The siren, horn, and visual warning lights are the primary ambulance warning devices. When misused, these devices can do more harm than good. Remember, the proper use of warning devices must be coupled with sound emergency driving practices and defensive driving techniques.

The Siren

The siren, _____, and visual warning _____ are the three primary warning devices used for ambulances. The excessive use of the siren can cause indifference in the general population. Along with danger of public indifference, studies have shown another danger with the excessive use of sirens. Many ambulance drivers tend to increase their speed when using this device. As with all warning devices, the siren must be properly used and coupled with _____ emergency driving practices and good _____ driving techniques. Use the siren sparingly (in accordance with local laws). Do not assume that all motorists will hear your signal. Be prepared for the erratic maneuvers of other drivers.

The siren has become the principal means of alerting other motorists. Learn to use it _____ . Since some motorists will not _____your signal, avoid sounding your siren after pulling up close to a vehicle that is directly ahead. Be prepared for _____ maneuvers by other drivers. Remember too, excessive use of the ambulance siren can have a psychological effect on you, other motorists, and the patient being transported.

The Horn

The horn, _____, and _____ _____ lights are the primary warning devices on an ambulance. As with the siren, the best results can be obtained by using the horn _____. Remember, excessive use of the horn may have a _____ effect on the patient.

---

weather

studded

pump
Reduced

pump

surface
curves

horn, lights

sound
defensive

sparingly
hear
erratic

siren, visual warning

sparingly
psychological

Visual Warning Signals

All visual warning devices should be in operation when responding to a call. Do not underestimate the use of headlights. They can be more effective in the daytime than the colored warning lights. Even though the headlights are very effective, be sure to use _____ visual warning devices when responding to a call.

all

BASIC AMBULANCE ACCIDENTS

Injuries and property damage occur most frequently when the ambulance collides with another vehicle. There are 7 varieties of such two-vehicle collisions including accidents while backing up. Of the _____ types of 2-vehicle accidents, the first 5 usually occur when the ambulance is responding.

7

An Accident with the Vehicle Ahead

Accidents can occur when the driver ahead either pulls his car to the left, stops, incorrectly signals his move, or has not noticed your approach. The driver who may cause the accident need not be the one in the car directly ahead of you. Be sure to watch the line of traffic some distance ahead, particularly at intersections.

Accidents can occur with the vehicle _____. The driver of this vehicle can cause an accident by pulling his car to the _____, by giving an incorrect signal, by being unaware of your approach, or by _____. Watch the line of traffic ahead, taking special precautions at _____.

ahead
left
stopping

intersections

Keep a safe distance from the vehicle ahead of the ambulance. Leave 1 vehicle length of distance for every 10 miles per hour of speed. Use good driving techniques by applying your brakes as soon as you see a hazard developing. In a potentially dangerous situation, poise your right food over the brake to reduce _____ distance and thus reduce stopping distance.

reaction

You should maintain a distance of _____ vehicle length between the ambulance and the vehicle ahead for every _____ miles per hour of speed. Learn proper braking techniques and how to steer around obstacles.

1
10

In addition to braking to avoid accidents, you may do better in some situations by _____ _____ obstacles.

steering around

An Accident with the Vehicle Behind

The driver who tailgates an ambulance can cause an accident. The techniques used by the responding ambulance driver cannot be the same as the ones used by a passenger car driver. Your only recourse is the proper use of directional signals and braking smoothly.

Since you cannot accelerate away from a tailgater or pull off the road, you must properly use directional signals and _____ _____.

brake
smoothly

An Accident with an Approaching Vehicle

Head-on collisions are the most deadly of two-car accidents. They can occur on straight roads, on curves, or at intersections. These accidents are caused by the ambulance or the approaching vehicle leaving its correct lane, usually trying to pass slower cars. Reduce speed, stay in your

_____ lane, and wait for vehicles ahead to pull to the right to let you around them. Head-on collisions on straight roads often occur when the ambulance driver attempts to steer too quickly back onto the road surface after the vehicle's right wheels have dropped off the pavement. _____ speed, wait for an opening, and steer back slowly with the wheels held at a sharp angle.

On right-hand curves, the ambulance may drift into oncoming traffic. On left-hand curves, oncoming traffic may drift into your path. As with most emergencies, _____ speed as you enter a curve, and accelerate as you approach a straightaway. Do not brake in a curve.

You may drift into oncoming traffic when the road curves to the _____. Reduce speed, do not _____, and accelerate as you approach the _____.

	correct
	Reduce
	reduce
	right, brake
	straightaway

An Accident at an Intersection

We have considered 3 types of basic ambulance accidents: an accident with the vehicle directly _____; an accident with the vehicle _____; and an accident with an _____ vehicle. Now we will consider accidents at intersections, the location of one-third of all traffic accidents.

One-third of all traffic accidents occur at _____. You can avoid most of these accidents by knowing where you are going to turn and by eliminating sudden stops. Since _____ - _____ of all traffic accidents occur at intersections, slow down for all intersections. Know where you are going to _____, signal properly, and make sure the way is clear in both directions.

When you approach an intersection, _____ _____. As in the case of any potentially dangerous situation, take your right foot from the accelerator and hold it over the _____ pedal. CAUTION: DO NOT ATTEMPT TO DRIVE WITH YOUR RIGHT FOOT ON THE ACCELERATOR AND YOUR LEFT FOOT OVER THE BRAKE PEDAL.

Other emergency vehicles may reach the intersection at the same time you do. The emergency vehicle with the green light, or if there is no traffic signal, the one on the right has the right of way.

If two emergency vehicles reach an intersection at the same time, you should yield to the one with the _____ light. If there is no traffic signal, yield to the vehicle on the _____.

Before you turn, _____ where you are going to turn, _____ properly, and _____ speed. If you must stop, keep your wheels in a straight line in case you are hit from the rear.

	ahead
	behind, approaching
	intersections
	one-third
	turn
	slow down
	brake
	green
	right
	know, signal
	reduce

An Accident with a Vehicle Being Passed

Check oncoming traffic to avoid a deadly _____ - _____ collision. Check traffic moving in the same direction to be sure you have enough room to reenter the traffic lane. This will help you avoid a collision with the vehicle _____ and the vehicle _____. Signal, move into the adjacent lane when the way is clear, alert other motorists of your intention to pass (it is best to signal with the horn), pass, and signal your return into the traffic lane. Be sure to check _____ traffic and the traffic _____ moving in the _____ direction as your vehicle. Always check your sideview mirror to be sure no one is attempting to pass you.

	head-on
	ahead, behind
	oncoming, ahead
	same

An Accident with a Vehicle that is Passing

The first 5 types of basic ambulance accidents usually occur when the ambulance is _____ to a call for help. The sixth type, an accident with a vehicle that is _____, usually occurs when the ambulance is returning to quarters.

responding
passing

Exercise good defensive driving skills. Help other motorists to pass by pulling to the _____ and, when necessary, _____ speed.

right, reducing

FACTORS THAT AFFECT RESPONSE

Seven major factors —the day of the week, the time of day, weather, detours, railroad crossings, bridges and tunnels, and schools—can affect response time and the selection of the route to the emergency scene.

Day of the Week

Two factors—the day of the week and the _____ of day—can affect response. Usually the heaviest traffic is encountered during weekdays. However, keep in mind that shopping, recreation, and holidays may all cause sharp increases in weekend traffic.

time

Time of Day

The time of day and the day of the _____ must both be considered when responding to a call for help. Morning and evening rush hour traffic will be the heaviest. However, main arteries may be crowded at all times.

week

Weather

Rain, fog, ice, snow, and high winds can all affect response. They can be an even greater problem during morning and evening _____ _____ traffic. Therefore, along with weather, you must also consider the _____ of the week and the _____ of day.

rush hour
day
time

Detours

Due to construction, road maintenance, and accidents, detours are a necessary part of driving. Knowledge ahead of time of their locations and the planning of alternate routes will save time, even if the alternate route appears longer than the normal route to the scene.

The only real answer to detours is to take an _____ route. Because of this, you must know the location of detours _____ of time.

alternate
ahead

Railroads

As with the day of the week, the time of day, weather, and _____, railroads can affect response. Bridges and underpasses help, but there are still situations where the route can be blocked by trains for long periods of time. Local schedules and plans for alternate routes can be of help.

detours

Bridges and Tunnels

Bridges and tunnels are subject to major traffic jams. This is particularly true during commuter hours, emphasizing once again the importance of the

164

_____ of the week and the _____ of day. The only answer again may be the selection of _____ _____.

To avoid long delays at railroad crossings, attempt to make full use of _____, _____, and underpasses.

day, time
alternate routes

bridges, tunnels

Schools

A school means that there may be children in the area. This potential hazard calls for _____ speed. Crossing guards, signals, and traffic jams that lead to delays are most likely to be encountered at the beginning and end of school and during lunch periods. Again, the _____ of day and the _____ of the week are very important.

reduced

time
day

ALTERNATE ROUTES

You should know several alternate routes to the emergency scene. Be sure to mark trouble spots on your maps. Keep in mind the _____ of the week and the _____ of day; note the effects of the weather, construction that may cause _____, and possible delays at _____ crossings, bridges and tunnels, and _____.

day
time
detours, railroad
schools

ARRIVING ON THE SCENE

FACTORS IN POSITIONING THE AMBULANCE

Three factors—the traffic, the roadway, and known hazards—affect the positioning of the ambulance at the emergency scene.

THE TRAFFIC. The traffic, the _____ , and known _____ can affect the positioning of the ambulance at the emergency scene. The effects from traffic may be unlimited. Remember, you will have to respond to emergencies that occur on 2 and 4 lane roads, at intersections, on 6 and 8 lane superhighways, on limited access roads, tunnels, crossovers, and cloverleafs.

roadway
hazards

THE ROADWAY. The roadway, the _____ , and known _____ can all be factors in the positioning of the ambulance at the emergency scene. If the ambulance must be positioned just off the roadway, or even more dangerously on the roadway, consider the type of road and the traffic conditions. Utilize the vehicle's warning lights, lock the brakes, and chock the wheels. Park between the wreckage and oncoming traffic (most officials favor this, but not all). The ambulance should be parked at least 50 feet from the involved vehicles.

traffic
hazards

Should you have to park the ambulance on the roadway, park between the _____ and _____ traffic, at least _____ feet from the involved vehicles. Use the warning lights, _____ the brakes, and _____ the wheels.

wreckage, oncoming, 50
lock
chock

CAUTION: Turn off the headlamps if the ambulance must be positioned facing oncoming traffic.

KNOWN HAZARDS. Known hazards, _____ , and the _____ all affect the positioning of an ambulance at the emergency scene. You must depend on the dispatcher, your own knowledge of emergency situations, and your own observations to determine what hazards are present at the emergency scene. Take particular note of damaged power and

traffic
roadway

utility poles and any downed wires. Depend on the _____, your own knowledge, and your own _____.

    Create a "danger zone" around damaged utility poles and downed or loose wires. Park beyond the reach of all wires and beyond each intact pole with dangling wires for a full span. Be sure that you are off to the side by a distance beyond that which the severed wires can reach.

    Do not attempt to remove any downed wires unless you have the special equipment needed and the training to use this equipment. You should create a "danger zone" and park outside of this _____ _____. Park beyond the reach of all downed and loose wires and beyond each _____ pole for a _____ _____. Be sure to park off to the side beyond the distance that can be reached by any _____ wires.

    Fire, threat of fire, leaking chemicals and fuels, and the possibility of explosion can all affect the positioning of the ambulance. Park no closer than 100 feet from burning vehicles at the scene of an accident that does not have leaking fuel or the possibility of explosions. This is in contrast to the recommended _____ feet for wreckage that is not on fire and is not leaking fuel.

    The presence of dangerous chemicals and explosives requires placing the ambulance at least 2000 feet from the involvement. Only _____ feet is required from burning vehicles when there are no dangerous chemicals or explosive.

    Avoid parking downhill or along the lines of flow from ruptured fuel tanks. If there are any dangerous chemicals at the scene, park upwind.

    The ambulance should be parked at least _____ feet from any involvement with explosives and dangerous chemicals. If there are fuel leaks, never park _____, and always park _____ and uphill from chemical leaks.

Margin answers:

dispatcher
observations

danger zone

intact, full span
severed

50

100

2000

downhill, upwind

TERMINOLOGY

Define the following terms. Check your definitions with those in the Glossary of your textbook or as directed.

Central dispatch *(p. 540)*—

Danger zone—

Defensive driving—

Hydroplaning—

Stopping distance *(p. 540)*—

MULTIPLE CHOICE

Circle the letter of the best answer for each question. The answers are given at the end of the chapter. Note that page references to *Emergency Care, 5th ed.*, are given.

1. The telephone number 911 is (*pp. 538-539*):
   A. A number used in the two-dispatch-center system
   B. An example of one-number calling
   C. The universal emergency number
   D. The number used for cross-communications access

2. The first thing a dispatcher should do when answering a call is to (*p. 540*):
   A. Ask, "Do you have an emergency?"
   B. Request the caller's name
   C. Identify the location of the caller
   D. Request the location of the caller

3. If there is an emergency, the next step is for the dispatcher to ask for (*p. 540*):
   A. Patient's name and age
   B. Patient's exact location
   C. Caller's name and call back number
   D. The nature of the emergency

4. The dispatcher should find out, as the next bit of information (*p. 540*):
   A. The location of the emergency
   B. The name of the caller
   C. The name of the sick or injured person
   D. The nature of the emergency

5. There is an emergency, the exact location and nature of which is known. The dispatcher must now find out the (*p. 540*):
   A. Patient's exact location
   B. Name and age of patient
   C. Caller's name
   D. Caller's telephone number

6. The dispatcher relays the following, "Ambulance Company 10, an emergency for a 50-year old female with acute shortness of breath. Respond to house at 7715 North Warren Street, Fulton Corners." What additional information do you need in order to make your run? (*p. 541*)
   A. The patient's name
   B. The caller's phone number
   C. The cross street
   D. The caller's name

7. You are responding to the scene of a traffic accident. Along with the standard bits of information, the dispatcher has told you the exact location of the accident, how many and what kinds of vehicles were involved, and how many people were injured and how seriously. You still need to know (*pp. 540-541*):
   A. The caller's location
   B. Specifics on each injury
   C. Any apparent hazards
   D. The time of the accident

8. When driving an ambulance, realize that there are NO state laws that grant the (*p. 542*):
   A. Use of controlled additional speed
   B. Safe passage through traffic signals
   C. Privilege of special parking at the scene
   D. Absolute right of way

9. Along with physical and mental capabilities, ambulance drivers should be noted for their (*p. 542*):
   A. Ability to move other vehicles off the roadway
   B. Cooperative attitude
   C. Ability to always be "up" for a run
   D. Justified feelings of superiority

10. To estimate the stopping distance, add the number of feet vehicle travels from start of actual braking until vehicle stops to (*p. 549*):
    A. The number of feet vehicle travels from the time driver decides to stop until his foot applies pressure to the pedal.
    B. The number of feet vehicle travels between lifting foot from accelerator and depressing brake pedal.
    C. The number of feet vehicle travels from driver's decision to stop until brakes actually lock.
    D. The number of feet vehicle travels from the moment driver's foot is above the brake pedal until pressure is applied to the pedal.

11. Stopping distance is defined as _____ distance plus the braking distance (*p. 549*):
    A. Reaction
    B. Nonacceleration
    C. Coasting
    D. Decision

12. When braking on ice (*p. 545*):
    A. Jam the brakes
    B. Brake with your left foot
    C. Don't brake, steer out of trouble
    D. Pump the brakes

13. When back-end skidding on a wet surface (*p. 544*):
    A. Turn in the direction opposite the skid
    B. Don't steer, just pump your brakes
    C. Turn in the direction of the skid
    D. Steer and accelerate

14. You can avoid an accident with the vehicle ahead by (p. 550):
    A. Quick passing
    B. Following at a safe distance
    C. Approaching closely and hitting your horn
    D. Flipping on your high beams

15. You can avoid an accident with a vehicle behind the ambulance by properly using your directional signals and by (p. 551):
    A. Accelerating
    B. Passing the car ahead
    C. Braking smoothly
    D. Pulling off the roadway

16. On left-hand curves, (p. 551):
    A. Oncoming traffic will drift into your path
    B. The ambulance may drift into oncoming traffic
    C. Avoid drift by accelerating into the curve
    D. Always apply firm braking action

17. One-third of all traffic accidents occur (p. 551):
    A. At intersections
    B. When passing
    C. With the vehicle ahead
    D. With the vehicle behind

18. The best technique to shorten braking distance is to (p. 549):
    A. Brake with your left foot
    B. Turn while braking
    C. Turn while pumping your brakes
    D. Reduce speed

19. For every 10 miles per hour of ambulance speed, you should allow _____ vehicle lengths between the ambulance and the car ahead (p. 550):
    A. 1/2
    B. 5
    C. 1
    D. 10

20. Your ambulance and another responding ambulance both reach an intersection at the same time. You are approaching from the south and they are approaching from the east. There is no traffic signal. Which ambulance has the right of way? (p. 551)
    A. The other ambulance
    B. Your ambulance

21. Most accidents involving an ambulance returning to quarters are between the ambulance and a vehicle that is (p. 552):
    A. Coming in the opposite direction
    B. Directly behind
    C. Directly ahead
    D. Passing

22. Which of the following should be in constant use when responding and transporting patients? (p. 543)
    A. Warning lights
    B. Horn
    C. Siren
    D. All of the above

23. When parking on a roadway at the emergency scene, use the ambulance warning lights, lock the brakes and (p. 557):
    A. Always leave the head lamps on
    B. Park at least 100 feet from any accident
    C. Chock the wheels
    D. Turn the wheels to the left

24. Where explosives are involved, park the ambulance at least _____ feet from the burning vehicles. (p. 557)
    A. 50
    B. 100
    C. 1000
    D. 2000

25. If there are ruptured fuel tanks at the emergency scene, always attempt to park the ambulance (p. 555):
    A. Downhill from the scene
    B. Parallel to the scene
    C. Perpendicular to the scene
    D. Uphill from the scene

EXERCISES

To check your answers to the Exercises, refer to *Emergency Care, 5th ed.*

1. List the eight major factors that affect response (p. 553).

2. Describe the physical and mental qualities of a good ambulance driver (p. 542).

3. Describe how to handle hydroplaning (*p. 544*).

4. Describe the danger zone if a utility pole has been damaged (*p. 557*).

5. List nine things you should always do when making a nighttime ambulance run (*pp. 546-547*).

ANSWERS: Multiple Choice

1. B	6. C	11. A	16. A	21. D
2. A	7. C	12. D	17. A	22. A
3. B	8. D	13. C	18. D	23. C
4. D	9. B	14. B	19. C	24. D
5. B	10. A	15. C	20. A	25. D

23 transferring patients to the ambulance

Reading Assignment: Emergency Care, 5th ed., pp. 563-583

BASIC PRINCIPLES OF MOVING PATIENTS

If there is no emergency, the EMT can complete on-the-scene care and transfer the patient to the ambulance stretcher using standard safe and effective methods. All movements are done so as to minimize aggravation to existing injuries and to prevent further injuries. A prime concern is whether or not the patient is in immediate danger. Such situations require the immediate use of special transfer techniques.

A method of transferring a patient should be selected that will minimize aggravation of _____ injuries and _____ further injuries. The EMT should consider whether or not the patient is in immediate danger, if there is a known or suspected spinal injury, if there are injuries to the extremities, and what help is available to move the patient.

existing, prevent

One of the prime factors to consider is whether the patient is in immediate _____. The EMT should be trained to handle patients in hazardous situations, when speed of transfer is important and help is limited.

danger

If a patient is found in a _____ situation, where speed of transfer is important and _____ is limited, the EMT may have to use a one-rescuer carry technique. Since _____ of transfer is important, injuries cannot be stabilized or fractures immobilized.

hazardous
help
speed

Care must be taken not to aggravate _____ injuries. During emergency removal, there is no time to _____ injuries or _____ fractures before the patient is moved. Before determining which method to use, the EMT has to be able to recognize the signs of spinal injury.

existing
stabilize
immobilize

ONE-RESCUER PROCEDURES

The 1-rescuer assist can be used for the slightly injured or confused person. With the person standing, place his arm around your neck and grasp his hand in yours. Put your other arm around his waist and help the person walk to safety.

The 1-rescuer _____ can be used to help persons who are slightly injured or _____. However, this can be a slow process, or the patient may not be able to walk. One-rescuer carries or 1-rescuer drags should then be used.

assist
confused

Should the patient be unable to walk, or if walking will be too _____, 1-rescuer drags or 1-rescuer _____ can be used. For the carries, the EMT must consider the patient's weight, whether there are any neck or _____ injuries, and the state of consciousness of the patient.

slow
carries

spinal

169

The piggyback carry, the front piggyback carry, the cradle carry, the firefighter's carry, and the pack strap carry are all examples of _____ - rescuer carries. To execute any of these carries correctly, the EMT must consider the patient's _____ and the state of _____. The EMT also must consider whether the patient has any _____ or _____ injuries.

The piggyback carry and the _____ piggyback carry both require the patient to be conscious and able to stand. The cradle carry can be used for unconscious patients, provided there are not neck or spinal injuries.

The firefighter's carry and the _____ carry are both useful for unconscious patients. However, neither is recommended for patients with _____ or _____ injuries.

The firefighter's carry requires that the patient be lifted and that the entire weight be carried by the rescuer. This method can aggravate any _____ injuries, particularly those of the _____ and _____. Because of this and the fact that the rescuer will be limited in his own actions due to the weight of the patient, this technique should be used only in dire emergencies.

When confronted with a dire emergency, the EMT can use the _____ carry, even though it may aggravate injuries. Once the EMT begins to use this method, it must be carried out in an unbroken sweep so that he can control the limiting factor of the patient's _____.

In addition to the 1-rescuer assist and the 1-rescuer carries, there are 1-rescuer _____. These drags can be used if the patient is too heavy to lift and carry. Some of these drags are safer to use because they help to prevent aggravation of _____ injuries.

The shoulder drag, the foot drag, the firefighter's drag, the incline drag, the blanket drag, and the clothes drag are all examples of _____ - _____ drags. To employ any of these drags, always pull the patient in the direction of the long axis of his body.

The EMT can select the blanket drag, the clothes drag, the firefighter's drag, the firefighter's carry, or the pack-strap carry. The method used depends on the immediate danger, if there are signs of a _____ injury, and somewhat on the state of consciousness of the patient.

The best protection to the patient's back and extremities is provided by the blanket drag or the clothes drag. During the pull, the patient's head should be as close to the floor as possible and guarded from bumping and other possible causes of injury. Care should be exercised not to close off the patient's airway.

The firefighter's drag can be used to move the patient. Since this method raises the upper part of the patient's body, it may aggravate spinal injuries. If there are known or suspected spinal injuries, the EMT would do better to use the _____ drag or _____ drag.

The pack-strap carry places fewer limitations on the rescuer that may be caused by patient weight. The state of _____ of the patient is significant. This method is very difficult to employ if the patient is unconscious. Since the patient is being lifted, aggravation to spinal injuries is possible, just as in the case of the firefighter's _____ or the firefighter's _____.

If there are spinal injuries, the EMT would do well to avoid the fire-

1

weight, consciousness
neck
spinal
front

cradle

neck, spinal

existing, neck
spine

firefighter's

weight

drags

existing

1
rescuer

spinal

blanket, clothes

consciousness

drag
carry

fighter's carry, the firefighter's drag, and the pack-strap carry. He can use the _____ or _____ drag.

blanket, clothes

TWO-RESCUER TECHNIQUES

Two-rescuer techniques include the 2-rescuer assist, the 2-rescuer seat carry, the 2-rescuer extremities carry, and the chair carry.

The 1-rescuer assist often can prove to be a very _____ process. The 2-rescuer assist does not usually have this problem since both rescuers can lift the patient if conditions worsen and greater speed is required in evacuation.

slow

Emergency 2-rescuer carries are not suitable for moving a patient with known or suspected injuries to the _____. The 2-rescuer seat and the 2-rescuer extremities carry are prime examples of such emergency carries.

spine

The 2-rescuer _____ carry has an advantage over the 2-rescuer seat carry in that it allows for transfer through narrow spaces.

extremities

THREE-RESCUER TECHNIQUES

Three-rescuer techniques employ 1 rescuer at the patient's head, 1 rescuer at the patient's midsection, and 1 rescuer at the patient's feet.

The 3-rescuer hammock carry and the 3-rescuer carry each have 1 rescuer at the patient's _____, _____, and _____. The 3-rescuer carry positions all 3 rescuers on the same side of the patient, whereas the 3-rescuer _____ carry places the head-end rescuer and the foot-end rescuer on the same side and the _____ rescuer on the opposite side of the patient.

head, midsection, feet

hammock
midsection

If no drag or carry is suitable, learn to improvise stretchers from coats and poles, blankets and poles, and rope or fire hose.

TRANSFERRING PATIENTS

After disentanglement, the patient can be transferred to the ambulance. This is a 4-step procedure. The EMTs must select the proper patient-carrying device, package the patient, move the patient to the ambulance and finally, load the patient into the ambulance.

The first step in transferring the patient to the ambulance is the selection of the proper _____ - _____ device. Selection should be based upon the nature of the patient's illness or injury and any factors that may impede the transfer. Before the patient is actually carried to the ambulance and loaded for transport, the EMTs must _____ the patient for transfer.

patient-carrying

package

SELECTION OF PATIENT-CARRYING DEVICES

Without Spinal Injury

Before transferring the patient, the EMTs must consider the nature of the patient's illness or injury and any factors that may _____ the transfer. Most standard patient-carrying devices can be used to transfer a patient with no spinal injury. When movement is unrestricted, the wheeled ambulance stretcher can be used.

impede

When considering the nature of patient illness or injury, the EMTs must give special consideration to _____ injury. If no such injury is

spinal

172

present or suspected and the transfer is unrestricted, the _____ _____ stretcher should be used. The patient may then be moved to the ambulance, and the wheeled stretcher can be secured to the floor or wall of the ambulance. Should door openings or hallways restrict the use of the wheeled ambulance stretcher, the folding ambulance stretcher can be used.

Once a patient is transferred onto a stretcher, he should be _____ securely into place. If the EMTs cannot use a wheeled ambulance stretcher and have decided to use the _____ ambulance stretcher, they should take care with the movements that bring this stretcher to the vertical position. The folding ambulance stretcher usually does not have the foot rest needed for this maneuver.

Stairs, narrow corridors, and small elevators can hinder transfer of the patient. In place of the wheeled stretcher, the EMTs can use the _____ ambulance stretcher, a folding stair chair, a slat stretcher, or a long spine board with a sturdy foot rest. Any of these devices can be used for a patient without _____ injury. Before transfer to the ambulance, the patient must be securely _____ to the patient-moving device.

When the stretcher must be moved down a ladder or at the end of a rope, the wire basket stretcher, the plastic basket stretcher, or a pole stretcher (Army stretcher, D-ring stretcher) should be used. If a long spine board is to be used, it must have a sturdy _____ _____.

Should transfer take place over obstacles and inclines, pole stretchers and long spine boards may be used, but they are not the devices of choice. The _____ basket or the _____ basket stretchers are selected because they are rigid and offer side protection.

With Spinal Injury

Any patient-carrying device used for a patient with known or suspected spinal injury must be a rigid device, and it must allow for straight-line neck and back immobilization. Care must be taken not to aggravate a spinal injury. The scoop-style stretcher can be employed without moving or lifting the patient.

A long spine board or a slat stretcher can be used to transfer a patient with _____ injuries. However, great care must be taken not to _____ the injury. Movement of the patient to the carrying device is greatly reduced if a _____ - style stretcher is used.

If the patient must be moved down a ladder or by rope, the selection of devices is the same as for the patient without spinal injuries. The EMTs may choose the wire or plastic _____ stretcher, the _____ stretcher, or a _____ spine board with a sturdy _____ _____.

When accident victims with possible spinal injuries are still in a vehicle, spine boards serve as the major patient-carrying device. If the patient is seated, a short spine board or one of the newer modified short spine boards or vests should be used before moving the patient onto the long spine board. The long spine board is used for patients found on the seat or floor of a vehicle.

Whenever possible, displace or remove the car seat so that the patient can be transferred with little or no movement of his body. Use a _____ - style stretcher and then transfer the patient to a long spine board. If this is not possible, a _____ spine board should be used.

Remember, selection of a patient-carrying device is based on the nature

wheeled
ambulance

strapped
folding

folding

spinal
strapped

foot rest

wire, plastic

spinal
aggravate
scoop

basket, pole
long, foot rest

scoop
long

of the patient's _____ or _____ , and any factors that may _____ the transfer.

illness, injury
impede (interfere with)

PACKAGING AND TRANSFERRING PATIENTS

In order to transfer the patient safely and quickly to the ambulance, the patient and the patient-carrying device must be combined into 1 unit. This will prevent aggravation to injury or patient condition. This process of unification is called *packaging*.

If movement is unrestricted, the _____ _____ stretcher may be used. The patient may be transferred from bed-level to this stretcher by the direct carry method or the draw sheet method. Should the patient have spinal injuries, then proper immobilization of the neck and back must be accomplished before the transfer to the stretcher takes place by these methods.

wheeled ambulance

The most popular technique for moving bed-level patients is the _____ carry method. The _____ sheet method is the next most popular, requiring the bottom sheet of the bed to be loosened on all sides and used as a draw sheet to move the patient to the center of the stretcher.

direct, draw

Should the patient be at ground-level or at floor-level, a variation of the direct _____ method can be used. The EMTs need to position the stretcher parallel to the patient rather than the 90° recommended for the direct carry method.

carry

EMTs may transfer a bed-level patient to the _____ ambulance stretcher by 1 of 2 methods: the _____ carry method or the draw _____ method. If the patient is at ground level, a modified _____ _____ method is used. Regardless of method used, the procedures are the same for positioning the patient on the stretcher. The patient is to be positioned on his back (in the _____ position), his head on the stretcher pillow, and his arms across his chest or along his sides.

wheeled
direct
sheet
direct carry

supine

When positioning the patient on a stretcher, his knees should be flexed slightly and the backrest should be slightly elevated. The patient should be in the _____ position with his head on the stretcher _____ and his arms across his _____ or along his sides. The patient should be covered with a sheet and blankets to help maintain body temperature, prevent exposure, and ensure privacy. The side rails are to be locked and the body straps fastened.

supine
pillow, chest

The patient may now be moved by rolling or carrying the wheeled ambulance stretcher. This is done after the _____ _____ are locked and the _____ _____ are fastened.

side rails
body straps
rolled

The wheeled ambulance stretcher may be carried or _____. If it has to be carried, the end carry or the side carry method is to be used. The end carry method should be used for moving the patient over any distance, while the side carry method is normally reserved for loading into the ambulance.

Before the loading into the ambulance, the stretcher should be locked to its lowest level. The _____ carry method is used to lift and position the stretcher. The stretcher and the ambulance doors must be firmly secured and latched.

side

Portable ambulance stretchers also may be used to transfer a patient to the ambulance. As in the case of the wheeled ambulance stretcher, a bed-

174

level patient can be transferred by the _____ carry method or the draw _____ method.

For patients at ground level, the same procedures as for the wheeled ambulance stretcher, the _____ direct carry method can be used. The patient should be covered to help maintain _____ _____ , prevent _____ , and ensure _____. After being covered, the patient should be _____ to the stretcher.

The patient can now be moved by the _____ carry method, or the patient and stretcher can be transferred to a wheeled ambulance stretcher. To load the ambulance when the patient is on a portable ambulance stretcher, the opposite of the wheeled ambulance stretcher procedure is used. That is, the _____ carry method is used, not the _____ carry method that is used for the wheeled ambulance stretcher.

For stairways and narrow or confined spaces, the folding stair chair can be used to transfer a patient. The stair chair should not be used for unconscious patients, disoriented patients, or patients with suspected spinal injuries or lower extremity fractures.

As with wheeled and portable stretchers, the _____ carry method is used to transfer a bed-level patient to a chair. This method has to be modified to bring the patient to a sitting position. The foot end EMT has to slide his arms under the patient's thighs before the patient is moved.

If a patient is unconscious or _____, the stair chair should not be used. This also applies to patients with suspected _____ injuries or fractures to the _____ extremities. The direct carry method is used to transfer a _____ - level patient to the stair chair. When the patient is at ground level, a _____ direct carry method can be used.

The extremity transfer can be used as long as the patient does not have a _____ injury or extremity _____. As with the direct carry method, the patient is transferred in the _____ position. The chair lift method can be used for a patient who is too heavy for the _____ transfer. This technique is used to place the patient in a _____ position and the chair is slid under the patient. The patient is covered and _____ to the chair.

For straight carries using the stair chair, a single waist belt can be used to secure the patient. If the carry is to take place down stairs, the chest, thighs, and lower legs should be secured by straps. For transfer, as with the ambulance stretcher, the stair chair should be _____ whenever possible.

Scoop-style stretchers give rigid support, making them useful for moving a patient with a _____ injury. As with portable stretchers, the _____ carry method is used for transfer to the ambulance. This is done after the patient is _____ and secured to the stretcher.

Since the _____ - style stretcher offers rigid support to the spine, the patient should not be removed from the stretcher. The patient and scoop-stretcher should be secured to the _____ ambulance stretcher for transport.

Basket stretchers can be made of either wire or plastic. The plastic basket stretcher can accommodate the scoop-style stretcher. For the patient with no spinal injury, transfer to a basket stretcher can be done by the _____ carry method, _____ transfer, or the draw

direct
sheet
modified
body
temperature, exposure
privacy, secured
end
end, side
direct
disoriented
spinal, lower
bed
modified
spinal, fracture
sitting
extremity
sitting
secured
rolled
spinal
end
covered
scoop
wheeled
direct, extremity

_____ method. In addition to these methods, the 3-rescuer lift or the blanket lift technique may be used. | sheet

The 3-rescuer lift can be used to transfer a patient to a _____ stretcher. Remember, transferring a patient with _____ injury by this method can be very dangerous for the patient. Application of an extrication collar is recommended before transferring any patient with possible spinal injuries. The 3-rescuer lift requires the patient to be kept as anatomically straight as possible, with a rescuer at the patient's head and back, another rescuer at the patient's lower back and thighs, and the third rescuer at the patient's knees and ankles. | basket
spinal

Patients may be transferred to the ambulance by way of the _____ ambulance stretcher, _____ stretchers, _____ chairs, _____ - style stretchers, or wire or plastic _____ stretchers. | wheeled, portable
stair, scoop
basket

Since the long spine board is often used for patients with _____ injuries, transferring the patient to this device requires careful execution of lifting and moving techniques. The 4-rescuer log roll is recommended for patients found at ground level in the supine position. | spinal

In addition to the 4-rescuer log roll, the 4-rescuer straddle slide can be used for moving a patient with a _____ injury onto a _____ spine board. Three rescuers handle the patient while the fourth rescuer slides the board into place. | spinal, long

TERMINOLOGY

Define the following terms. Check your definitions with those in the Glossary at the end of your textbook, or as directed.

Basket stretcher *(p. 571)*—

Packaging—

MULTIPLE CHOICE

Circle the letter of the correct answer for each question. The answers are at the end of this chapter. Note page references to *Emergency Care, 5th ed.*

1. You wish to transfer a patient without spinal injury. Movement is unrestricted. The patient-carrying device of choice is the *(p. 571)*:
   A. Folding ambulance stretcher
   B. Wire basket stretcher
   C. Wheeled ambulance stretcher
   D. Slat stretcher

2. Which of the following would be best suited for moving a patient without spinal injuries through a narrow hallway? *(p. 571)*
   A. Wheeled ambulance stretcher
   B. Folding ambulance stretcher
   C. Wire basket stretcher
   D. Long spine board

3. You have a patient positioned on a scoop-style stretcher and wish to lower him from a roof top. You should *(p. 571)*:
   A. Place the stretcher and patient in a plastic basket stretcher
   B. Transfer the patient to a spine board
   C. Place the patient in a wire basket stretcher
   D. Lower the patient in the scoop-style stretcher

4. To avoid trauma to an injured spine, the best patient-carrying device would be the *(p. 571)*:
   A. Long spine board
   B. Wheeled ambulance stretcher
   C. Wire basket stretcher
   D. Portable ambulance stretcher

5. The most commonly used method for transferring a bed-level patient to a wheeled ambulance stretcher is the *(pp. 573, 574)*:
   A. Draw sheet method
   B. Side carry method

C. Direct carry method
D. Slide transfer method

6. Which of the following procedures is used to load the wheeled ambulance stretcher onto the ambulance? *(p. 576)*
   A. Direct carry
   B. Side carry
   C. Modified direct carry
   D. End carry

7. The final steps in packaging a patient on a wheeled ambulance stretcher are *(p. 573)*:
   A. Locking side rails and fastening body straps
   B. Placing a towel under the patient's head and drawing it over his chest
   C. Covering the patient with a top sheet and then a blanket
   D. Covering the patient with a top sheet and then 2 blankets

8. The most common practice used for carrying a wheeled ambulance stretcher is the *(p. 573)*:
   A. Direct carry
   B. Slide transfer
   C. Side carry
   D. End carry

9. A patient without fractures or spinal injuries must be moved from the floor to a stair chair. The technique used is the *(p. 573)*:
   A. Direct carry
   B. Extremity transfer
   C. Slide transfer
   D. Chair lift

10. A stair chair is best carried with 1 rescuer *(p. 577)*:
    A. On each side
    B. Gripping the top and 1 rescuer gripping the chair legs
    C. Gripping the top and 1 rescuer on each side
    D. Gripping the chair legs and 1 rescuer on each side

11. For moving a patient on a stair chair over rough ground, secure the patient with straps positioned *(pp. 573, 577)*:
    A. Only at the waist
    B. At the chest and waist
    C. At the chest, thighs, and lower legs
    D. At the chest and thighs

12. A patient without a spinal injury has been correctly positioned on a scoop style stretcher. The best method for transporting this patient would be *(p. 578)*:
    A. With the patient removed from the scoop-style stretcher and transferred to a long spine board
    B. With the patient transferred to the ambulance stretcher and the scoop-style stretcher then removed
    C. With the patient and the scoop-style stretcher transferred as a package to the ambulance stretcher
    D. Any of the above would be acceptable.

13. A victim with an obvious spinal injury is found on the floor of a burning building. The EMT rates the situation hazardous, but not yet dire. Being alone and without special equipment, the EMT should use the *(pp. 566-567)*:
    A. Cradle carry
    B. Clothes drag
    C. Firefighter's carry
    D. Pack-strap method

14. Which of the following carries must be performed in one unbroken sweep? *(p. 567)*
    A. Pack-strap carry
    B. Front piggyback carry
    C. Firefighter's carry
    D. Four-rescuer log roll

15. An EMT finds a patient in a burning building. He rates the situation as a dire emergency. The EMT should *(p. 566)*:
    A. Use the firefighter's carry
    B. Check respiration
    C. Use the firefighter's drag
    D. Check for spinal injuries

16. Which of the following is a two-rescuer carry that can be used to move a patient through a narrow space? *(p. 569)*
    A. Hammock carry
    B. Traction-blanket lift
    C. Extremities carry
    D. Seat carry

17. Which of the following is considered very difficult to use with an unconscious person? *(p. 566)*
    A. Cradle carry
    B. Three-rescuer carry
    C. Shoulder drag
    D. Piggyback carry

EXERCISES

To check your answers to the Exercises, refer to the textbook.

1. Describe transferring a bed-level patient without spinal injuries to a wheeled ambulance stretcher by the direct carry method *(p. 574)*.

2. Describe using the draw sheet method to transfer a bed-level patient without spinal injuries to a wheeled ambulance stretcher *(p. 575)*.

3. Describe how you would transfer a ground-level patient without spinal injuries to a wheeled ambulance stretcher *(p. 575)*.

4. List the steps involved in the 3-rescuer carry *(p. 569)*.

5. Describe 1 method in which guide ropes can be used to help carry a basket stretcher *(pp. 580-581)*.

6. Describe the basic procedure for the six-rescuer shift *(p. 581)*.

ANSWERS: Multiple Choice

1.	C	7.	A	13.	B
2.	B	8.	D	14.	C
3.	A	9.	B	15.	A
4.	A	10.	B	16.	C
5.	B	11.	C	17.	D
6.	B	12.	C		

24 transporting the patient to the hospital

Reading Assignment: Emergency Care, 5th ed., pp. 585-593

TRANSPORT

Transport takes place after the completion of any necessary disentaglement and the proper _____ of the patient to the ambulance. Transport is more than the simple moving of the patient from the scene to the hospital. Emergency care activities are carried out before the ambulance moves, while en route to the hospital, and on arrival at the hospital.

| transfer |

Emergency care procedures occur while en route and on arrival at the hospital or medical facility. However, the EMT should not neglect certain activities that occur before the _____ _____. The EMT should make certain that the cot is secured in place, checking both forward and rear positive locking devices.

| ambulance moves |

Once the cot is secured by both _____ and _____ positive locking devices, the EMT should properly position the patient. The patient should be positioned according to the nature of illness or injury.

| forward, rear |

The position of the patient, once the cot has been secured by _____ _____ devices, depends on the nature of his _____ or _____. To promote an open airway and to allow for the proper drainage of fluids, some unconscious patients are best moved into a lateral recumbent position.

| positive locking |
| illness, injury |

Some unconscious patients should be placed in the _____ position to promote an _____ _____ and allow for the proper _____ of fluids. Take special care with security straps to allow for the safe transport of a patient in the lateral recumbent position.

| lateral |
| open airway |
| drainage |

For patients with heart problems or difficulty in breathing, transport in a position that allows the patient to breathe freely. If you believe the patient might be a candidate for cardiac arrest, position a short spine board between him and the ambulance cot.

The positioning of a patient for transport depends on the nature of his _____ or _____. For heart and respiratory problems, transport in a position that allows the patient to _____ freely. If there is a possibility that the patient will go into cardiac arrest, place a _____ _____ board between the patient and the _____.

| illness, injury |
| breathe |
| short spine, cot |

When an unconscious patient is placed into the _____ position, be sure to take special care with the _____ _____ to allow for safe transport. For all patients, adjust the straps for safety, making certain that these constricting straps do not interfere with respiration or circulation, or cause pain. Take care that these straps do not bind over an injury site. While checking straps, loosen any constricting clothing.

| lateral |
| security straps |

180

After properly securing the cot, positioning the patient, adjusting the security straps, and _____ constricting clothing on the patient, the EMT should turn his attention directly to the patient. The patient's airway should be checked, all bandages and splints should be checked, and vital signs should be taken and recorded.

loosening

The EMT should check the patient's breathing and make sure that there is an open _____. If the patient has been moved into the lateral recumbent position because he is _____, make certain that he has adequate air exchange.

airway
unconscious

After checking the airway, the EMT should check all _____ and _____ to be sure they are not too loose or too tight. Once this is done, the EMT should determine and record the patient's _____ _____.

bandages, splints

Once the patient is on board the ambulance, vital signs should be determined. These signs include blood pressure, pulse rate, and respiratory rate. Vital signs should not only be determined, they should also be _____.

vital signs

recorded

The EMT should take and record vital signs, including pulse rate, _____ rate and _____ _____. As soon as this task is completed, the EMT should determine if a relative or friend of the patient should be transported along with the patient. The EMT should also make sure that all of the patient's personal effects which are at the scene are, when possible, loaded into the ambulance.

respiratory, blood pressure

It is often beneficial to transport a _____ or _____ of the patient as you take the patient to a medical facility. Be certain that this companion is emotionally stable and will not interfere with patient care activities. Many patients will be very concerned about their personal effects. Be sure these items, if possible, are transported along with the patient.

friend, relative

Many patients become more apprehensive once they are loaded into an ambulance. If possible, transport the patient along with a friend or relative and attempt to carry along the patient's _____ effects. Take time to reassure the patient. Talk to the patient, touch him, offer a toy to a frightened child. Make certain the patient is ready for transport before signaling the driver to begin the trip to the hospital.

personal

EN ROUTE TO THE HOSPITAL

The trip to the hospital should not begin until _____ are sure that the patient is ready for transport. While en route, continue life support measures, gather patient information, continue to monitor and record vital signs, and check splints and bandages.

you

Emergency care does not stop during transport. Continue all _____ _____ measures and tend to all the needs of the patient. Continue to monitor and record _____ _____, collect vomitus, and check to see if _____ and _____ have become too tight or too loose.

life support
vital signs
splints, bandages

Continue to reassure the patient. If emergency care activities will not be compromised, gather patient _____. An EMT should remember to control his emotions at all times. Reassuring conversation by a professional will be beneficial to the patient.

information

If cardiac arrest occurs, have the driver stop the ambulance while you initiate CPR. The CPR effort will not be effective unless there is a short

_____ _____ placed between the patient and the cot, and the patient has been properly positioned for CPR chest compressions. Signal the driver to continue transport while you continue CPR.   **spine board**

In cases where cardiac arrest develops, the EMT should signal the driver to _____ the ambulance so that _____ can be initiated. For any changing patient condition, the EMT should advise the driver so that the driving technique and the route can be adjusted for maximum patient benefit.   **stop, CPR**

While en route to the hospital, the EMT should radio ahead information about the patient and the incident. The radio message should be brief and complete. This message will have 8 essential elements.

All radio communications between the ambulance and the _____ should be complete and _____. The message should begin with the hospital identification and the ambulance or rescue unit identification. Next, a brief description of the situation should be radioed ahead.   **hospital, brief**

The radio message to the hospital begins with two identifications: first, the _____ identification and then the _____ or _____ _____ identification. Next, the situation is described. Remember, both patient information and information about the _____ are needed by the hospital staff.   **hospital, ambulance rescue unit** **incident**

After a brief description of the _____, the message should include a review of the subjective examination and the objective examination. The subjective examination review should provide the patient's _____, his _____, primary _____, medical history, known allergies, and other relevant information.   **situation** **name, age, complaint**

A review of the objective examination is given after the _____ findings. Assess the patient's overall condition, provide _____ signs and any positive findings from your observations. Once this is done, you should inform the emergency department staff of the patient's suspected illness or injury and indicate the emergency care plan.   **subjective** **vital**

The staff at the hospital needs to know of any _____ illness or injury and the _____ _____ plan for the patient. This is transmitted after the review of the _____ examination.   **suspected** **emergency care** **objective**

The last of the _____ essential elements of two-way radio contact with the hospital is to give your estimated time of arrival (ETA). After these eight elements are covered, you are ready to receive hospital advice. Continue to transmit patient information if necessary and to obtain advice from the hospital staff. Always continue to monitor and record _____ _____ and inform the hospital staff and the _____ of changing conditions.   **eight** **vital signs** **driver**

ON ARRIVAL AT THE HOSPITAL

EMTs are responsible for the orderly transfer of the patient to the care of the emergency department staff. This transfer is called the handoff. It has five steps: two are concerned with patient care activities, and three are accomplished after the EMTs are free from patient care activities.

The orderly transfer of the patient to the hospital emergency department staff is a _____ -step procedure called the _____. The first   **five, handoff**

two steps are of primary concern since they deal with the continuation of
_____ _____ activities. | patient care

The first step of the handoff may vary depending upon the situation. For the non-emergency patient, first check to see what is to be done with the patient. Then decide if off-loading is to be immediate or delayed. In an emergency situation, off-load the patient and wheel him to the designated area. Continue emergency care procedures until someone from the emergency department can assume responsibility. *Do not* transfer the patient from the ambulance cot until directed to do so.

Off-load the patient and wheel him to the designated area if the situation is an _____ . In the non-emergency situation, first | emergency
check to see what is to be done with the patient. Never abandon a patient. Continue emergency care activities until someone from the emergency department can assume _____ . | responsibility

After _____ - _____ the patient, the second step of the | off-loading
handoff is for the EMTs to assist the emergency department staff as required and according to local policy. When the emergency department staff has taken over completely, the EMTs should remain in the area of patient care in case they can be of assistance.

Even when the responsibility for the patient care has been transferred over to the emergency department staff, the EMTs should remain to _____ the emergency department staff. | assist

After the EMTs are free from _____ _____ activities, they | patient care
are still not finished with patient transfer. They should transfer not only the patient, but also the patient _____ and his personal | information
_____ . The transfer is complete once the EMTs have obtained a | effects
release from the hospital.

MULTIPLE CHOICE

Circle the letter of the best answer for each question. The answers are given at the end of this chapter. Note page references to *Emergency Care, 5th ed.*

1. Once the patient has been loaded into the ambulance, the EMT should first *(p. 586):*
   A. Position the patient
   B. Secure the cot
   C. Take vital signs
   D. Check the patient's airway

2. Some unconscious patients should be transported in the _____ position *(p. 586).*
   A. Supine
   B. Semi-erect
   C. Lateral recumbent
   D. Prone

3. When the patient has been loaded into the ambulance, three vital signs are always taken. Which of the following vital signs is NOT taken in every case? *(p. 587):*
   A. Temperature
   B. Blood pressure
   C. Pulse rate
   D. Respiratory rate

4. If cardiac arrest occurs during transport, the EMT's first step is to *(p. 589):*
   A. Request the driver to stop the ambulance
   B. Radio the hospital
   C. Initiate CPR
   D. Insert an airway

5. When a radio message is sent to the hospital, the correct order of essential elements is *(pp. 589-590):*
   A. Ambulance identification, description of the situation, subjective findings, objective findings.
   B. Hospital identification, ambulance identification, objective findings, subjective findings.
   C. Ambulance identification, description of situation, objective findings, subjective findings.
   D. Hospital identification, ambulance identification, description of the situation, subjective findings.

6. After transmitting your objective review you should transmit (p. 590):
   A. Suspected illnesses and injuries
   B. Emergency care plan
   C. Subjective review
   D. Estimated time of arrival

7. The last essential element of your radio transmission should be (p. 590):
   A. Emergency care plan
   B. Objective review
   C. Estimated time of arrival
   D. Suspected diagnosis

8. For the handoff of a non-emergency patient, (pp. 591-593):
   A. Off-load, wheel to the designated area and stay with patient
   B. Check to see what is to be done with the patient
   C. Off-load, wheel to the designated area and leave the patient
   D. Wait for the emergency staff to call for the patient

9. The last step of the handoff is (p. 593):
   A. Transfer personal effects
   B. Transfer patient information
   C. Wait to help the emergency staff
   D. Obtain your release

EXERCISES

To check your answers to the Exercises, refer to *Emergency Care, 5th ed.*

1. Write out a hypothetical en route radio transmission. Be sure that you include all eight essential elements and that they are in the correct order (pp. 590-591).

2. Describe all the essential steps in the handoff of an emergency situation patient (pp. 591-593):

3. What factors would you use to decide if a relative or friend of the patient should be transported along with the patient? (p. 587)

4. List the tasks you must perform before the ambulance moves to transport a patient (pp. 586-589).

ANSWERS: Multiple Choice

1. B	6. A
2. C	7. C
3. A	8. B
4. A	9. D
5. D	

25 terminating the run

Reading Assignment: Emergency Care, 5th ed., pp. 595–601

TERMINATION OF ACTIVITIES

The termination of activities begins while at the hospital, continues en route to quarters, and is completed when in quarters. All these activities are directed toward making the ambulance ready for another call.

While at the hospital, the procedures started for termination of activities are directed toward making ready for another _____ prior to the return to quarters. **call**

So that the ambulance could respond prior to returning to quarters, seven activities can be carried out while at the _____. First, whatever cleaning is required for the ambulance interior, including deodorizing, can be done. Interior equipment must also be wiped down. During this cleaning, _____ gloves should be worn to protect against _____ _____. **hospital**

latex, infectious disease

After cleaning and _____ the ambulance interior, the EMTs should turn their attention to equipment. They should replace respiratory equipment as required, replace expendable items, and exchange equipment according to local policies. **deodorizing**

In addition to replacing expendable items and exchanging equipment in accordance with _____ policies, the EMTs should replace _____ equipment as required. Since cross-infection is possible with respiratory assist and inhalation therapy devices, all nondisposable items must be bagged to be thoroughly cleaned in quarters. **local**

respiratory

If local policies permit, equipment can be _____ at the hospital. Be certain to check this equipment for both completeness and operability. **exchanged**

The making up of the ambulance stretcher should be done while at the hospital. You should carry out your local standard operating procedures. These procedures should include care of both the linens and the stretcher mattress and blankets. All linen and blankets should be folded or tucked so that they are contained within the stretcher frame.

When the _____ is made up, the EMTs should replace the cot in the ambulance. Finally, the EMTs should check for any equipment left in the hospital and check once again to be sure that appropriate nondisposables have been _____ and all _____ items have been replaced. **stretcher**

exchanged, expendable

EN ROUTE TO QUARTERS

A safe return is essential to any ambulance run. As noted in Chapter 22, ambulance accidents often occur en route to quarters, with cars attempting

185

to _____ the ambulance. Always practice _____ driving | pass, defensive
techniques. When leaving the hospital, report your status. While en route,
air the ambulance and also buy gas if necessary according to local policies.
Remember, report your _____ as you leave the hospital. | status

IN QUARTERS

The final procedure for the _____ of activities in- | termination
volves completion of cleaning and disinfecting activities. The first part of
the in-quarters activities involves disposal, cleaning, and sanitizing. Dispose
of dirty linen, being sure to use a sealable container for contaminated linen.
Remove and clean all patient care equipment as required. Remember, the
final procedure for the termination activities involves both cleaning and | disinfecting
_____ activities.

After disposing of dirty _____ , remove and clean _____ | linen, patient
_____ equipment as required. Any nondisposable respiratory equipment | care
should be cleaned and sanitized as required. Next, clean and sanitize the
ambulance interior as required.

Disposal, cleaning, and sanitizing are followed by replacing and replen-
ishing. Replace expendable items, replace patient care equipment, and replenish oxygen and air in their proper cylinders so that the ambulance
carries only full cylinders.

All nondisposable _____ equipment should be cleaned | respiratory
and _____ as required. The EMTs should complete the cleaning | sanitized
procedures they started at the hospital by cleaning and _____ | sanitizing
the _____ of the ambulance. Disposal, cleaning, and sanitizing are | interior
then followed by replacing _____ items and patient care | expendable
equipment. The EMTs should replenish all _____ and | oxygen
_____ cylinders. | air

Maintenance and cleaning of the ambulance exterior should be done after each call, in accordance with local policies. All reports should be finished
and the EMTs should ready themselves to be clean and professional looking
for the next run.

TERMINOLOGY

Define the following terms. Check your definitions
with those in the Glossary at the end of your textbook.

Disinfect—

Sanitize—

MATCHING

Match the following locations to the tasks listed below, putting the correct letter before each activity.

A. At the hospital
B. En route to quarters
C. In quarters
_____ 1. Dispose of dirty linens
_____ 2. Finish report forms
_____ 3. Exchange equipment
_____ 4. Air the ambulance
_____ 5. Replace respiratory equipment
_____ 6. Make up the ambulance stretcher
_____ 7. Clean and sanitize respiratory equipment
_____ 8. Replenish fuel supply

EXERCISE

After practicing the skills involved, make up a
step-by-step list of the local procedures for making
up an ambulance stretcher. Check your answer
with your own local procedures and pp. 596 and
598 in *Emergency Care, 5th ed.*

ANSWERS: Matching

1. C 2. C 3. A 4. B 5. A 6. A 7. C 8. B

26 communications and reports

Reading Assignment: Emergency Care, 5th ed., pp. 603–611 and 589–591

COMMUNICATION

Communication means more than radio transmissions. As an EMT, you must be able to use proper oral communication techniques when talking with patients, bystanders, and other members of the EMS System.

As an EMT, you must develop the written skills that apply to your duties. These written skills, along with the proper _____ communication techniques, will allow you to communicate with _____, _____, and other members of the EMS System.

You must be able to speak clearly and calmly, using the correct terminology to allow for effective _____ _____. Since your written reports are very important, make certain they are complete, accurate, and the correct terminology has been used.

Proper _____ and _____ communications require the EMT to use correct _____.

	oral
	patients, bystanders
	oral communications
	oral, written
	terminology

RADIO COMMUNICATIONS

The basic communications system consists of the dispatcher base station, the ambulance transmitter/receiver, the emergency department remote center, and telephone backup.

While in the ambulance, the EMTs can use the ambulance _____ / _____ for emergency communications. They can send and receive messages at the scene even when they are away from the ambulance if they have portable transmitter/receivers. These units require an ambulance repeater station to retransmit between the _____ transmitter/receiver and the portable transmitter/receiver.

When the crew is in the ambulance, they can send and receive radio messages by way of the ambulance transmitter/receiver. They can use portable units if the ambulance has a _____ station. They may have expanded capabilities if they can send biotelemetry to the emergency department _____ _____, or if they have _____ line backup. Telephone patches can be done via the dispatcher _____ _____ to allow radio communications to be connected with telephones.

Radio communications should be limited to official use. They should be as brief and as accurate as possible.

Do not interrupt transmissions from the dispatcher or from other members of the EMS System. Remember to limit radio communications to

transmitter/receiver
ambulance
repeater
remote center, telephone
base
station

_____ use. Know what you are going to say before you go on the air so that your transmission will be as _____ and as _____ as possible.	official brief, accurate

REPORTS

Reports are a form of official communication. They can be written or _____. Remember that your written report becomes part of the patient's medical record.	oral
Written reports must be complete, accurate, and contain the correct _____. They become part of the patient's official _____ _____. They help keep track of patient information, serve as a way to provide this information to the staff of the emergency department, and supply information on personnel and equipment usage.	terminology, medical records
The patient _____in your written report becomes part of the _____ medical record. The EMTs written report can be used to supply information on _____ and _____ usage.	information patient's personnel equipment

TERMINOLOGY

Define the following terms. Check your definitions as directed.

Ambulance repeater station *(p. 604)*—

Base communication station *(p. 604)*—

Communications *(p. 604)*—

EXERCISES

To check your answers to the Exercises, refer to *Emergency Care, 5th ed.*

1. List 4 ways to improve your oral communications skills *(p. 604)*.

2. An EMT at the scene is away from the ambulance. What communications equipment must be on hand to allow him to communicate with the dispatcher? *(p. 604)*

3. List 10 rules to follow when using the radio for official communications *(p. 605)*.

4. When is it proper to use codes in an official radio communication? *(p. 605)*

5. List 4 duties performed by an EMT that usually require a written report *(p. 607)*.

6. List at least 10 pieces of information that should be obtainable by someone reading your official report of an ambulance run *(p. 607)*.

27 vehicle rescue

Reading Assignment: Emergency Care, 5th ed., pp. 613–624

THE VEHICLE RESCUE OPERATION

At the scene of accidents and disasters, you may be faced with the problem of gaining access to the patients. This is often true in vehicle rescue operations. Emergency care and rescue activities take precedence over all other operations. However, these activities cannot be carried out unless you can safely reach and care for the patient. Always assess the scene so that you will know what is needed and what is present.

If a seriously injured person can reach a trauma center so that advanced care can be started within an hour of the injury, that person's chances of surviving are reasonably good. This first hour after the injury is called the Golden Hour. For victims who are trapped in a motor vehicle, your skills in extricating them swiftly and safely could make the difference in determining whether or not they reach a trauma center within the _____ _____.

golden hour

Before gaining _____ to the patients, assessment and hazard control are needed. You may be called upon to assess the situation to determine what resources are needed and what resources are present at the scene. Hazard control and _____ may have to be done before gaining access to the patient. The assessment involves finding out what is _____ and what is _____ at the scene.

access

assessment

needed, present

During the assessment, you should consider the number and types of vehicles involved, the mechanisms of entrapment, the number of people injured, the extent of their injuries, and the hazards present at the scene. The assessment matches what has to be done to the on-scene capabilities. The EMT should then call for help as required.

There are times when you will need to call for additional _____. You must know about community resources and how to bring them quickly to your aid.

help

In assessing the situation, be certain that you have located all the victims. Realize that injured people may walk or be led away from the accident scene. Talking to occupants and witnesses and looking over the contents of the vehicles may help you figure out how many _____ were in the vehicle.

victims

SECTION ONE: EQUIPMENT FOR VEHICLE RESCUE

Protective gear should be worn during vehicle rescue operations. There are many ways that an EMT can be injured during a vehicle rescue operation. Potential dangers include broken glass and metal debris, unstable vehicles, smoke, toxic gases, flames, and the elements. Human factors can also increase the possibility of injury. These include unfamiliarity with rescue procedures and tools, and unsafe actions. But the unsafe act that contributes most to EMT accident scene injuries is the failure to wear _____ gear during rescue operations.

protective

During rescue operations, the following equipment is recommended to protect the EMT from injury: to protect the head, a rescue _____ or construction hard hat; to protect the eyes, _____ goggles or glasses; to protect the trunk, a turnout coat; to protect the hands, leather _____, to protect the legs, turnout pants or fire-resistant trousers or coveralls; and to protect the feet, high-top shoes or boots. Also useful on icy road surfaces are ice _____.

helmet
safety

gloves

cleats

For rescue operations in oxygen-deficient or toxic atmosphere, self-contained _____ apparatus is needed. When it is necessary to work near active traffic lanes, flourescent and _____ vests make the EMT highly visible.

breathing
reflective

EMS personnel must also consider the danger of infectious disease. Three additional items of equipment are needed to protect the EMT from exposure to a victim's blood or body fluids. To protect the hands, medical grade _____ gloves are used. In situations where blood or body fluids might be splashed in the eyes, nose, or mouth, a medical grade face _____ is needed. Finally, midweight plastic or rubber gloves should be used for non-patient care tasks that involve handling items contaminated with a victim's _____ or body _____.

latex

mask

blood, fluids

During rescue operations, equipment is also needed to protect entrapped patients from further _____. To shield patients from fire, cold, or rain and to provide limited protection from glass and metal particles, an aluminized rescue _____ can be used. Where there is no danger of fire, a lightweight vinyl-coated paper tarpaulin might be used to protect victims from the elements or debris. Wool blankets will also protect patients from the cold, but should not be used to protect the patients from _____ or metal particles. This protection is best provided by an _____ rescue blanket.

injury

blanket

glass
aluminized

TERMINOLOGY

Define the following term. Check your definition with the one given in the Glossary of your textbook.

Extrication—

EXERCISES

1. List the 12 phases of a vehicle rescue operation (pp. 614–615).

2. Describe the protection gear to be worn by an EMT at a vehicle accident scene (pp. 616–619).

3. List nine hazard management procedures that an EMT should be able to carry out. (p. 623).

4. List six disentanglement procedures that an EMT should be able to carry out. (p. 623).

Reading Assignment: Emergency Care, 5th ed., pp. 624–638

SECTION TWO: MANAGING ACCIDENT-RELATED HAZARDS

WARNING: Do only what you have been trained to do. Make certain that you have all the necessary equipment and personnel.

TRAFFIC AND NONTRAFFIC HAZARDS

After assessment activities are completed, you reach the _____ _____ phase. You may have to deal with traffic, downed wires, fire, and unstable vehicles. Remember, _____ _____ and _____ activities take precedence over all other operations. However, to perform these activities you must be able to safely gain access to the victims. | hazard
control
emergency care
rescue

During the_____ control phase, you may have to deal with _____ wires, fire, _____ vehicles, and _____ hazards. In cases of possible traffic hazards, establish an accident zone and utilize flares. | hazard
downed, unstable, traffic

When you establish an area that is included in a circle with a radius of 50 feet with the crashed vehicle as the center, you are establishing an _____ _____ . Once this area is established, you can alert others through the use of_____. | accident zone
flares

The farthest warning flare from the accident zone is placed at the stopping distance for the posted speed plus the number of feet equal to the posted speed. At 20 mph, the stopping distance is 50 feet. Take 50 feet + _____ feet and post the farthest flare _____ feet from the accident zone. This means that for this example, the farthest flare from the crashed vehicle will be _____ feet away. Place all other flares at 10-foot intervals. | 20, 70

120

In addition to traffic hazards, fire, and unstable vehicles, you may have to deal with _____ _____ . In doing so, there are 3 things you should never do. NEVER assume a downed wire is dead. NEVER assume a downed wire is not energized because the surrounding area is dark (without power). NEVER assume guy wires are not energized. | downed wires

Consider all downed wires and _____ wires to be _____, even if the surrounding area is _____. | guy, energized
dark

In addition to traffic hazards, downed wires, and unstable vehicles, you may have to confront_____ at the accident scene. For this reason, your ambulance should carry a portable fire extinguisher. You should know the classes of fires the extinguisher was designed to fight and how to use the extinguisher for these types of fires. | fire

REMEMBER: Even if the fire is small, you should call for a fire department response.

If the fire is in the engine compartment of a wrecked vehicle and the hood is open, attack the fire with short bursts from the hand-held _____ extinguisher carried on the ambulance. If the hood is closed, keep it closed and attack through the grill, hood openings, or, for some vehicles, the wheel wells. | portable

To attack a fire in the engine compartment of a wrecked vehicle, use _____ bursts from the extinguisher. Remember, if the hood is | short closed, keep it closed. If the fire is a spilled fuel fire, do not use short bursts, attempt to sweep the flames away from the passenger compartment. Be sure that there are no sources for later ignition after you have _____ away and extinguished the flames.

| swept

Besides _____ hazards, downed wires, and fire, the EMT may have to deal with _____ vehicles at the accident scene. Obviously you must know the techniques of stabilization using chocks, cribbing, jacks, and even spare tires. Every accident vehicle must be stabilized.

| traffic
| unstable

REMEMBER: Stabilize the vehicle. Do not roll the vehicle or set the vehicle upright while the victims are still inside or near it.

In order to stabilize a vehicle you must increase the number of contact points with the ground and spread these contact points over as wide an area as possible.

Before assessing the possible access route, _____ the vehicle. Regardless of techniques used, always work to _____ the number of _____ points with the ground and to spread these points over an area as _____ as possible.

| stabilize
| increase
| ccontact
| wide

EXERCISES

To check your answers, refer to *Emergency Care, 5th ed.*

1. List six factors that must be considered when setting out a string of flares at a vehicle accident scene *(p. 626)*.

2. If the posted speed on a straight section of highway is 40 mph and the stopping distance is 125 feet, what is the distance for the farthest warning device? *(p. 627)*

3. Describe the actions that an EMT should take when the accident zone contains downed electrical wires *(pp. 629–630)*.

4. Describe how to stabilize a vehicle that is resting on its side *(pp. 634–636)*.

Reading Assignment: Emergency Care, 5th ed., pp. 638–649

SECTION THREE: GAINING ACCESS TO VEHICLE OCCUPANTS

ENTERING A VEHICLE

Gaining access and disentanglement often overlap. Keep in mind that gaining access means that an EMT reaches the trapped person, while disentanglement means the release of the trapped person. By gaining access, surveys and care can begin. Do *not* delay care by initiating disentanglement procedures unless there is a dire emergency.

The term _____ _____ means that the EMT reaches the trapped person. The release of a trapped person is called _____.

gaining access

disentanglement

If the vehicle is stabilized, determine if the victims are trapped. The best indicator is structural damage to the vehicle. If the victims are trapped, consider the best access route to be the vehicle doors. If access through the doors is impossible, then consider first the windows and then the vehicle body.

No access attempt should be made until the vehicle is _____. Once this is done, the best route of access is through the vehicle's _____. Check to see if *all* the doors are locked or jammed. *Easy access may be on the other side of the vehicle!* If the doors are locked, see if the patient can help by unlocking the doors.

stabilized
doors

If the first door you approach is locked, first check to see if _____ the doors are _____. If they are, check to see if the _____ can unlock a door. If the patient cannot help, check to see if the vehicle has electric door locks. If so, you can break a window and unlock all the doors at one time. If the vehicle does not have an electric door _____, you may be able to unlock the door with a piece of hooked wire. Unframed windows may require prying with a bar, flat-blade screwdriver, or windshield wiper before using the wire. Straight-shank locking buttons can be opened with a wire and washer to drop over the shank.

all
locked, patient

lock

If the vehicle has electric door locks, break a _____ and unlock all the doors at one time. If the locks are not electric, use a tool to unlock the doors. Noose tools, awls and hammers are commonly used. For a door with an accessible lock, a _____ tool can be used. If the lock is not accessible, use an _____ and _____.

window

noose
awl, hammer
bent, wire

If you have to unlock a door, the best tool is a _____ piece of _____. However, some locking mechanisms are inside the door or armrest. Either power tools or hand tools may have to be used to cut away part of the door to expose the locking mechanism

If the door is unlocked, but is jammed, the latch mechanism must be _____. Then pry the door open with a bar. The first step in opening a damaged door is to _____ the door. Once this is done, use a long _____ to pry the door open.

disabled

unlock
bar

NOTE: If there is a life-threatening emergency, and you can ensure the patient safety, going through a window by glass removal or breaking may be necessary since speed of access is so important.

When gaining access through a vehicle window, windshield, or rear window (also called a back light), the EMT must consider the dangers of broken glass. Danger exists for the rescuer, for the patient and for bystanders. Flying glass can not only lacerate the patients, but glass entering open wounds can turn minor injuries into serious medical problems.

Since there is danger associated with _____ _____, the EMT would do better to remove the glass rather than attempting to shatter it. Windshields and rear window glass are the easiest to remove. Before beginning the procedures, check to see if the glass is channel-mounted, mounted in soft adhesive tape or thermosetting plastic, or set in mastic material. If you can see only chrome, the glass is mastic mounted. This is the most common form used in cars since 1969. **broken glass**

When it is necessary to gain access through a vehicle window, the best procedure is to _____ the glass. Since 1969, both the windshields and rear windows of cars have been mounted in _____ materials, easily identified if the recuer can see only _____ around the glass. **remove mastic chrome**

Regardless of the mounting, begin by removing the side and top pieces of chrome trim with a pry bar, screwdriver, or baling hook. When removing glass set in rubber molding, cut away part of the rubber, force the point of a linoleum knife or the blade of a screwdriver behind the glass, and pry.

You may first have to remove the _____ and _____ pieces of _____ _____ before removing a windshield. Part of the rubber will have to be cut away for glass set in rubber molding. If you can see only chrome trim and no rubber is apparent, the glass is _____-mounted. In this case, you will have to separate the glass from the adhesive and pry. Your tool of choice is a glazier's tool. **top, side chrome trim mastic**

If you cannot remove the glass, you will have to break it. Keep in mind that windshields are made of laminated glass, and side and rear windows are made of tempered glass. When broken, laminated glass will actually hold its own shards. Boken tempered glass will not form shards, but small, often round-edged pieces. NOTE; Tempered glass that has been fractured clear through may have sharp pieces which break away as the glass shatters.

Windshields are made of _____ glass. They can be cut with an ax. Remember to protect yourself, taking care to have hand, eye, and head protection. Cut as far away from the patients as is possible. **laminated**

Side windows are made of _____ glass. Unlike removing windshields, which are composed of _____ glass, an _____ is of little use. Tempered glass should be broken with a sharp-pointed tool. The center punch from the door and windshield kit is recommended. **tempered laminated ax**

You can break a windshield with an ax. Side windows, being composed of _____ _____, should be broken with a _____-_____ tool such as the _____ _____ in the door and windshield kit. Regardless of which window is being broken, remember to protect your _____, _____, and _____. Always break the window as _____ _____ from the patient as possible. **tempered glass, sharp-pointed, center pnnch hands, eyes, head far away**

Gaining access through the vehicle body can take place through the roof, floor, or trunk. Most vehicle body access is made through the roof. Efforts made through the vehicle trunk will seldom pay off.

Whereas the trunk is the least likely route, the _____ is the most common approach. A hack saw can be used. Do not attempt access through the roof until the vehicle is _____ and you are properly protected with gloves, goggles, and a helmet. **roof stabilized**

It is unlikely that a crushed roof can be raised without tools. Both _____ tools and power tools should be considered. A hand-operated jack can be used between the body and the roof line to raise the portion of the roof behind the A-posts. Once the posts are exposed. they can be cut, and the roof can be folded back.

When you are attempting to raise a crushed roof, the power tool of choice is the hydraulic jack and spreader unit. If hand tools are used, the best choice is some form of hand-operated _____ that can be used to raise the roof behind the _____-posts.

When gaining access through a vehicle floor, the hand tools of choice are the _____ and _____ _____.

If the roof line is very close to the vehicle body, select a power tool such as the _____ _____ and _____ unit. As with hand tools, raise the section of roof _____ the A-posts. Alternately raise and block the roof section until the _____ can be cut.

Once you have _____ a crushed roof, it may be necessary to remove the top of the vehicle. When using hand tools, the procedure calls for removal or breaking away of the windshield glass.

hand

jack
A

hammer, panel cutter

hydraulic jack, spreader
behind
posts
raised

TERMINOLOGY

Define the following terms. Check your definitions with the ones given in the Glossary of your textbook.

A-post—

Tempered glass (*p. 643*)—

MATCHING

Matching the letter of the tool to the vehicle access problem stated below. There may be more than one correct tool for each problem. See the end of this section for the answers.

_____ 1. Mushroom head lock
_____ 2. Damaged door
_____ 3. Inaccessible lock knob
_____ 4. Mastic-mounted windshield
_____ 5. Breaking side window
_____ 6. Roof
_____ 7. Floor

A. Panel cutter

B. Hacksaw

C. Glazier's tool

D. Noose tool

E. Ax

F. Awl

G. Long bar

H. Center punch

I. Hammer

EXERCISES

To check your answers, refer to *Emergency Care, 5th ed.*

1. What is the recommended order of access routes during an emergency situation at the scene of a motor vehicle accident? (*p. 640*)

198

2. Describe how you can unlock most vehicle doors through non-destructive methods *(pp. 640–641)*.

3. Describe how to open a jammed vehicle door *(p. 642)*.

4. Describe how to gain access through a mastic mounted windshield *(pp. 643, 645)*.

ANSWERS

Matching
1. D
2. G
3. F, I or A, I
4. C, E
5. H, I (if punch is not spring-loaded)
6. B
7. A, I

Reading Assignment: Emergency Care, 5th ed., pp. 650-666

SECTION FOUR: DISENTANGLING TRAPPED PERSONS

INTRODUCTION

After gaining access and initiating care, disentanglement of the patient must be accomplished. The EMT will have to be able to carry out activities designed to make a pathway through the wreckage to allow removal of packaged patients, or to remove wreckage from the patient so that preparation for safe transfer to the ambulance can begin.

PATIENT PROTECTION

Before a patient can be transferred to the ambulance, disentanglement activities may be necessary. These activities come after gaining _____ and initiating _____. Disentanglement has three parts: 1) protecting the vehicle occupants, 2) creating openings in the wreckage, and 3) removing mechanisms of entrapment from around the occupants.

access
care

The patient may be exposed to broken glass, sharp metal edges, and other hazards during _____ procedures. Because of these diverse hazards, accident victims should be _____ with blankets, safety goggles, industrial hearing protectors, hard hats, and other appropriate protective gear. The EMT must be sure to protect the patient's eyes and to allow for adequate ventilation.

disentanglement
protected

Rigid protection, such as that offered by a spine board, may be required to keep a victim from coming into contact with tools being used during disentanglement or the metal parts of the wreckage. Whatever the form of protection used, be certain to protect the victim's _____ and make sure that there is adequate _____.

eyes
ventilation
glass, metal

Protect the victim from broken _____ and _____ parts of the wreckage. You should also protect the victim from the elements. Remember that fire can be a real problem at the accident scene. Practice sound fire prevention and suppression techniques.

CREATING OPENINGS IN THE WRECKAGE

As part of the disentanglement procedures, the EMT might have to make a pathway through the _____ or he might have to remove wreckage from the _____. When making a pathway through the wreckage the EMT might have to use hand tools, power tools, or, in some cases, no tools at all. Regardless of the methods, making a _____ will allow other rescuers to reach the patient and will provide a route for patient removal.

wreckage
patient

pathway

There are three common problems at the scene of vehicle accidents that require special techniques in establishing a pathway to the victim. These problems are raising a crushed roof, removing the top of a vehicle, and widening door openings. Once these problems are corrected, a pathway can be established to allow other _____ to reach the patient and to provide a _____ for _____ of the patient.

rescuers
route, removal

The primary hand tool for removing a vehicle top is a hacksaw. This tool is not used until after the _____ has been removed or broken away and all _____, _____ and _____ have been removed. Working with a partner on the other side of the vehicle, cut first the A-posts and then the B-posts. Make sure the roof is being supported while you cut. Do not cut the C-posts.

windshield

trim, stripping, sealant

The hand tool of choice for removing a vehicle top (roof) is the _____. First, cut through the _____-posts and then the _____-posts. Do not cut the _____-posts. A right angle cut, as deep as the hacksaw frame will allow should be made just ahead of the C-posts.

hacksaw

A, B

C

After making a _____ _____ cut just ahead of the _____-posts, have someone stand on the roof where it will fold. While others lift the roof, this person can dimple the metal with his foot. Be sure to cover all sharp edges and severed pillars.

right angle

C

If the car is a compact model with narrow C pillars, cut the C pillars and remove the _____.

roof (top)

In many cases, particularly when a long spine board must be used in the packaging of a patient, door openings need to be widened. This can be done without tools simply by chocking the wheels and having several rescuers push and pull on the opened door. If hand tools are to be used, the hand winch with 2 chains is the best choice.

Widening of door openings is possible without using any tools. Have several rescuers push and pull on the _____ door after the wheels have been _____. The hand tool of choice is the hand _____ used with _____ chains. Secure the short chain to the vehicle door and the long chain around the frame. The winch can be set on the hood, with its fixed hook secured to the ring of the long chain.

open

chocked, winch

2

The hand winch has a 2-_____ system. The short chain is secured to the vehicle_____, and the long chain is fastened around the vehicle _____.

chain

frame

door

CAUTION: Do not use a "cheater bar" or any other device to lengthen the winch handle. The handle should be turned only until the door is opened the required distance. Should this method fail, a hydraulic jack and ram, with appropriate extension bars, can be used.

REMOVING WRECKAGE FROM THE PATIENTS

The EMTs should direct efforts toward removing or displacing items in direct contact with the patient. There are 6 commonly seen problems: cutting seat belts; removing steering wheels, displacing steering columns, displacing floor pedals, displacing the dash, and displacing seats. These problems can be solved with hand or power tools.

The quick-release buckles of seat belts usually still work after an accident. If they don't, the web of the belt can be cut with scissors or aircraft snips. However, remember that the sudden release of tension often can worsen many abdominal and shoulder injuries.

The steering wheel may have to be removed, and/or the steering column may have to be _____. As with seat belts, the sudden release of _____ can worsen certain injuries.

displaced

tension

Before attempting to remove the _____ _____ or displace the _____ _____, see if the vehicle has

steering wheel

steering column

a tilt or telescoping steering wheel. These can be moved to give you better access to the patient. Next carefully try to move the seat backward on its track. If the seat mechanism is manual, apply a rigid collar before moving the seat to avoid aggravating cervical spine injuries.

If you cannot move the seat, cut away the steering wheel with a hacksaw.

The steering column can be displaced from the inside or from the outside of the vehicle. However, before attempting displacement, first try to _____ the seat _____ on its track. If that fails, _____ the steering wheel. First, protect the patient with a rigid shield. Then use a _____ to cut away the plastic covering and the _____ _____.
move, back, remove
hacksaw
inner core

If removing the steering wheel fails to free the victim, displace the _____ _____. Work from the inside of the vehicle if there is no danger to the patient's legs. A bumper jack or a hydraulic jack and ram can be used. If the foot or base of any of these tools is to be placed on the vehicle floor, use blocks to prevent it from pushing through.
steering column

If there is no danger to the patient's legs, a steering _____ can be displaced from the _____ by using a _____ jack or a _____ jack. When there is a chance of injury to the patient's legs, displacement is done from the outside. A hand winch can be used after a hole has been made in the windshield or the windshield has been removed.
column
inside, bumper
hydraulic

When working from the outside of the vehicle, the steering column can be displaced by using a _____ winch. This requires a hole to be made in the _____. The column needs to be displaced only a few inches.
hand
windshield

There are times when a foot can be caught under a brake or clutch pedal. After carefully protecting the patient's foot, disassemble the pedal, remove the driver's foot from the shoe, or displace the pedal.

To disentangle an entrapped patient from a vehicle, seatbelts can be _____, the steering column can be moved or cut, the foot pedals can be disassembled, severed or _____. Sometimes removing the driver's shoe also helps to disentangle a patient who is entrapped by the vehicle's pedals.
cut
displaced

A wrecker's winch and cable is not recommended for most dash displacements. The recommended tool is the _____ _____. This is also the hand tool of choice for displacing seats.
hand winch

Before the _____ _____ can be used to displace a seat, be certain that the patient is stabilized in place. Two helpers can support the patient, or a long spine board can be used between the patient and the seat. The patient should be protected from debris.
hand winch

To set up the hand winch, make a hole in the rear window to allow the chain to run through. Then follow the same basic procedures used to displace a steering column. The anchoring chain is to be attached to the vehicle's _____ at the trunk end. Place the winch on the trunk lid, and run the winch chain through the rear window opening. The lock on this chain is snapped over the ring of the short chain that has been wrapped around the seat.
frame

With the long chain anchored to the _____ frame and the short chain wrapped around the lower _____, have a rescuer depress the seat adjustment mechanism while another rescuer operates the winch handle. Cut the seat adjustment springs as soon as they come into view.
vehicle
seat

Before turning the winch handle, and also while the winch handle is being turned, the _____ _____ mechanism should be
seat adjustment

depressed. As the seat is being displaced, the seat adjustment _____ should be cut as soon as they can be seen. If necessary, repeat the procedure for the other side of the seat.

| springs

Be certain to protect the patient from the effects of sudden movement that may occur when you cut the seat _____ _____.

| adjustment springs

TERMINOLOGY

Define the following terms. Check your definitions with those in the Glossary at the end of your textbook.

A-posts—

B-posts—

C-posts—

Disentanglement—

MATCHING

For each of the disentanglement situations listed below, identify the correct tools. There can be more than one tool for each situation.

_____ 1. Removing a vehicle roof
_____ 2. Widening door openings
_____ 3. Cutting seat belts
_____ 4. Removing the steering wheel
_____ 5. Displacing the steering column
_____ 6. Disassembling or severing the floor pedals
_____ 7. Displacing the floor pedals
_____ 8. Displacing the dash
_____ 9. Displacing the seats

A. Hacksaw

B. Pliers

C. High-lift jack

D. Hand winch

E. Utility shears

MULTIPLE CHOICE

Circle the letter of the correct answer to each question. The answers are given at the end of this section. Note that page references to *Emergency Care, 5th ed.*, are given.

1. The two objectives of a disentanglement operation are to expand or create openings through which the patient can be removed and to *(p. 651):*
   A. Remove the wreckage from the patient
   B. Remove the patient
   C. Package the patient
   D. Stabilize the vehicle

2. When removing a vehicle's crushed roof, fold the roof just ahead of the *(p. 654):*
   A. A-posts
   B. B-posts
   C. C-posts
   D. D-posts

3. Which of the following is the correct order for cutting posts when removing a vehicle's crushed top? *(pp. 654–655):*
   A. A-post, C-post; A-post, C-post
   B. A-post, B-post; A-post, B-post
   C. A-post, A-post; B-post, B-post
   D. A-posts, B-posts, C-posts

4. For widening door openings with a hand winch, the short chain is anchored to the vehicle's *(p. 652):*
   A. Hood
   B. Door frame
   C. Door handle
   D. Frame

5. For widening door openings with a hand winch, the long chain is fastened around the vehicle's *(p. 653):*
   A. Frame
   B. Hood
   C. Door
   D. Door handle

6. The recommended hand tool for displacing a dash is *(p. 665)*:
   A. Hand winch
   B. Chains
   C. Pry bar
   D. Wrecker's winch and cable

7. The first step in displacing a vehicle seat is to *(p. 663)*:
   A. Cut the seat bolts from underneath
   B. Stabilize the patient's position
   C. Cut the seat adjustment springs
   D. Depress the seat adjustment mechanism

EXERCISES

To check your answers to the Exercises, refer to the textbook. Page numbers given.

1. Describe how to use the hand winch to move a crushed dash *(p. 665)*.

2. Describe how to use the hand winch to displace a steering column from outside the vehicle *(p. 660)*.

3. Describe how to use the hand winch to displace a vehcile seat *(p. 663)*.

4. Describe the technique for folding back a vehicle's roof *(pp. 654–655)*.

ANSWERS

Matching
1. A
2. D
3. E
4. A
5. C, D
6. B, A
7. D
8. D
9. D

Multiple Choice
1. A
2. C
3. D
4. B
5. A
6. A
7. B

appendices

Reading Assignment: Emergency Care, 5th ed., pp. 667-671

APPENDIX 1: ESOPHAGEAL OBTURATOR
AIRWAY (EOA)

The esophageal obturator airway (EOA) is used to establish and maintain an airway in a person who is in respiratory or cardiac arrest, or in a person who is deeply unconscious. It is used for patients who are over 16 years of age and over 5 feet tall. Insertion must be done without hyperextending the neck.

The EOA (esophageal _____ airway) kit should contain an inflatable face mask, a tube with a one-way valve, a syringe, and surgical lubricant (a water-soluble gel).
    obturator

The face mask of the EOA is _____ . Fill the syringe with _____ cc of air and use this to inject air into the mask's one-way valve to inflate the cushion. Repeat until the cushion is inflated, but still soft.
    inflatable
    35

In the EOA kit is a tube with a _____-_____ valve. Inject 20 _____ of air through this valve to test the tube cuff for leaks (15 cc for new tubes). Withdraw the air and remove the syringe. After testing the tube _____ for leaks, remember to _____ the air and remove the _____. Attach the tube to the _____ mask and lubricate the tip of the tube with _____ lubricant.
    one-way, cc

    cuff
    withdraw, syringe
    inflated
    surgical

Begin insertion by positioning yourself at the supine patient's head, holding the EOA just below the mask so that the tube follows the natural curve of the pharynx. Have your partner continue to provide ventilation until you start the actual insertion.

Grasp the patient's tongue by inserting your thumb into the mouth. At the same time, grasp the lower jaw with your index finger so that you can lift the tongue and jaw upward. You should not _____ the neck.
    hyperextend

Still holding the tube just below the _____ and keeping its curvature the same as the natural curvature of the _____ , insert the _____ tip and advance the tube carefully until the mask settles on the patient's face. Throughout this entire process you should continue to lift the patient's _____ and _____.
    mask
    pharynx
    lubricated

    tongue, jaw

Test the EOA by blowing a full breath into the tube mouthpiece while firmly holding the cuff in place. The patient's chest should rise. If it does not, remove the tube, continue resuscitation, and reinsert.

If the _____ is correctly inserted, inflate the tube cuff with _____ cc of air. Begin to ventilate by mouth-to-mask methods, a bag-valve-mask unit, or an oxygen-powered ventilator that is manually triggered.
    EOA, 15

To remove the EOA, turn the patient on his side, withdraw the air from the tube _____, and carefully remove the tube. Be sure to _____ the tube cuff before withdrawing the tube.
    cuff, deflate

1. Define "esophageal obturator airway." *(p. 667).*

2. The tube cuff of an EOA is inflated with _____ cc of air *(p. 670).*

3. The tip of the EOA tube is lubricated with a _____ - _____ _____ _____ *(p. 670).*

4. Is a pronounced hyperextension of the neck recommended when inserting an EOA? *(p. 670)*

5. When removing an EOA, you must *(p. 670):*
   A. Deflate the mask cushion
   B. Inflate the mask cushion
   C. Deflate the cuff
   D. Inflate the cuff

6. Describe, step by step, the insertion of an EOA *(p. 670).*

Reading Assignment: Emergency Care, 5th ed., pp. 672-677

APPENDIX 2: USING THE PHARYNGO-TRACHAEL LUMEN (PtL)™ AIRWAY

1. Describe the advantages of using an endotracheal tube to establish and maintain a patient's airway *(p. 672).*

2. Describe the procedure for inserting a PtL airway *(pp. 674–676).*

PtL is a trademark of Resperonics, Inc.

3. What procedure can be used to determine if the PtL has been placed in the esophagus *(p. 676)?*

4. If your patient does not seem to be responding to ventilations through the PtL Airway, what should you do *(p. 676)?*

5. Describe when you should remove a PtL Airway and the procedure for doing so *(pp. 676–677).*

Reading Assignment: Emergency Care, 5th ed., pp. 678–687

APPENDIX 3: IV THERAPY

1. Distingush between "transfusion" and "infusion" *(p. 678).*

2. List the 5 major components of a sterile infusion set *(pp. 678–679).*

3. Is the macro-drip or micro-drip set used for maintenance of a life-line *(pp. 679–680)?*

4. Describe how to open an infusion set and connect the extension tubing *(p. 684).*

5. How do you flush air from the tubing *(p. 684)?*

6. A 14 gauge over-the-needle catheter is generally recommended for _____ _____ *(p. 684).*

7. Why is the vein in the forearm below the crease in the elbow usually selected for IV insertion *(p. 684)?*

8. Describe how to prepare the insertion site *(p. 684).*

9. Describe, in 6 steps, insertion of the cannula *(p. 685).*

10. Describe how to start the infusion *(p. 685).*

11. List the 3 things you must know to allow the fluid rate to be adjusted according to the instructions of the physician *(p. 686).*

12. If a physician wants a patient to receive 500 ml of fluid in 2 hours, and you have an infusion set that is capable of delivering 10 drops per ml, you would have to deliver _____ drops per minute *(p. 686).*

13. List the 7 steps to take when troubleshooting an IV that is not running properly *(p. 686).*

14. List 4 local complications that may arise during or after IV therapy *(pp. 686–687).*

15. List 6 systemic complications that may arise during or after IV therapy *(p. 687).*

Reading Assignment: Emergency Care, 5th ed., pp. 688–697

APPENDIX 4: AUTOMATED DEFIBRILLATION

1. Describe why EMS systems should consider providing EMTs and first responders with automated defibrillators *(p. 688)?*

2. Indicate which cardiac rhythms can and cannot be helped with defibrillators *(pp. 689–690).*

3. Describe the components of the collapse-to-defibrillation interval *(p. 691).*

4. Describe three strategies for shortening the collapse-to-defibrillation interval *(p. 691).*

5. Describe how to attach the defibrillator to the patient *(p. 692).*

6. Describe the procedure for operating a fully automatic defibrillator *(pp. 694–696).*

7. Describe the procedure for operating a semi-automatic defibrillator *(pp. 696-697).*

Reading Assignment: Emergency Care, 5th ed., pp. 698-702

APPENDIX 5: HELICOPTER AMBULANCE OPERATIONS

1. Sketch a night-landing zone for a small helicopter. Indicate the location of flares, wind direction markers, and approach and departure paths *(pp. 700–702)*.

2. List five medical problems that warrant helicopter transport when ground travel time is likely to be long *(p. 699)*.

3. List five safety precautions you should take if you are asked to assist the helicopter crew in loading *(p. 702)*.

study problems: 10 emergency care situations

When you begin to learn the information and procedures that go into providing emergency care, the problems are presented to you in an orderly fashion. Only materials dealing with one day's lesson need to be considered. But this is not the case for professionals dealing with actual emergencies. These people must constantly bring together all their knowledge of emergency medicine and all their skills in care delivery to meet emergency situations.

The following 10 situations are presented to give you a chance to "bring together" the things you have studied concerning emergency care. Look over each situation and decide what you would do, step by step. Better yet, study each problem and write out what you would do. This will not only serve as a way for you to check your solutions with the ones offered on the following pages, but it will also allow you to check back on your solutions once you have refined your knowledge through field experience.

SITUATION 1

You respond to an emergency at an industrial site. A worker, having been exposed to high temperatures, is found lying on the ground. He is conscious, lying in the supine position. Before you can question him, he loses consciousness. You notice his skin is hot, dry, and flushed. His pulse is now rapid and weak and his respirations are shallow.

SITUATION 2

You are called to the scene of a falling accident. The patient, a 40-year-old male, is lying on his back with his arms raised flat above his head. Witnesses are trying to stop profuse bleeding from his right forearm.

SITUATION 3

You are called to the home of a 65-year-old woman and find her unresponsive to your voice but not unconscious. The neighbors who called keep saying that she has "bad lungs." You note that she is cyanotic and has noisy dyspnea. Her feet and ankles are swollen, and she appears bloated in the right upper quadrant.

SITUATION 4

A woman has fallen from her bicycle and is found lying along the roadside. She is bleeding profusely from her face and lightly on her left forearm. Her left leg is found in a flexed position with observable deformity of the left knee.

SITUATION 5

At the scene of an accident involving three passenger cars, you and your partner are the only two EMTs present. There are five victims lying in the roadway and one victim is sitting up against a guardrail. You see the following:

A. A man around 70 years of age. He is not moving or showing any signs of life.
B. A man in respiratory distress, making gurgling sounds.
C. A woman with an open fracture of the left humerus.
D. A man with severe crushing injuries to the skull. Portions of his brain are visible and there is almost complete deformity of the face. He is in a large pool of blood.
E. A young woman is lying on her right side. She is conscious, has minor bleeding and is clutching her abdomen.
F. A woman is sitting up against the guardrail. She is bleeding from the face and is screaming for help.

SITUATION 6

You arrive at the home of a 55-year-old male. He is obviously having chest pains and dyspnea. The patient will not sit down. He is becoming more and more irritable. You talk to his wife, the one who called for emergency services. The man begins to take turns being angry with her and then with you. He refuses care.

SITUATION 7

You arrive at the scene of an automobile accident to find that a car has swerved off the road and struck a utility pole. The sole occupant of the vehicle is the driver who appears to be unconscious. The car was clearly traveling at a high rate of speed before the impact. The passenger compartment is badly deformed. The door on the passenger side of the vehicle is open.

SITUATION 8

At the scene of a one-car accident, you find the driver to be the only victim. He is unconscious, cyanotic, and his head and neck are a noticeable blue color.

SITUATION 9

You respond to an emergency childbirth situation. The expectant mother is in greater pain than normally associated with delivery. She says that she thought she was delivering just before you arrived, but now something is "very wrong." You check for crowning and find a breech presentation.

SITUATION 10

It is 10 PM on a clear summer night. You arrive at the scene shown in the figure. Describe your procedure, step by step.

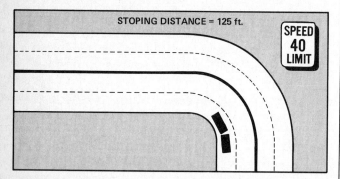

COMMENTS

Here are some comments on the situations just presented. These are not step-by-step procedural answers to the problems, but merely guidelines to solving the problems. In each case it is assumed that you carried out the basics, including the subjective interview and the objective examination. If you read through these comments and find that you left out a specific technique or procedure, go back to your textbook and refresh your memory.

Situation 1

Apparently you are dealing with a case of heatstroke—a true emergency. Did you elicit information from the witnesses? Did you check for other injuries? How much heat was involved in this case? If the amount of heat was very high, then checking around the lips and nose for even minor burns could warn you of the possibility of laryngeal and/or pulmonary edema.

Assuming that there were no other injuries, you should have followed the procedures found on page 482 of your textbook.

Did you consider how to transfer patient information?

Situation 2

Let's assume that there is adequate respiration and circulation. Your first concern is the bleeding. However, there is an apparent injury to the spine, indicating great care must be taken with any procedures carried out on this patient. Did you consider how you would move the witnesses away from the patient without having them disturb patient position?

How were the witnesses trying to stop the bleeding? You may be faced with having to leave their dressings in place, or worst yet, leaving a fixed tourniquet on the patient's arm. If these problems do not exist, then direct pressure would be your best approach, provided there are no severe injuries to the patient's arm. You should have made a very quick inspection before deciding the method of control.

After considering bleeding, did you turn your attention to the application of an extrication collar, immobilizing the spine, giving oxygen and treating for shock? If you did, good. If you remembered to check for possible spinal injuries, that is even better.

Some of the procedures you may have to carry out will depend on the information obtained from witnesses. Did you ask for this information? Nothing was said about the patient being unconscious. Did you question him?

Many new rescuers make the mistake of not considering the possibility that a heart attack led to the fall. Don't be fooled by the patient's age. Many men in their early 40s experience their first heart attack. Close observation of pulse and respiration are called for in this case.

Situation 3

In this case you are probably dealing with congestive heart failure, involving both right and left heart failure. The neighbor's comments may not be of much help, but they have to be considered. This patient may be in heart failure because of the problems associated with emphysema, asthma, or chronic bronchitis. Talk to the patient and try to find out her history, even if you feel she will not be able to acknowledge your presence.

Do not make the mistake of trying to walk the patient around to "bring her to her senses." Follow the procedures outlined on page 393 of your textbook. Remember the recommended procedures for respiratory patients. Did you consider a Venturi mask to deliver 24 percent oxygen (p. 393 in your textbook)? Did you consider what to do if the patient fought the face-mask?

Finally, did you consider the scene? Was there anything there that could have caused carbon monoxide or another toxic gas to reduce the oxygen intake of this patient?

Situation 4

First of all, who is controlling the scene? After this is considered, did you consider respiration, circulation and bleeding before worrying about the apparent fracture to the knee? Were there any other injuries with a higher priority than the knee? Did you follow the procedures on page 310 of your textbook, including pulse and nerve function?

How did you transfer this patient to the ambulance?

Did you make the mistake that many rescuers make? Is there only one victim? Unless you can find out the cause of the accident, assume that she may have struck someone such as a child or an elderly person. Check the bicycle for damage that may indicate such an accident. If this sounds a little hard to take seriously, consider what damage could be caused if someone were struck at the speed a ten speed bicycle can achieve.

Situation 5

If you thought of triage, you are on the right track. However, who is controlling the scene? Would you expect only six victims in a three-car accident? Would you expect all the victims to be out of the cars? Your triage of the scene must include all the victims.

Let's consider the victims from the situation:

A. This could be high priority—perhaps the highest. Respiration and pulse must be checked.

B. This is high priority. A good rescue team would have one person check patient A while the other tried to correct patient B's apparent airway obstruction.

C. One major fracture would place patient C into the second priority classification. Be sure that severe bleeding is not involved. If she's conscious, at least let her know you see her and you will be there to help.

D. This patient will be given a third or delayed priority. Can you really do anything to help? What happens to A and B if you try?

E. Is this an open wound? Nothing was said about bleeding. However, the patient may have severe internal bleeding. Only a survey will tell if she goes after A and B, but before C. Also, is she pregnant and will this change her status in triage?

F. Possibly a low priority, provided the bleeding is not severe. Her bleeding will, until checked closely, place her ahead of C and D. Usually a close check will place her back to the third priority. As you approach patient A, ask a bystander to try to comfort her and to see if the bleeding appears to be very serious. You have no other choice with only you and your partner.

This accident sounds almost impossible to handle. Perhaps your first course of action should have been to radio for help as soon as you saw the scene.

Situation 6

You have arrived at the scene of an impending AMI. Trying to help this patient is making the problem worse. Do ask if you can help. Do request his permission to take blood pressure, and so forth. If he says no, then you cannot give physical care.

With this patient's attitude, psychological care may not be very successful. Suggest to his wife that she or you contact the family physician. It may be better if you do it through your communications system so as not to aggravate the patient. Do not leave the scene. Wait—he may change his mind as the situation worsens. If the AMI occurs, the sooner you can begin care, the better it will be for the patient. Once the AMI strikes, his wife's permission and implied consent will take over, negating the patient's refusal to give actual consent.

Situation 7

Your initial view of the scene should suggest some important questions. Did you consider hazards that should be identified and controlled before you begin to provide care? Common hazards at the scene of motor vehicle accidents include traffic and leaking gasoline.

At this scene, the utility pole should suggest the possibility of live electrical wires. How will you be certain that this hazard is controlled? What information will your dispatcher need? Do you know how to establish an accident zone around this kind of hazard to protect bystanders and other EMS personnel?

If you are certain that there are no downed

wires, you can begin to approach the vehicle to provide care. The open door should lead you to consider the possibility of a passenger who might have been thrown from the car. This open door may also provide some initial access to the driver to allow you to begin care.

Did you consider the possibility that this patient might require helicopter transport to a trauma center?

Situation 8

This sounds like traumatic asphyxia—a group of signs and symptoms, not a condition. Transport this patient as soon as possible with artificial ventilation with oxygen as your main procedure of care. Treat the signs of shock. Is there flail chest or pneumothorax involved here? Even if there is, the problems caused by the sudden pressure on the heart need medical facility attention. Do not waste time at the scene. Do what you can during transport.

Situation 9

An airway for the infant is critical. Calm the mother; tell her what you are going to do and do it all in one smooth move. Do not waste any time. Do not assume that you cannot deliver a breech presentation. Follow the procedures given on page 453 of your textbook.

Situation 10

Note in the illustration that an accident zone was established. The ambulance is parked before the curve, in the same lane as the accident, between the wreckage and traffic. The flares extend to 165 feet beyond the accident zone. You should have placed them about 10 feet apart.

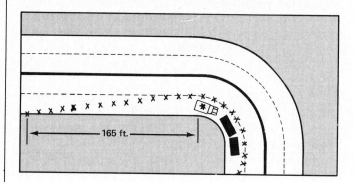

emergency care
post-test

This post-test is to be taken after you have completed your study of emergency care. By taking this test, you will be able to determine how much you have understood and retained throughout your studies. If you have completed all of the objectives presented for each phase of emergency care, you should have little difficulty doing well on the test.

Another purpose for this test is to give you practice in taking an exam on emergency care. If you are taking the entire exam, allow yourself 3 hours and 10 minutes total time. A built-in break of 10 minutes occurs after question 100. Do not take any other breaks or try taking the test in small segments over a longer time period.

You may be taking an emergency care course that covers only the materials found in Chapters 2 through 20. For this type of course, begin taking the exam with question 26 and continue through 175. Allow yourself 2 hours to take this portion of the post-test. Do not take any breaks.

Be sure to follow all the directions given for this exam and use only the time allotted to you. Do not stop to check your answers until you have completed all the questions assigned to you. At the end of the test you will find the answers to the post-test questions, a way to analyze your score, and references back to your textbook, *Emergency Care, 5th ed.*

DIRECTIONS: Circle the letter of the correct answer to each question.

1. At the scene of an accident, an EMT provides care to the victims, acting in good faith and to the best of his abilities. In many states this EMT is protected from care-related lawsuits by:

    A. Applied consent laws
    B. Laws of total immunity
    C. Good Samaritan laws
    D. Jeopardy laws

2. When confronted with a dire emergency care situation involving a minor without parents or legal guardians present, the EMT should:

    A. Seek a physician's approval before beginning care
    B. Consider consent for care to be implied and begin care
    C. Ask the child for consent and begin care
    D. Consider consent to be actual and begin care

3. A standard size, van-type ambulance in which the body and cab form an integral unit is a _____ ambulance.

    A. Type I
    B. Type II
    C. Type III
    D. Type IV

4. Which of the following must be proven to establish negligence on the part of the EMT?

    A. A duty to act
    B. The standard of care was not provided
    C. The patient was harmed or injured by inappropriate actions
    D. All of the above

5. Which of the following is classified under the heading of basic supplies?

    A. Wheeled ambulance stretcher
    B. Oropharyngeal airway
    C. Sheets
    D. Padded board splints

6. To have access into an emergency services system with one-number calling, the person should dial:

    A. 911
    B. 9
    C. 555
    D. 949

7. The first piece of information given to the crew by the dispatcher is:

    A. Address
    B. If this is an emergency or a routine transport
    C. Nature of emergency
    D. Injured person's name

8. "Stopping distance" is:

   A. Reaction distance plus braking distance
   B. Reaction distance minus braking distance
   C. Braking distance minus reaction distance
   D. Reaction time in seconds plus breaking distance

9. The solution to hydroplaning is to:

   A. Jam on the brakes
   B. Rapidly pump the brakes
   C. Slow down
   D. Maintain speed, but slowly steer back and forth

10. One-third of all traffic accidents occur:

    A. At intersections
    B. With the car ahead
    C. With a car that is passing
    D. With an approaching vehicle

11. You are heading south in an ambulance, using its warning devices. As you approach an intersection without traffic signals, another responding ambulance approaches from the east. Which vehicle should yield?

    A. Your ambulance approaching from the north
    B. The ambulance approaching from the east

12. Which of the following occurs more frequently when the ambulance is returning to quarters?

    A. An accident at an intersection
    B. An accident with the vehicle behind
    C. An accident with a vehicle being passed
    D. An accident with a vehicle that is passing

13. At the scene of an accident most officials favor placing the ambulance between the wreckage and oncoming traffic, not less than _____ feet from the involved vehicles.

    A. 15
    B. 25
    C. 50
    D. 75

14. The ambulance should be parked no closer than _____ feet from a burning vehicle.

    A. 50
    B. 100
    C. 500
    D. 1000

15. The dispatcher has told you the exact location of an accident, what kinds of vehicles are involved, how many vehicles, and any known hazards. What other information would you

like the dispatcher to provide concerning this accident?

    A. How many people are injured and how seriously
    B. The direction designator
    C. How to contact the person who reported the accident
    D. The nearest cross street

16. When should an EMT use latex gloves to protect against infectious disease?

    A. Whenever there is patient contact
    B. Only if a patient is known to have an infectious disease
    C. For all adult patients
    D. Whenever there may be contact with a patient's blood or body fluids

17. Research on shock has shown that in order to have the best chance of survival, a seriously injured patient must reach a trauma center within:

    A. 15 minutes
    B. 30 minutes
    C. one hour
    D. two hours

18. Which of the following is recommended for the emergency evacuation of the unconscious patient?

    A. Piggyback carry
    B. Front piggyback carry
    C. Standard pack strap carry
    D. Cradle carry

19. Which of the following, when used properly, can be employed to evacuate a patient with spinal injuries?

    A. Blanket drag
    B. Firefighter's drag
    C. Two-rescuer seat carry
    D. Three-rescuer hammock carry

20. Which of the following is the best way to evacuate a patient in a dire emergency?

    A. Pack strap carry
    B. Cradle carry
    C. Shoulder drag
    D. Firefighter's carry

21. Which of the following is the best method to use in evacuating a patient without spinal injuries when he must be moved through a narrow opening?

    A. Two-rescuer seat carry
    B. Three-rescuer carry

C. Two-rescuer extremities carry
D. Two-rescuer assist

22. Assessing the situation at a vehicle accident scene includes:

A. Gaining access
B. Locating the victims
C. Hazard control
D. All of the above

23. After establishing an accident zone you wish to position flares. The speed limit is 40 mph. The stopping distance is 125 feet. How far from the *accident zone* should the farthest warning device be placed?

A. 85 feet
B. 165 feet
C. 205 feet
D. 125 feet

24. The tool of choice for removing a mastic-mounted windshield is a:

A. Glazier's tool
B. Pry-Axe
C. Linoleum knife
D. Baling hook

25. Which tool can be used to expose a car door locking mechanism?

A. Flat-blade screwdriver
B. Pry-Axe
C. Panel cutter
D. Center punch

STUDENTS TAKING THE SHORT TEST BEGIN HERE

26. A person laying flat on his back is in the _____ position.

A. Supine
B. Prone
C. Coma
D. Recumbent

27. When you move a patient's arm toward his body, the process is called:

A. Flexion
B. Abduction
C. Extension
D. Adduction

28. The bulk of the liver is situated in the _____ quadrant.

A. Right lower
B. Left lower
C. Right upper
D. Left upper

29. The first step in the primary survey after establishing unresponsiveness is to:

A. Ensure an open airway
B. Check for adequate breathing
C. Check for circulation
D. Look for profuse bleeding

30. The fastest and most reliable way to check for heart action is the:

A. Radial pulse
B. Use of the stethoscope over the heart
C. Carotid pulse
D. Presence of respiration

31. When you obtain the circumstances of a patient's complaint, you are conducting the:

A. Objective examination
B. Subjective interview
C. Subjective examination
D. Objective interview

32. Which of the following is a *true* vital sign?

A. Skin color
B. Skin temperature
C. Body temperature
D. All of the above

33. The normal pulse rate for an adult at rest is between:

A. 50 and 70 beats per minute
B. 80 and 100 beats per minute
C. 60 and 80 beats per minute
D. 65 and 92 beats per minute

34. During the secondary survey, the pulse rate is normally taken with the:

A. Carotid pulse
B. Femoral pulse
C. Pedal pulse
D. Radial pulse

35. The term for weak pulse force is:

A. Thin
B. Weak
C. Partial
D. Thready

36. Normal "at rest" breathing rates for adults vary from:

A. 12 to 30 breaths per minute
B. 15 to 30 breaths per minute
C. 5 to 10 breaths per minute
D. 20 to 32 breaths per minute

37. Which of the following will be observed in a patient with spasms of the larynx?

   A. Gurgling
   B. Snoring
   C. Stertorous respirations
   D. Crowing

38. Systolic blood pressure indicates the pressure when the:

   A. Artery is contracting
   B. Artery is relaxing
   C. Heart is contracting
   D. Heart is relaxing

39. Diastolic blood pressure indicates the pressure when the:

   A. Heart is contracting
   B. Heart is relaxing
   C. Artery is contracting
   D. Artery is relaxing

40. The technique of measuring blood pressure with a sphygmomanometer and a stethoscope, basing measurements on pressure related to characteristic sounds, is called:

   A. Palpation
   B. Auscultation
   C. Oscillation
   D. None of the above

41. The characteristic sound heard through the stethoscope for the diastolic reading is the:

   A. First tapping sound
   B. Second set of tapping sounds
   C. End of all tapping sounds
   D. Fading of tapping sounds

42. A usual sign of shock is:

   A. Cool, clammy skin
   B. Cold, moist skin
   C. Cold, dry skin
   D. Hot, dry skin

43. During the secondary survey, bleeding under the scalp can be detected by feeling for a:

   A. Soft spot
   B. Sticky spot
   C. "Goose egg"
   D. Depression

44. During the secondary survey, a quick check for skull fractures includes inspecting the:

   A. Ears and nose for blood and clear fluids
   B. Inner surface of the eyelids
   C. Skin color of the cheeks
   D. Mouth for blood and clear fluids

45. During the secondary survey, before you inspect the neck for a stoma and anterior injury:

   A. Palpate the cervical spine for point tenderness
   B. Inspect the chest for penetrations
   C. Inspect the chest for fractures
   D. Check the upper extremities for fractures and paralysis

46. Just prior to inspecting the abdomen for penetration:

   A. Inspect the chest for fractures
   B. Inspect the chest for penetration
   C. Listen to the chest for sounds of equal air entry
   D. Inspect the chest for equal expansion

47. The final step in checking the lower extremity for injury or paralysis is:

   A. Checking for a distal pulse
   B. Having the patient press his foot against your hand
   C. Checking for foot wave
   D. Confirming sensitivity

48. The first step in a disaster scene operation is to establish:

   A. A supply pool
   B. Triage points
   C. Communication with hospitals
   D. A command post

49. Upon arrival at the emergency scene, you find an injured patient displaying intense fear. Initially, you should consider this to be a(n):

   A. Psychiatric emergency
   B. Emotional emergency
   C. Stress reaction
   D. All of the above

50. In most triage systems, which of the following is a second priority casualty?

   A. Severe shock
   B. A breathing emergency
   C. A back injury with spinal cord damage
   D. Head injury with unconsciousness

51. Atmospheric air contains _____ oxygen.

    A. 14 percent
    B. 21 percent
    C. 36 percent
    D. 73 percent

52. Brain cells will usually begin to die if they are deprived of oxygen for more than _____ minutes.

    A. 15
    B. 10
    C. 6
    D. 4

53. The correct term for "windpipe" is:

    A. Trachea
    B. Larynx
    C. Pharynx
    D. Bronchus

54. An unconscious patient's head flexes forward. This could cause an airway obstruction by the:

    A. Epiglottis
    B. Uvula
    C. Tongue
    D. Larynx

55. Complete airway obstruction is indicated by:

    A. Crowing sounds
    B. The lack of the usual signs of breathing
    C. Gurgling sounds
    D. Cyanosis; snoring sounds

56. When you have recognized complete airway obstruction in a conscious patient, you should immediately:

    A. Place the patient in the supine position
    B. Deliver 4 back blows in rapid succession
    C. Deliver 6 to 10 abdominal thrusts in rapid succession
    D. Attempt to ventilate the patient

57. You are attempting to dislodge a complete airway obstruction in an unconscious adult patient. All efforts have failed. Which of the following is the correct sequence you should now follow?

    A. Finger sweeps, back blows, manual thrusts
    B. Manual thrusts, finger sweeps, back blows
    C. Ventilations, finger sweeps, manual thrusts
    D. Manual thrusts, finger sweeps, ventilations

58. To correct for a complete airway obstruction in an infant, position the patient in the _____ position.

    A. Upright
    B. Supine
    C. Head-down
    D. Prone

59. To deliver abdominal thrusts to a patient lying down, place the patient in the _____ position.

    A. Upright
    B. Prone
    C. Coma
    D. Supine

60. For chest thrusts on an adult victim your hands should be positioned two finger-widths superior to the:

    A. Xiphoid process
    B. Supraclavicular notch
    C. Navel
    D. Lower margin of the ribs

61. While you are trying to correct a complete airway obstruction, the patient becomes unconscious. You place him in a supine position, open the airway, perform finger sweep, and attempt to provide 2 ventilations. This fails. Your next step is to:

    A. Deliver 6 to 10 abdominal thrusts
    B. Retilt the head and again attempt to ventilate
    C. Deliver 4 back blows
    D. Attempt another finger sweep

62. The easiest and quickest way to relieve an airway obstruction due to the positioning of the patient's tongue is the:

    A. Jaw-thrust maneuver
    B. Abdominal thrust maneuver
    C. Head-tilt; chin-lift maneuver
    D. Jaw-lift maneuver

63. The recommended maneuver for opening the airway of a patient with possible cervical spine injury is the _____ maneuver.

    A. Jaw-thrust
    B. Mouth-to-nose
    C. Head-tilt, chin-lift
    D. Jaw-lift

64. Before beginning mouth-to-mouth ventilation, you should assess the patient's breathing for _____ seconds.

   A. 30
   B. 15
   C. 5 to 10
   D. 3 to 5

65. To determine if spontaneous respiration has occurred after opening the patient's airway:

   A. Look for chest movements
   B. Listen for airflow
   C. Feel for air exchange
   D. All of the above

66. The rescuer in mouth-to-mouth ventilation provides _____ breaths every minute to the adult patient.

   A. 5
   B. 12
   C. 15
   D. 21

67. You have ventilated a patient with 2 adequate breaths using the mouth-to-mouth technique. Spontaneous respiration does not occur. Your next step is to:

   A. Begin the standard mouth-to-mouth ventilations
   B. Repeat the process
   C. Check for a carotid pulse
   D. Deliver four quick breaths, giving time for deflation

68. Infants should be ventilated at the rate of one adequate breath every:

   A. 10 seconds
   B. 8 seconds
   C. 5 seconds
   D. 3 seconds

69. Before attempting any form of resuscitation on a laryngectomee check for:

   A. Pharyngeal obstructions
   B. Tracheal obstructions
   C. Tracheal spasms
   D. Laryngeal collapse

70. When opening the airway of an infant use the:

   A. Full head-tilt method
   B. Jaw-thrust maneuver
   C. Head-tilt, chin-lift maneuver
   D. Neck hyperextension method

71. When breathing and circulation cease, *clinical death* begins:

   A. Immediately
   B. In 3–5 minutes
   C. In 10 minutes
   D. In 12–15 minutes

72. The CPR compression site for an adult is selected:

   A. About two finger-widths below the sternal manubrium
   B. About two finger-widths above the substernal notch
   C. The vertical midsternal plane
   D. The direct center of the chest

73. The adult CPR compression rate in one-rescuer CPR is:

   A. 30/minute
   B. 60 to 80/minute
   C. 80 to 100/minute
   D. 100/minute

74. The rate of ventilations during one-rescuer CPR on an adult is:

   A. 2 every 15 compressions
   B. 2 every 5 compressions
   C. 1 every 5 compressions
   D. 2 every 10 compressions

75. During CPR the most reliable pulse site in the adult is the:

   A. Pedal pulse
   B. Radial pulse
   C. Femoral pulse
   D. Carotid pulse

76. The rate of compressions in two-rescuer CPR is:

   A. 60 to 80/minute
   B. 80 to 100/minute
   C. 50/minute
   D. 100/minute

77. In two-rescuer CPR, the ventilations are given at the rate of:

   A. 2 every 10 seconds
   B. 2 every 5 compressions
   C. 1 every 5 compressions
   D. 1 every 10 seconds

78. During CPR for an adult, the sternum is depressed:

   A. 3/4 to 1 inch
   B. 1 1/2 to 2 inches
   C. 1/2 to 3/4 inch
   D. 2 1/2 to 3 inches

79. If CPR is effective, the patient's pupils may:

   A. Dilate
   B. Constrict
   C. Assume a ground-glass appearance
   D. Begin to move

80. During CPR on an infant, the sternum is depressed:

   A. 1 to 1 1/2 inches
   B. 1/4 to 1/2 inch
   C. 1/2 to 1 inch
   D. 3/4 to 1 1/2 inches

81. During CPR on a small child, the sternum is compressed:

   A. 1 to 1 1/2 inches
   B. 1/2 to 3/4 inch
   C. 1/4 to 1/2 inch
   D. 3/4 to 1 1/2 inches

82. CPR compressions are delivered to children:

   A. The same as to adults
   B. With the tips of the index and middle fingers
   C. With the palm of one hand
   D. With the heel of one hand

83. The compression rate during CPR on an infant is at least:

   A. 150/minute
   B. 100/minute
   C. 80/minute
   D. 55/minute

84. Unless the patient is being moved, CPR should not be interrupted for more than:

   A. 7 seconds
   B. 10 seconds
   C. 15 seconds
   D. 20 seconds

85. The most common complication of CPR is:

   A. Liver laceration
   B. Injury to rib cage
   C. Contusion of the lung
   D. Hemothorax

86. The lower pumping chambers of the heart are the:

   A. Atria
   B. Auricles
   C. Semicardials
   D. Ventricles

87. The typical adult male has approximately _____ liters of blood.

   A. 6
   B. 10
   C. 12
   D. 24

88. In the adult, bleeding must be considered as life-threatening if there is a blood loss of:

   A. 1/2 liter
   B. 1 liter
   C. 5 liters
   D. 10 liters

89. Red blood flowing in distinctive spurts indicates _____ bleeding.

   A. Arterial
   B. Venous
   C. Capillary
   D. Lymphatic

90. The best method to control external bleeding is by:

   A. Pressure point
   B. Tourniquet
   C. Elevation
   D. Direct pressure

91. The pressure point for controlling bleeding from the arm is the _____ _____ pressure point.

   A. Carotid artery
   B. Brachial artery
   C. Subclavian vein
   D. Radial artery

92. The best method for control of nasal bleeding is:

   A. Packing the nose with cotton
   B. Pinching the nostrils together
   C. Packing the nose with gauze
   D. Applying pressure to the facial artery

93. The estimated blood loss from badly contused tissue is approximately _____ for each area the size of a man's fist.

   A. 30 percent
   B. 25 percent
   C. 15 percent
   D. 10 percent

94. The first step in caring for possible internal bleeding, after ensuring respiration and circulation, and controlling life-threatening external bleeding, is to:

   A. Administer liquids by mouth to the patient
   B. Apply a bulky dressing
   C. Treat for shock
   D. Place the patient in a sitting position

95. A scratch is an example of:

   A. An incision
   B. An abrasion
   C. A contusion
   D. A minor laceration

96. Which of the following is the condition where skin is torn loose, but not pulled off?

   A. A laceration
   B. An abrasion
   C. An incision
   D. An avulsion

97. After the control of profuse bleeding in the case of an object impaled in the forearm, you should:

   A. Remove the object
   B. Place a pressure dressing over the site
   C. Stabilize the object
   D. Slowly allow a little bleeding to decontaminate the site

98. Severe external bleeding will lead to _____ shock.

   A. Cardiogenic
   B. Metabolic
   C. Hemorrhagic
   D. Neurogenic

99. Which of the following is a sign of shock?

   A. High blood pressure
   B. Constricted pupils
   C. Slowed pulse rate
   D. Moist, cool skin

100. Which condition requires immediate transport even when the initial signs are mild?

   A. Septic shock
   B. Anaphylactic shock
   C. Neurogenic shock
   D. Psychogenic shock

IF YOU ARE TAKING THE ENTIRE 200–QUESTION TEST, STOP NOW AND RETURN IN 10 MINUTES. IF YOU ARE TAKING THE SHORT TEST, CONTINUE WORKING.

101. An oropharyngeal airway is inserted with the tip pointing toward the:

   A. Roof of the patient's mouth
   B. Patient's uvula
   C. Patient's tongue
   D. Lower teeth of the patient

102. In mouth-to-adjunct ventilation, you should deliver breaths to the adult patient at the rate of:

   A. 1 every 5 seconds
   B. 1 every 12 seconds
   C. 2 quick breaths every 10 seconds
   D. 2 quick breaths every 15 seconds

103. When delivering oxygen to a patient with emphysema, deliver:

   A. 100 percent with a non-rebreathing mask
   B. 50 percent with a nasal cannula
   C. 35 percent with a partial rebreathing mask
   D. 24 percent with a Venturi mask

104. Which of the following devices is recommended for nonbreathing patients?

   A. Non-rebreathing mask
   B. Venturi mask
   C. Manual positive pressure resuscitator
   D. Patient demand resuscitator

105. In cases of skull fracture, the pupils will tend to be:

   A. Equal
   B. Dilated
   C. Constricted
   D. Unequal

106. Which of the following describes the blood pressure and pulse for a patient with a brain injury?

    A. Low blood pressure, fast pulse
    B. Low blood pressure, slow pulse
    C. High blood pressure, fast pulse
    D. High blood pressure, slow pulse

107. The patient with mild head injury should be positioned in the _____ position if there is no reason to suspect neck or spinal injuries.

    A. Supine
    B. Upper body elevated
    C. Recumbent
    D. Coma

108. A patient is having a grand mal seizure. The primary element of care is to:

    A. Protect the patient
    B. Cover the patient to maintain body temperature
    C. Administer 100 percent oxygen
    D. Insert a bite stick in the patient's mouth

109. The first step in care for a patient having a CVA is to:

    A. Administer 100 percent oxygen
    B. Place the patient in the coma position
    C. Maintain body temperature
    D. Ensure an open airway

110. The first 7 vertebrae are the _____ vertebrae.

    A. Lumbar
    B. Thoracic
    C. Cervical
    D. Sacral

111. A patient with a spinal injury can raise his arms, but he cannot wiggle his toes. The injury is probably:

    A. In the area of the neck
    B. In an area somewhere below the neck
    C. At the neck and below
    D. Not spinal but to the brain

112. Priapism is:

    A. A persistent erection of the penis
    B. Spasms to the hands and feet
    C. Apparent only in unconscious patients
    D. Uncontrolled muscle twitches of the thighs

113. Often with spinal injury the patient's arms will be:

    A. Straight out at his side
    B. Raised above his head
    C. Down at his side
    E. Across his chest

114. The first step in the care of a scalp wound is to:

    A. Clean the wound
    B. Apply a sterile dressing
    C. Cut away hair around the site
    D. Apply a water-moistened dressing

115. Unstable objects impaled in the cheek that have passed through the wall should be:

    A. Stabilized from the outside
    B. Stabilized from the inside
    C. Removed
    D. Stabilized from the inside and from the outside

116. A patient with facial fractures should be transported in the _____ position.

    A. Supine
    B. Recumbent—opposite side of wound
    C. Head-elevated
    D. Prone

117. An object impaled in the eye should be

    A. Stabilized with a dressing, then shielded
    B. Removed carefully and a pressure dressing applied
    C. Shielded with a cup taped over the orbit
    D. Removed and a dressing applied with minimum pressure

118. An avulsed part should be kept:

    A. Warm
    B. At body temperature
    C. Cool
    D. Cold

119. An object protruding from the nose should be:

    A. Left in place
    B. Pulled loose
    C. Pulled loose after probing for its hidden end
    D. Washed free with a stream of water from a syringe

120. Before moving a supine patient with possible spinal injuries onto a long spine board, you should always:

 A. Align the teeth and tape the jaw in place
 B. Apply a short spine board
 C. Apply an extrication collar
 D. Secure a K.E.D. to the patient

121. Initial efforts to control bleeding from a severed neck artery should be:

 A. Direct pressure
 B. Pinching off the severed ends with your fingers
 C. Pressure point
 D. Occlusive dressing

122. A severed major neck vein can be cared for by:

 A. Pressure point
 B. Occlusive dressing
 C. Direct pressure
 D. Pinching off the severed ends with your fingers

123. A sucking chest wound should be cared for with:

 A. Trauma dressing
 B. Multi-trauma dressing
 C. Packed dressing
 D. Occlusive dressing

124. Rib fractures usually occur to the:

 A. first 5 ribs
 B. 11th and 12th ribs
 C. 5th through 10th ribs
 D. 2nd through 5th ribs

125. To care for fractured ribs:

 A. Place the arm of the affected side in a sling and swathe
 B. Tape the chest
 C. Apply cravats and support the arm of the opposite side
 D. Apply cravats and support the arm on the same side

126. When giving care to a patient with a flail chest:

 A. Tape around the chest
 B. Place the patient in the sitting position
 C. Stabilize with a bulky pressure dressing
 D. Stabilize with a firm pressure dressing

127. When caring for a patient who has a sucking chest wound, tension pneumothorax may be avoided by applying:

 A. Occlusive dressing

 B. Bulky dressing
 C. Moist gauze dressing
 D. Dry multitrauma dressing

128. Traumatic asphyxia is best cared for:

 A. With a bulky dressing
 B. As a true emergency requiring immediate transport
 C. With an occlusive dressing
 D. By taping the chest

129. When caring for an open abdominal wound with evisceration:

 A. Replace the organ and cover with occlusive material
 B. Replace the organ and cover with a bulky dressing
 C. Do not replace the organ and cover with occlusive material
 D. Do not replace the organ and cover with a moistened dressing only

130. A patient in acute abdominal distress without vomiting should be transported in the:

 A. Prone position
 B. Coma position
 C. Supine position with his knees bent
 D. In the recumbent position with one knee bent

131. A fractured clavicle is best cared for with a:

 A. Padded splint
 B. Sling and swathe
 C. Wrist sling
 D. A bulky pressure dressing

132. A fracture to the humerus shaft is best cared for by immobilizing with a:

 A. Wrist sling
 B. Padded board splint, sling and swathe
 C. Air-inflated splint
 D. Sling and swathe

133. A fracture to the proximal end of the humerus is best cared for by immobilizing with a:

 A. Wrist sling and swathe
 B. Padded board, sling and swathe
 C. Air-inflated splint
 D. sling and swathe

134. Your best approach to immobilizing a fractured elbow when the arm is found in the bent position, and there is a distal pulse, is to:

 A. Straighten the arm and apply an air-inflated splint

B. Keep the arm in its found position and apply a short padded board splint
C. Keep the arm in its found position and apply an air-inflated splint
D. Straighten the arm and apply a wire ladder splint

135. The correct pressure for an air-inflated splint is when:

A. Resistance stops you from blowing in more air
B. You can make a slight dent in the plastic with your finger
C. The patient says that his pain is gone
D. Resistance stops the hand pump

136. The first step in immobilizing a fractured wrist with distal pulse is to:

A. Correct angulation of the wrist
B. Secure to a padded board splint
C. Place the hand in position of function
D. Secure as found

137. A patient with a fractured pelvis should be immobilized on an orthopedic stretcher or long spine board with:

A. Legs bound together
B. Long padded boards secured down each side of his body
C. Sandbags used for stabilization
D. Simply secured with straps

138. A fractured femur is best immobilized with a(n):

A. Long padded board
B. Air-inflated splint
C. Short padded board
D. Traction splint

139. Before immobilizing a fractured knee:

A. Check for a distal pulse
B. Straighten the angulation
C. Straighten the leg
D. Flex the leg at the knee

140. The best method for immobilizing a fractured ankle is to use a(n):

A. Traction splint
B. Pillow splint
C. Padded board splint
D. Air-inflated splint

141. A sprain is an injury where:

A. Tendons are torn
B. Ligament are torn
C. Cartilage is crushed
D. Muscles are torn

142. In which of the following is there usually no deformity of the joint?

A. Dislocation
B. Sprains
C. Fractures
D. There is deformity in all of the above

143. Muscle is attached to bone by:

A. Cartilage
B. Ligaments
C. Smooth muscles
D. Tendons

144. Which of the following is the condition where a portion of the heart muscle dies because of oxygen starvation?

A. Angina pectoris
B. Mechanical pump failure
C. Cardiogenic shock
D. Acute myocardial infarction

145. A patient has pains in his chest. Each pain lasts about 3 minutes. He has shortness of breath, and he is sweating profusely. When he sits and rests, the pains go away quickly. The patient is probably suffering from:

A. Congestive heart failure
B. Acute myocardial infarction
C. Angina pectoris
D. Mechanical pump failure

146. For several days a patient has had pain in his lower jaw. This morning he started having compressing substernal pains and dyspnea. The problem of concern here is:

A. Acute myocardial infarction
B. Left heart failure
C. Right heart failure
D. Mechanical pump failure

147. A patient with no history of respiratory problems complains of dyspnea. Your survey discovers tachycardia, edema of the lower extremities, and an engorged liver. You quiet the patient and place him in a sitting position. Your next step should be to:

A. Suggest he take nitroglycerin tablets
B. Begin care for internal abdominal bleeding
C. Administer oxygen
D. Begin care for septic shock

148. A heart rate below 60 beats per minute is called:

A. Bradycardia
B. Tachycardia
C. Isocardia
D. Neurocardia

149. A conscious patient who is an AMI victim is best placed in the _____ position.

   A. Supine
   B. Coma
   C. Traumatic coma
   D. Sitting

150. An unconscious patient with "acetone breath," deep sighing respirations, and a rapid, weak pulse is probably suffering from

   A. Diabetic coma (hyperglycemia)
   B. Septic shock
   C. Insulin shock (hypoglycemia)
   D. Pulmonary edema

151. After calming a snakebite victim, treating for shock, you locate the fang marks. There is no way to contact a poison control center. Your next procedure is to:

   A. Immobilize the affected extremity
   B. Conserve patient body heat
   C. Cleanse the wound site
   D. Apply a full tourniquet

152. A patient has ingested a non-corrosive poison. You cannot reach a poison control center. Your first act of care is to:

   A. Induce vomiting with Syrup of Ipecac
   B. Dilute the ingested poison with milk or water
   C. Attempt to neutralize the poison
   D. Administer an oily substance to induce vomiting

153. A patient is in insulin shock. The recommended care procedure is to:

   A. Have the patient take his insulin shot
   B. Transport immediately
   C. Administer sugar
   D. Administer oxygen

154. A patient who was working in a hot environment complains of painful leg muscle spasms. He feels weak, You should move him to a cool place and begin care by:

   A. Applying manual pressure to the cramped leg muscles
   B. Transporting immediately after cooling
   C. Administering 24 percent oxygen by Venturi mask
   D. Giving him sips of water

155. A second degree burn involves the:

   A. Epidermis
   B. Epidermis and dermis
   C. Epidermis, dermis, and subcutaneous layers
   D. Epidermis, dermis, and subcutaneous layers and muscles

156. A patient's right upper limb and his entire chest have been burned. What percentage of surface burn would you report?

   A. 18 percent
   B. 27 percent
   C. 9 percent
   D. 36 percent

157. A patient receives a minor partial thickness burn to his left forearm. After checking for and finding no respiratory distress, your next step is to:

   A. Cover the area with a water-moistened sterile dressing
   B. Immerse the affected area in cool water
   C. Wash the area with sterile saline
   D. Immerse the area in warm water

158. A patient has extensive second degree burns. After checking for and finding no respiratory distress, your next step is to:

   A. Check for other injuries
   B. Cover the area with a sterile dressing
   C. Wet down the area with sterile water
   D. Wet down the area with sterile saline

159. A patient is suffering from chemical burns to the skin caused by dry lime. Your first step in care should be to:

   A. Wash the area with running water
   B. Remove the lime with phenol
   C. Remove the lime with alcohol
   D. Brush away the lime

160. Acid burns to the eyes should be washed for at least:

   A. 20 minutes
   B. 10 minutes
   C. 5 minutes
   D. 1 minute

161. Your patient has superficial frostbite to the fingers of the right hand. Transfer of this patient will be delayed. You should:

   A. Rub the area with warm water
   B. Immerse in cool water
   C. Rub the area with cold water
   D. Immerse in warm water

162. The first step in caring for a rescued near-drowning victim is to:

    A. Expel water from his lungs
    B. Administer oxygen under positive pressure
    C. Establish an airway
    D. Initiate CPR

163. Which of the following radiations cannot penetrate heavy clothing?

    A. Alpha
    B. Beta
    C. Gamma
    D. All of the above

164. The second stage of labor begins when the:

    A. Cervix dilates
    B. Baby moves into the birth canal
    C. Amniotic sac breaks
    D. Placenta is to be delivered

165. The average time of labor for women having their first baby is about:

    A. 16 hours
    B. 24 hours
    C. 10 hours
    D. 5 hours

166. To make a final decision about transporting an expectant mother in labor, you should:

    A. Check for crowning
    B. Check for bleeding
    C. Time the contractions
    D. Palpate for pelvic movements

167. The first clamp placed on the umbilical cord should be _____ inches from the baby.

    A. 5
    B. 12
    C. 10
    D. 2

168. Difficulties arise during the delivery of the baby's upper shoulder. You should gently:

    A. Pull the baby's shoulder
    B. Guide the baby's head upward
    C. Guide the baby's head downward
    D. Push the baby's lower shoulder

169. After the umbilical cord has been clamped and cut, bleeding continues from the baby's segment of the cord. You should:

    A. Unclamp and tie the cord
    B. Apply a sterile pressure dressing
    C. Tie, unclamp, and clamp again
    D. Clamp again, close to the original

170. If there are no complications you can wait up to _____ for the placenta to deliver.

    A. 2 hours
    B. 20 minutes
    C. 45 minutes
    D. 1 hour

171. The first step in dealing with maternal bleeding after delivery of the placenta is to:

    A. Massage the mother's abdomen over the uterus
    B. Apply a pressure dressing
    C. Pack the vagina with sterile gauze
    D. Place a sanitary napkin over the vaginal opening

172. If a breech presentation is noticed:

    A. Prepare to ensure an airway for the baby with your gloved fingers
    B. Attempt to turn the baby
    C. Do nothing but wait to assist the mother
    D. Transport immediately

173. A premature baby is one that weighs less than 5.5 pounds or is born before the _____ week.

    A. 19th
    B. 28th
    C. 37th
    D. 46th

174. A bike fork compression injury in a child should be cared for the same as a broken:

    A. Pelvis
    B. Ankle
    C. Hip
    D. Femur

175. When called to the scene of an attempted suicide where the patient does not have a weapon, you should:

    A. Wait for the police
    B. Establish contact with the patient as soon as possible
    C. Inform the patient of your authority
    D. Gain access without the patient seeing you

END SHORT TEST, ALL OTHERS CONTINUE

DIRECTIONS: Questions 176 through 181 are part of a matching problem. Match the recommended tools listed to the disentanglement problems.

_____ 176. Displacing a seat
_____ 177. Raising a crushed roof
_____ 178. Widening door openings
_____ 179. Displacing a floor pedal
_____ 180. Removing the steering wheel
_____ 181. Displacing the steering column

A. Hacksaw

B. Pliers

C. High-lift jack

D. Hand winch

E. Utility shears

DIRECTIONS: Circle the letter of the correct answer for each question.

182. Which of the following is the best patient-carrying device to use for a patient with a spinal injury?

A. Wheeled ambulance stretcher
B. Scoop-style stretcher
C. Wire basket stretcher
D. Long spine board

183. One commonly used method of transferring a bed-level patient without spinal injuries to a wheeled ambulance stretcher is the _____ method.

A. Slide carry
B. Slide transfer
C. Packstrap carry
D. Direct carry

184. You are about to load a wheeled stretcher onto the floor of an ambulance. Which of the following methods should you use?

A. Side carry
B. Modified direct carry
C. Direct carry
D. End carry

185. You wish to move a patient without spinal injuries from the floor to a stair chair. Which of the following methods should you use?

A. Slide transfer
B. Direct carry
C. Extremity transfer
D. Two-rescuer assist

186. You are about to move a supine, conscious patient with a spinal injury onto a long spine board. The patient is in an anatomically straight position with someone applying in-line stabilization to his head and neck. The patient's arms are folded across his chest. The next step is to:

A. Apply an extrication collar
B. Log roll the patient onto the long spine board
C. Lift the patient as a unit onto the spine board
D. Adjust the stretcher's head support

187. After an extrication collar has been secured during the placement of a K.E.D., the head-end rescuer:

A. Continues to apply in-line stabilization
B. Places himself on the opposite side of the patient, directly across from the other rescuer
C. Releases manual traction to the head and neck
D. Assumes a position at the patient's feet

188. Which of the following devices is best suited for transferring a patient from a high elevation?

A. Orthopedic stretcher
B. Basket stretcher
C. Portable stretcher
D. Pole stretcher

189. You have applied an extrication collar to a patient still seated in his car. Your next step would be to:

A. Reposition the patient and secure him to a long spine board
B. Secure the patient to a short spine board
C. Reposition the patient on the car's floor and use a scoop-style stretcher
D. Use the two-rescuer extremities lift to place him on a wheeled ambulance stretcher.

190. A patient with spinal injuries is found on the floor in a very narrow hallway. After applying an extrication collar you should:

    A. Move the patient onto a scoop-style stretcher
    B. Use the three-rescuer lift to place him on a long spine board
    C. Use the four-rescuer straddle to move him onto a long spine board
    D. Use the blanket drag to move him to a larger work area

191. The basic EMS communication system includes the dispatcher base station, ambulance transmitter/receiver, emergency department remote center, and:

    A. Telephone line backup
    B. Portable transmitter/receiver
    C. Ambulance repeater station
    D. Biotelemetry

192. Written reports in an EMS System:

    A. Keep track of patient information
    B. Transfer patient information
    C. Serve as part of the medical record
    D. All of the above

193. A patient goes into cardiac arrest while in transport. Your first task is to:

    A. Initiate CPR
    B. Radio the hospital
    C. Request the driver to stop the ambulance
    D. Insert an airway

194. You are transferring a non-emergency patient. The procedure for handoff (patient transfer) is:

    A. Wait for emergency staff to call for the patient
    B. Off-load, wheel to the designated area, and stay with the patient
    C. Check to see what is to be done with the patient
    D. Off-load, wheel to the designated area, and leave the patient

195. The last step of the handoff is to:

    A. Wait to help the emergency room staff
    B. Transfer patient information
    C. Obtain your release
    D. Transfer patient's valuables

DIRECTIONS: Mach the following locations to the tasks listed below.

A. At the hospital
B. En route to quarters
C. In quarters

_____ 196. Clean and sanitize respiratory equipment
_____ 197. Air the ambulance patient compartment
_____ 198. Exchange equipment
_____ 199. Replace respiratory equipment
_____ 200. Dispose of dirty linens

END POST-TEST

POST-TEST ANSWERS

SHORT TEST

You should have completed all the questions from question 26 through question 175. Subtract 1 point for each incorrect answer. Total the number you had wrong and subtract this number from 150 to obtain your final score.

Range of Scores

135–150: Excellent
120–134: Good
105–119: Passing, but you will probably have trouble on a certification exam
90–104: It will be difficult for you to pass a certification exam
89 and below: It is doubtful that you can pass a certification exam without additional study

LONG TEST

You should have completed all 200 questions. Subtract 1 point for each incorrect answer. Total the number you had wrong and subtract this number from 200 to obtain your final score.

Range of Scores

180–200: Excellent
160–179: Good
140–159: Passing, but you will probably have trouble on a certification exam
120–139: It will be difficult for you to pass a certification exam
119 and below: It is doubtful that you can pass a certification exam without additional study

ANSWERS:

1. C (p. 19)
2. B (p. 19)
3. B (p. 22)
4. D (p. 17)
5. C (p. 22)
6. A (p. 538)
7. B (p. 541)
8. A (p. 549)
9. C (p. 544)
10. A (p. 551)
11. B (p. 551)
12. D (p. 552)
13. C (p. 557)
14. B (p. 557)
15. A (p. 541)
16. D (p. 409)
17. C (p. 613)
18. D (p. 566)
19. A (p. 568)
20. D (p. 568)
21. C (p. 569)
22. B (p. 614)
23. B (p. 627)
24. A (p. 643)
25. C (p. 642)

BEGIN SHORT TEST

26. A (p. 34)
27. D (p. 34)
28. C (p. 38)
29. A (p. 70)
30. C (p. 72)
31. B (p. 79)
32. C (p. 82)
33. C (p. 85)
34. D (p. 86)
35. D (p. 85)
36. A (p. 87)
37. D (p. 87)
38. C (p. 88)
39. B (p. 88)
40. B (p. 88)

41. D (p. 89)
42. A (p. 90)
43. C (p. 92)
44. A (p. 95)
45. A (p. 91)
46. C (p. 98)
47. B (p. 102)
48. D (p. 523)
49. C (p. 505)
50. C (p. 516)
51. B (p. 120)
52. B (p. 114)
53. A (p. 114)
54. C (p. 117)
55. B (p. 126)
56. C (p. 127)
57. D (p. 132)
58. C (p. 132)
59. D (p. 132
60. A (p. 128)
61. A (p. 131)
62. C (p. 118)
63. A (p. 118)
64. D (p. 120)
65. D (p. 120)
66. B (p. 121)
67. C (p. 121)
68. D (p. 123)
69. B (p. 123)
70. C (p. 122)
71. A (p. 114)
72. B (p. 144)
73. C (p. 145)
74. A (p. 145)
75. D (p. 143)
76. B (p. 152)
77. C (p. 152)
78. B (p. 145)
79. B (p. 146)
80. C (p. 155)
81. A (p. 156)
82. D (p. 155)
83. B (p. 156)
84. A (p. 156)
85. B (p. 147)
86. D (p. 139)
87. A (p. 194)

88. B (p. 195)
89. A (p. 194)
90. D (p. 195)
91. B (p. 198)
92. B (p. 342)
93. D (p. 201)
94. C (p. 202)
95. B (p. 221)
96. D (p. 223)
97. C (p. 228)
98. C (p. 203)
99. D (p. 204)
100. B (p. 207)
101. A (p. 165)
102. A (p. 121)
103. D (p. 175)
104. C (p. 183)
105. D (p. 302)
106. A (p. 302)
107. B (p. 304)
NOTE: A is correct in some systems.

108. A (p. 406)
109. D (p. 395)
110. C (p. 297)
111. B (p. 311)
112. A (p. 309)
113. B (p. 309)
114. B (p. 328)
115. C (p. 331)
116. B (p. 332)
117. A (p. 336)
118. C (p. 230)
119. A (p. 341)
120. C (p. 312)
121. A (p. 346)
122. B (p. 346)
123. D (p. 352)
124. C (p. 355)
125. A (p. 356)
126. C (p. 357)
127. A (p. 354)
128. B (p. 359)
129. C (p. 362)
130. C (p. 408)

131. B (p. 257)
132. B (p. 260)
133. B (p. 260)
134. B (p. 261)
135. B (p. 264)
136. C (p. 263)
137. A (p. 274)
138. D (p. 276)
139. A (p. 276)
140. B (p. 293)
141. B (p. 247)
142. B (p. 247)
143. D (p. 247)
144. D (p. 388)
145. C (p. 388)
146. A (p. 390)
147. C (p. 393)
148. A (p. 392)
149. D (p. 391)
150. A (p. 405)
151. C (p. 381)
152. B (p. 376)
153. C (p. 404)
154. D (p. 482)
155. B (p. 461)
156. A (p. 463)
157. A (p. 465)
NOTE: Your System may require a dry dressing.

158. A (p. 466)
159. D (p. 468)
160. A (p. 468)
161. D (p. 486)
162. C (p. 491)
163. A (p. 474)
164. B (p. 438)
165. A (p. 439)
166. A (p. 440)
167. C (p. 446)
168. C (p. 442)
169. D (p. 446)
170. B (p. 447)
171. D (p. 447)
172. A (p. 453)

173. C (p. 455)
174. B (p. 425)
175. B (p. 509)

END SHORT TEST

176. D (p. 663)
177. C (p. 647)
178. D (p. 652)
179. D. (p. 662)
180. A (p. 659)
181. D (p. 660)
182. D (p. 577)
183. D (p. 573)
184. A (p. 573)
185. C (p. 573)
186. A (p. 312)
187. A (p. 321)
188. B (p. 571)
189. B (p. 322)
190. C (p. 317)
191. A (p. 604)
192. D (p. 605)
193. C (p. 589)
194. C (p. 591)
195. C (p. 593)
196. A or C (p. 596 and p. 601)
197. B (p. 598)
198. A (p. 596)
199. A (p. 596)
200. C (p. 601)